5·001

C19124

Experiments:
Design and Analysis

Other books on experimental design and cognate subjects

Experimental design: selected papers	F. Yates
Biomathematics	Cedric A. B. Smith
*The mathematics of experimental design**	S. Vajda
*Patterns and configurations in finite spaces**	S. Vajda
*Statistical models and their experimental application**	P. Ottestad
*The method of paired comparisons**	H. A. David
*The analysis of variance: a basic course**	A. Huitson
The advanced theory of statistics	Sir Maurice Kendall & A. Stuart
Rank correlation methods	Sir Maurice Kendall
Statistical method in biological assay	D. J. Finney
Estimation of animal abundance and related parameters	G. A. F. Seber

* A volume in Griffin's Statistical Monographs and Courses

Descriptive catalogue giving a complete list of statistical and mathematical books
is available from the Publishers

Experiments:
Design and Analysis

J. A. JOHN

B.Sc.(Econ.), Ph.D.
Lecturer in Mathematical Statistics
University of Southampton

and

M. H. QUENOUILLE

M.A., Sc.D., F.B.A.
Late Professor of Statistics
University of Southampton

Second Edition

Quis separabit nos

CHARLES GRIFFIN & COMPANY LTD
London and High Wycombe

CHARLES GRIFFIN & COMPANY LIMITED

Registered Office:

5A Crendon Street, High Wycombe, Bucks HP13 6LE
England

First published 1953
(Entitled *The Design and Analysis of Experiment*)
Second edition 1977

ISBN: 0 85264 222 9

Set and printed in Great Britain by
The Garden City Press Limited
Letchworth, Hertfordshire SG6 1JS

Contents

Preface

The death of Maurice Quenouille during the early days of the preparation of a new edition of his *Design and Analysis of Experiment* was deeply felt. I owe him a very considerable debt. I was fortunate to have been a student of his, both as an undergraduate and as a postgraduate at London University. I became a member of his staff at Southampton University and benefited enormously from his advice, encouragement and interest in my early years as a university teacher.

In preparing this new edition, it has been my aim throughout to preserve the spirit in which the first edition was written. The emphasis is on the principles and concepts involved in conducting experiments, and on illustrating the different methods of design and analysis by numerical example rather than by mathematical and statistical theory. It is hoped that as such the book will be of value to those statisticians, researchers and experimenters who wish to acquire a working knowledge of experimental design and an understanding of the principles governing it.

During the years since publication of the first edition very considerable progress has taken place in statistical theory and methodology. New techniques for the design and analysis of experiments have appeared. The electronic digital computer now routinely undertakes complex statistical analyses and is also used increasingly in the design of the experiment. Obviously, not all the developments can be described in a book of this size. However, in addition to a revision of the text there has been some rearrangement of the material and the inclusion of two new chapters on fractional factorial experiments (Chapter 7) and response surface methods (Chapter 9). Although the emphasis is on the more common and widely used types of designs, those wishing to pursue the subject in greater detail will find guidance to further reading in the text and an extensive bibliography at the end of the book. As in the first edition, the importance of adequate inspection of the raw results is constantly stressed. With the advent of easily accessible computer packages to analyse data, such an inspection is now even more important.

During the preparation of the book, I had many valuable discussions with Mr H. D. Patterson of the ARC Unit of Statistics at Edinburgh and I am very grateful to him for his advice and comments. My thanks are also due to Mr Patterson and to my colleagues Mrs S. M. Lewis and Dr P. Prescott for their detailed criticisms of earlier drafts of some of the chapters. I, of course, accept full responsibility for the actual contents and for any errors that may be found.

Finally, I would like to thank the Biometrika Trustees for permission to reprint percentage points of the studentized range from the *Biometrika Tables for Statisticians*, Vol. 1.

J. A. JOHN

Southampton,
January 1977

1 The Design and Analysis of Experiments

1.1 Introduction

This book is intended to help the experimenter with the design and analysis of his experiments. It is hoped that its use will lead to the application of more efficient designs, with consequent savings in time and expense, and gains in information. However, the uses and limitations of experimental designs need to be understood at the outset if the selection of designs for specific purposes is to be carried out rapidly and effectively. For this reason, this chapter is devoted to a general discussion of different types of experimental designs and what can and cannot be achieved by their use. Since most of this book is devoted to illustrating what can be achieved by the use of efficient designs, it is perhaps worth while to start by outlining their limitations.

There is a saying to the effect that it is possible to prove anything by statistics. While this may seem true for bad statistics, the converse applies equally to good statistics: it is impossible to prove anything by statistics, since correctly applied statistical methods never allow anything to be experimentally *proved*. What they will do, however, is to ascertain the likelihood of error in any statement, or the confidence that can be placed in any experimental value. A little reflection will show that this is, in fact, all that should be expected. There is no proof, for instance, that the sun will rise tomorrow. Experience has taught us that it is very likely to do so, and indeed we are content to believe that it will continue to rise every morning in agreement with previous observations and laws based upon them.

Similarly, statistical method will not provide any absolute proof to the experimenter of the effectiveness of his treatments. It will, however, enable him to estimate the likelihood of their continued performance at the level indicated by his experiments. For example, an experiment may be carried out to estimate the effect on the growth of a group of experimental rats of supplementing their normal diet with particular ingredients. This experiment may indicate that the supplement increases the total weight at six weeks of age by, on average, 20 grams. However, this provides no proof that if the experiment were repeated under similar conditions a similar increase would be observed, or even that any increase would be observed. The experimenter may thus be left in considerable doubt about the worth of his conclusions.

The use of a suitable experimental design followed by statistical analysis of the results will not necessarily remove any such doubt, but it will enable the experimenter to set a value to the reliability of his results. If he is interested solely in demonstrating the existence of an effect of the supplement, he should be able to estimate just how frequently or infrequently results such as his would arise if no such effect existed, and to use this as a basis for his conclusions. For instance, if he is able to demonstrate that such extreme differences as those he has obtained would arise less than once in a thousand times if the supplement had no effect, he is fairly safe in discounting the possibility of its ineffectiveness and concluding that it is effective. The possibility of its being ineffective nevertheless remains, but some measure of the possibility is now available and can be used to demonstrate to others the plausibility of the existence of an effect of the supplement.

More often in experimentation, it is necessary not only to infer the existence of an effect but also to measure its size. Here again the application of statistical methods helps in assessing the reproducibility of the results. Not only are effects estimated in well-planned experiments, but also limits can be found within which the true values for the effects will almost certainly lie. Thus, in the above illustration, the experimenter may ultimately be able to say that his supplement causes a weight increase, the true value of which lies almost certainly between, say, 16 and 24 grams. He then knows how much confidence he can put in his experimental values and, when using them in any particular instance, how far he is likely to be misled. Even here, however, the experimenter cannot specify limits within which the true values of effects will certainly fall, except by including the whole possible range of values. He has, in general, to be content with specifying a range within which the true value will fall with a given high degree of probability.

The first important point then, in planning an experiment, is to realize that perfection cannot be achieved from a limited number of observations and, since this is so, that designs and methods which will allow the reproducibility of the results to be assessed have to be employed. The principles and methods involved are discussed in the next few sections.

1.2   Principles involved in experimentation

Once it has been realized that good experimental design requires the reproducibility of any effects to be estimated at the same time as the effects themselves, the basic principles involved in experimental design become easier to understand. Three main considerations enter into the design of experiments—

(1) The conclusions drawn from an experiment must have *validity*. Consider an example in which two different diets are to be tested on rats. Diet *A* is always given to male rats and diet *B* to female rats. In such an experiment it will be impossible to distinguish the differences between the diets from any systematic differences that may exist between the sexes of the rats. The systematic arrangement of the treatments may coincide with a pattern in the uncontrolled variation to produce a systematic error in the estimated treatment effects, thereby invalidating the conclusions to be drawn from the experiment.

An interesting example of the systematic assignment of treatments to experimental material has been given by Greenberg (1951). He reports an experiment designed to test the immunity of pairs of mice to a particular ringworm, by giving them solutions supposed to contain 200 larvae per 0.05 cm^3. The experimental group had previously been given stimulating injections and the differences in reaction between the experimental and control groups were to be examined. Mice from the two groups were injected with the solution alternately in the hope that this would cancel variations in dosage. In fact what happened was that the number of larvae successively increased so that the control group, which was injected alternately after the experimental group, received a higher mean number of larvae. Hence there was a systematic error in the estimated treatment effects that would persist even over a long experiment.

To ensure the absence of these systematic errors it is necessary to allot the treatments to the available experimental material at random. Then the estimated treatment effects found from a large number of independent repetitions of the experiment would tend to average out to the true treatment effects. That is, randomization ensures that unbiased estimates of treatment effects are obtained. The valid experiment, therefore, will be one that is planned so that the conclusions are free from the biases, either consciously or unconsciously, of the experimenter. Even if a non-random arrangement is in fact felt to be satisfactory there is always the suspicion that it may not be so, and this may detract considerably from the cogency of the experiment, especially if surprising results are found. Randomization provides a form of insurance for the experimenter.

(2) The conclusions drawn from an experiment must have *precision*. If the absence of systematic errors is achieved by randomization, the estimation of treatment effects will differ from their true values only by random variation. A true experiment is one which furnishes a measure of this variation. Such a measure is provided by replicating or repeating some or all of the treatments, so that an estimate of experimental error can be obtained by a comparison of similar experimental units, i.e. units which are similar with respect to the effects which are consciously controlled. Replication, therefore, permits the reproducibility of the results to be assessed.

(3) Finally, the experimental conclusions must have wide *coverage*. The precision of the experiment depends not only on the size of the experiment as reflected in the number of replications but also on the inherent variability of the experimental units; the experimental error will be smaller if the experimental units are more homogeneous. However, in order to achieve wide coverage of the results, heterogeneous units will have to be used in the experiment. There are techniques available for achieving a compromise, i.e. of increasing precision without an undue sacrifice of coverage. This is the design problem: to choose a design to estimate the effects of the treatments as accurately as possible. It is to a consideration of this problem that a large portion of the remainder of this book is devoted.

1.3 Statistical methods used in the analysis of experiments

In the following pages, certain statistical methods and terms will be used. For a full explanation of these, reference should be made to a text on statistics. However, a brief summary may be given here for the convenience of those wishing to avoid any deeper contact with statistical methods.

The reliability of estimated effects is usually indicated by their *standard errors*, which may be used to set limits within which the true values fall with any degree of confidence. These are called *confidence limits*. Thus, for example, if the estimated effect is $\bar{x}$ and its standard error (accurately estimated) is s, the 95 percent confidence limits for the effect are $\bar{x} - 1\cdot96s$ and $\bar{x} + 1\cdot96s$, i.e. 95 times out of 100 the true value for the effect will fall within these limits. Similarly, the 99 percent confidence limits are $\bar{x} - 2\cdot58s$ and $\bar{x} + 2\cdot58s$; and further limits corresponding to different degrees of confidence can be found by adding and subtracting a suitable multiple of the standard error from the estimated effect.

In general, the appropriate multiple of the standard error to be added and subtracted from any estimate depends not only on the degree of confidence that is required but also upon how accurately the standard error has been estimated. Tables such as the t table (Appendix Table A.1) provide values of the appropriate multiple for the standard error in determining confidence limits. In this case, the possible inaccuracy in the standard error is indicated by its *degrees of freedom* (or the effective number of independent observations used in its estimation).

Normally, in what follows, standard errors will be estimated using an *analysis of variance* which partitions the variation in any series of observations into components due to ascribable causes, such as treatment effects or differences between groups of the treatment material, and a component unascribable to any individual cause—a *residual* or *error* component. The components due to particular causes may be used to test whether these causes contribute significantly to the total variation; for example, the treatments component may be used to test whether the treatment effects are significant.

The test that is commonly used in the analysis of variance is the *variance-ratio* test. This is carried out by estimating *variances* or calculating *mean squares* in the analysis of variance and using the ratios of each mean square to the error mean square. The appropriate significance levels for ratios of this type are tabulated in tables such as Appendix Tables A.2 and A.3. For instance, reference to the tables shows that the ratio of two variances based on 3 and 12 degrees of freedom would exceed the value $3\cdot49$ by pure chance in only 5 percent of cases, and the value $5\cdot95$ by pure chance in only 1 percent of cases. A higher value would certainly indicate the existence of treatment effects or whatever else is being tested.

Other tests and methods may sometimes be employed, but no great difficulty should be experienced, provided the reader is familiar with the two ideas of setting confidence limits and of using the analysis of variance for partitioning variation and testing significance.

1.4   Example of the interpretation of an experiment

As a simple illustration of the interpretation of experimental results, we shall consider the results of an experiment to compare the effects of methyl methacrylate and paraffin on the clotting time of human blood. The following results were reported by Hirschboeck (1941) of the clotting times observed in 10 pairs of blood samples. One out of each pair was chosen at random and treated with methacrylate and the other was treated with paraffin. The results are shown in Table 1.4.1.

The main purpose of the experiment is to estimate the mean difference between clotting times for paraffin and methacrylate and to decide whether or not it is likely to be due to chance.

Table 1.4.1 Results of clotting-time experiment

| Sample | Clotting time in minutes | | |
	Paraffin	Methacrylate	Difference, d
1	10	13	−3
2	27	20	7
3	11	9	2
4	18	12	6
5	19	11	8
6	16	14	2
7	16	19	−3
8	18	12	6
9	22	11	11
10	26	18	8
Mean	18·3	13·9	4·4

Examination of Table 1.4.1 shows that, in individual pairs of samples, paraffin tends to give a longer clotting time than methacrylate, the average difference being 4·4 minutes. However, owing to the variability of results, it is difficult to gauge the reliability of this difference or to assess whether paraffin is likely to continue to give a longer clotting time in further experiments. Statistical analysis is required for this purpose.

An analysis of the results in this instance gives a mean difference of 4·4 minutes whose standard error (with 9 degrees of freedom) is 1·5 minutes. Use of Appendix Table A.1 then shows that the 95 percent confidence limits for the effect are

$$4·4 - 2·26 \times 1·5 = 1·01$$
and $$4·4 + 2·26 \times 1·5 = 7·79.$$

Thus, with 95 percent certainty, it can be stated that the true mean value of the difference in clotting times lies between 1·01 and 7·79 and is not zero, i.e. with 95 percent certainty there is a difference in the mean clotting times of paraffin and methacrylate.

Similarly the 99 percent confidence limits are

$$4·4 - 3·25 \times 1·5 = -0·475$$
and $$4·4 + 3·25 \times 1·5 = 9·275,$$

indicating that on the basis of these figures we cannot state with 99 percent certainty that there is a real difference in mean clotting times.

To indicate the reliability or reality of any estimated difference it is quite common to indicate the proportion of cases in which such an extreme estimate would occur if the true difference were zero. Here, the proportion lies between 0·05 and 0·01, and consequently a summary of the difference in clotting times is provided in the form

$$\text{Mean difference in clotting times} = 4·4 \pm 1·5 \ (0·05 > P > 0·01).$$

The bracketed expression assesses the confidence that may be placed in the reality of the difference.

In general, the existence of any treatment effect is regarded as highly likely if $0·01 > P$, and as probable if $0·05 > P > 0·01$. If $P > 0·05$, then any observed difference may more readily be attributed to chance, and the existence of a treatment effect cannot be regarded as having been demonstrated with any strength. Of course, the level at which an experimenter decides to accept the existence of any effect as being sufficiently well proven must depend upon the circumstances, including possible outside evidence. What should, however, be avoided, is the attitude that a value of P provides a hard-and-fast basis for action, and that, for instance, if $P = 0·051$, the existence of an effect is disproved, and that, if $P = 0·049$, its existence is proved. Since the value of P reflects the accuracy and size of the experiment as well as the size of any effect, such an attitude must undoubtedly lead to incorrect conclusions.

1.5 Example of the use of the analysis of variance

To illustrate the use of the analysis of variance, the example of the last section may be used. Details of the numerical procedure for calculating the analysis of variance need not concern us here. The layout and interpretation of the analysis of variance is more important.

Table 1.5.1 Analysis of variance of clotting-time experiment

	Degrees of freedom, d.f.	Sum of squares, s.s.	Mean square, m.s.
Between pairs of samples	9	309·8	34·42
Between treatments	1	96·8	96·80
Residual	9	101·2	11·24
Total	19	507·8	

Table 1.5.1 gives the analysis of variance appropriate to the results of the clotting-time experiment of the previous section. The total variation, as indicated by the total sum of squares, 507·8, is divided up into three parts: the variation

between pairs of samples, 309·8; the variation between methods of treatment, 96·8; and a residual "unaccountable' portion, 101·2.

Mean squares are calculated from these sums of squares by dividing them by their degrees of freedom. The residual mean square may then be used to estimate the reliability of the observed treatment effects and differences between blood samples. First, variance ratios need to be calculated to test the significance of the differences between treatments and between pairs of samples. Thus, for instance, $96·80/11·24 = 8·61$ tests the difference between methacrylate and paraffin, and reference to Appendix Tables A.2 and A.3 with $n_1 = 1$, $n_2 = 9$ shows that such a large value would occur by chance in less than 5 percent but more than 1 percent of cases, i.e. $0·05 > P > 0·01$. Similarly, $34·42/11·24 = 3·06$ tests whether the differences between pairs of samples are larger than can be accounted for by the residual variability, i.e. the variability within pairs, and reference to Appendix Tables A.2 and A.3 with $n_1 = n_2 = 9$ gives $P \doteq 0·06$. The analysis thus indicates that the observed difference between the treatments is likely to be real and suggests that the variability between pairs of samples is greater than the variability within pairs, i.e. apart from the treatment effect, samples from the same pair tend to be more alike than samples from different pairs.

Secondly, the residual mean square, denoted by s^2, may be used to derive the standard errors of means and differences between means. Usually, the standard error of the mean of n observations is

$$\sqrt{\left(\frac{s^2}{n}\right)},$$

while the standard error of the difference between means of n and m observations is

$$\sqrt{\left[s^2\left(\frac{1}{n} + \frac{1}{m}\right)\right]}.$$

This is true here.

Thus the standard error of the individual treatment mean is

$$\sqrt{\left(\frac{11·24}{10}\right)} = \pm 1·06,$$

while the standard error of the difference between treatment means is

$$\sqrt{\left[11·24\left(\frac{1}{10} + \frac{1}{10}\right)\right]} = \pm 1·50,$$

as was reported in the previous section. Confidence limits may now be set for the means or for the difference between means in the manner described in that section.

1.6 Assumptions involved in the analysis of experiments

In order to facilitate the analysis and to simplify the tests of significance, it is usual to make some assumptions about the nature of the observations or responses obtained from an experiment. Three important assumptions are commonly made—

    (1) the unaccountable variation or error in different measurements has a normal law of error;

    (2) different measurements are independent;

    (3) the relative sizes of errors in different measurements are unrelated to any factor of the experiment.

The meanings and consequences of each of these assumptions will be examined in turn.

First, the assumptions that the unaccountable variation follows a normal law of error is equivalent to assuming that the frequencies of errors of different sizes follow a given law, such as is shown diagrammatically in Fig. 1.6.1. The scale of measurement can, of course, be altered in this figure to make any range of error

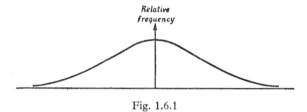

Fig. 1.6.1

feasible, but it is important to note that whatever scale is used the distribution will have the same basic properties. Most important of these are that large errors occur less frequently than small errors, and that very large errors hardly ever occur. Also positive and negative errors of the same magnitude occur with equal frequency.

Secondly, it is important that the assumption about the independence of measurements should hold if the experimenter is not to be misled about the reproducibility of his results. Obviously, by repeating some or all of the measurements a number of times an artificial idea of their general applicability may be conceived. If growth observations repeated on the same animals were treated as if they were independent observations on different animals, individual irregularities might be over-emphasized and an unjustified confidence might be placed in their general existence. In such situations a multivariate analysis of the data would be more appropriate. For such analyses, which are beyond the scope of this book, reference should be made to texts on multivariate statistical analysis, such as Morrison (1967) and Kendall (1975). In most cases the requirement of independence can be met by randomization. For instance, operations that must necessarily be carried out successively in time or space are likely to be more homogeneous than those separated by time or space. The operations may be affected by various slight changes in the experimental conditions that would cause fluctuations in the results. The observations from neighbouring plots in field experiments, for example, tend to be positively correlated. It is essential, therefore, to allocate the treatments to the experimental material at random so as to ensure the independence of the observations and hence to validate the tests of significance.

Thirdly, the errors in the measurements should be uninfluenced by the nature of the measurements. For if larger errors tend to be associated with certain treatments or groups of treatment material, the use of one overall estimate of the experimental error cannot be a valid procedure. At the same time, the estimated error will usually be heterogeneous and, equally, tests of significance will no longer be valid. In general, it is the less stringent assumption that the error is homogeneous that is important in assigning a standard error and confidence limits to estimated treatment effects.

Usually, slight deviations from these assumptions will not unduly influence an analysis for practical purposes. Thus, for instance, an error distribution approximating to the normal distribution will give comparable significance levels, while slight error heterogeneity will barely affect the usual confidence limits.

Where, however, large deviations from these assumptions occur, misleading conclusions may be obtained by the use of the standard methods of analysis. It is thus necessary, before carrying out an analysis, to consider whether any of these three assumptions is likely to be invalid and, if so, how to overcome this difficulty. Sometimes this can be done by changing the scale of measurements to make the error distribution normal or the error homogeneous. Such methods are described in Chapter 14. On other occasions, the use of combinations of the observations, instead of the observations themselves, will allow the assumption of independence to be made. These methods are described in Chapter 13.

Usually, where the experiment has been well planned the methods of Chapter 14 make it possible to assure the truth of the above assumptions. However, in planning experiments, some initial consideration has to be given to the type and number of observations that are to be taken to ensure that they provide what is needed.

1.7   First steps in planning an experiment

The first and obviously most important step in planning an experiment is to decide what the experiment is intended to do. This is not as easy as it sounds, since it is often necessary not only to state what is to be tested, but also to specify clearly the population to which results of the test are intended to apply. For example, it may be desired to estimate the increase in the yield of potatoes resulting from a fertilizer application. The dressing and type of fertilizer and time and method of application need first to be decided in specifying the treatment. This should not be difficult. It is then necessary to decide to what population the results are to apply. The total possible population consists of all varieties of potatoes and the whole range of conditions under which they might be cultivated, i.e. all possible soil types, fertilizers and other cultivations, weather conditions and so on.

Obviously a larger experiment is likely to be needed to obtain results applicable to a wide population than to obtain results applicable to a small population. In fact, any one experiment is unlikely to be sufficiently wide to give results applicable to the whole population of possible conditions, and so the limitations to be placed on the experiment usually need to be considered first.

In its most limited form, the experiment is restricted to just one set of conditions. For example, the variety and cultivations to be used may be determined beforehand, and the responses to the fertilizer accepted as referring only to the prevailing weather and soil conditions, etc. This is the *unifactor* type of experiment.

More extensive would be an experiment in which a range of cultivations and varieties were tested with the fertilizer. The effects of different cultivations and varieties could then be estimated at the same time as the effect of the fertilizer. This is the *factorial* type of experiment.

Still more general results could be obtained by carrying out a series of unifactor or factorial experiments under variable conditions so that, for instance, the average effect of a fertilizer could be estimated over several seasons. This requires the carrying out of a series of experiments.

The experimenter thus has to choose to how wide a population his final results are to refer. Naturally his preference will be for results as widely applicable as possible; but at the same time it has to be remembered that much extra work may be required to obtain accurate values for such results, since more variation will be introduced as the field of experimentation is widened. It is therefore necessary to inquire how accurate the results are likely to be when deciding the design of any experiment. If the design is unable to give results of the required accuracy, there is little point in carrying out the experiment, and either a modification in the design has to be sought or the experiment must be abandoned.

Thus, normally, the second step in setting up an experiment is to gauge the probably accuracy of the results likely to be obtained from the experiment. To do this, it is necessary to gauge the unaccountable variability in the individual observations of the experiment and thereby to assess how many replications are likely to be needed for a difference of a given magnitude to have confidence limits of a given width. In consequence, three things are needed to estimate whether an experiment is likely to be large enough. These are—

(1) An estimate of the percentage variation in the observations that cannot be accounted for by any of the factors in the experiment. This quantity is commonly called the *coefficient of variation* and, for most biological observations, takes a value between 5 percent and 15 percent. For instance, the unaccountable variation in yield in a field-plot experiment may be about 12 percent, i.e. the yield of any particular plot may easily vary between 88 per cent and 112 percent of what might be expected.

(2) A value for the accuracy desired in the treatment effect, expressed as a percentage of the overall mean. Thus, it may be desired to measure treatment effects to within 5 percent since any effect smaller than this may be of no practical importance.

(3) The probability for the true value of the difference to fall within the assigned limits. For example, it may be desired to measure a treatment effect to within 5 percent, but it is impossible to be absolutely certain that this has been

achieved; 95 percent or 99 percent or some similar degree of certainty has to be decided upon, and the corresponding confidence limits used.

The level of probability that is used will often depend upon the possible consequences of concluding that the difference is real. If the conclusion is liable to lead to expensive or irrevocable action, then a high probability level might be used to make a more stringent test of the reality of any difference.

Table 1.7.1 gives the number of replications, r, needed to estimate the percentage difference between a pair of means with a given accuracy. It should be noted that this table is compiled upon the assumption that $2(r - 1)$ degrees of freedom are available for error. Where several treatments are tested at the same time, fewer replications may be required than are indicated in this table since the number of degrees of freedom may be larger.

It must be noted that the use of the numbers of replications indicated in this table gives no guarantee that an error of the size shown will be realized. The *average* error will be of the size shown, but the actual error will be larger in half of the cases and smaller in the other half. This means that if it is desired to test for significance a difference of the size indicated in the first column of Table 1.7.1, only in about 50 percent of cases will the number of replications be sufficient for significance at the level shown.

It is, of course, impossible to ensure that significance should be achieved at any levels; but by increasing the number of replications, the probability of any given difference achieving significance can be correspondingly increased. Thus Table 1.7.2 gives the number of replications required to achieve significance at the indicated levels with 90 percent certainty. For instance, when the coefficient of variation is 8 percent, at least 18 replications are required to ensure (with 90 percent certainty) that a difference of 10 percent between two means is significant at the 95 percent level.

Tables 1.7.1 and 1.7.2 should be regarded here as indicating whether the experimenter is being too ambitious in hoping for a result of a given accuracy from his experiment, and whether it may be necessary to limit his objectives. Before this is done, however, other methods of improving the accuracy of an experiment should be considered.

1.8 Methods of improving the accuracy of an experiment

As mentioned above, an obvious method to improve the accuracy of an experiment is to limit the population to which its results are to apply. By using uniform material, the accuracy of the experiment may be greatly improved, but at the same time much of the applicability of the results may be lost. To avoid this loss, it is necessary to use heterogeneous material and account and adjust for some of the causes of variability.

Some increase in accuracy may often be obtained by improvements in the methods of applying the treatments and measuring and recording the results of the experiment, but usually these improvements are the direct concern of the experimenter and, as far as this book is concerned, are of secondary importance compared with the improvements to be obtained by statistical design and analysis.

Table 1.7.1 Number of replications needed to estimate a percentage difference between two means with a given accuracy

Coefficient of variation		2			4			6			8		
Confidence probability		90	95	99	90	95	99	90	95	99	90	95	99
Error ($\pm$) in estimate as a percentage of overall mean	4	3	4	6	7	9	16	14	19	32	23	32	—
	6	2	3	4	4	5	8	7	9	16	11	15	26
	8	2	3	3	3	4	6	5	6	10	7	9	16
	10	2	2	3	3	3	5	4	5	7	5	7	11
	12	2	2	3	2	3	4	3	4	6	4	5	8
	14	2	2	3	2	3	4	3	3	5	3	4	7

Coefficient of variation		10			12			14			16		
Confidence probability		90	95	99	90	95	99	90	95	99	90	95	99
Error ($\pm$) in estimate as a percentage of overall mean	6	17	23	40	23	32	—	31	44	—	40	—	—
	8	10	14	23	14	19	32	18	25	43	23	32	—
	10	7	9	16	9	13	22	12	17	29	15	21	37
	12	5	7	12	7	9	16	9	12	21	11	15	26
	14	4	6	9	6	7	12	7	9	16	9	12	20
	16	4	5	8	5	6	10	6	8	13	7	9	16

Coefficient of variation		20			30			40			50		
Confidence probability		90	95	99	90	95	99	90	95	99	90	95	99
Error ($\pm$) in estimate as a percentage of overall mean	15	11	15	26	23	32	—	40	—	—	—	—	—
	20	7	9	16	14	19	32	23	32	—	35	50	—
	25	5	7	11	9	13	22	15	21	37	23	32	—
	30	4	5	8	7	9	16	11	15	26	17	23	40
	35	3	4	7	6	7	12	9	12	20	13	17	30
	40	3	4	6	5	6	10	7	9	16	10	14	23

Two main statistical methods can be used to improve the accuracy of any experiment. First, if the treatment material is grouped so that each group is as homogeneous as possible, the treatments may be arranged so that treatment comparisons are made *within* each group, thereby eliminating the variability between groups but retaining a wide generality in the results. The arrangement or stratification of treatments in blocks gives rise to a wide variety of experi-

Table 1.7.2 Number of replications needed to detect a percentage difference between two means at a given confidence probability with 90 percent certainty

Coefficient of variation		2			4			6			8		
Confidence probability		90	95	99	90	95	99	90	95	99	90	95	99
Percentage difference	4	7	8	11	23	28	38	50	—	—	—	—	—
	6	4	5	6	11	13	18	23	28	38	40	48	—
	8	3	4	4	7	8	11	14	16	22	23	28	38
	10	3	3	4	5	6	8	9	11	15	15	18	25
	12	2	3	3	4	5	6	7	8	11	11	13	18
	14	2	3	3	3	4	5	6	6	9	9	10	14

Coefficient of variation		10			12			14			16		
Confidence probability		90	95	99	90	95	99	90	95	99	90	95	99
Percentage difference	8	35	42	—	50	—	—	—	—	—	—	—	—
	10	23	28	38	33	39	—	44	—	—	—	—	—
	12	17	20	27	23	28	38	31	37	—	40	48	—
	14	13	15	20	17	21	28	23	28	38	30	36	49
	16	10	12	16	14	16	22	18	22	29	23	28	38

Coefficient of variation		20			30			40			50		
Confidence probability		90	95	99	90	95	99	90	95	99	90	95	99
Percentage difference	20	23	28	38	50	—	—	—	—	—	—	—	—
	25	15	18	25	33	39	—	—	—	—	—	—	—
	30	11	13	18	23	28	38	40	48	—	—	—	—
	35	9	10	14	17	21	28	30	36	49	46	—	—
	40	7	8	11	14	16	22	23	28	38	35	42	—

mental designs which are enumerated in the next section and explained in the following chapters. These designs automatically eliminate much of the variation in the observations from treatment comparisons.

Secondly, if a series of observations can be taken to account for some of the variability in the final measurements, an *analysis of covariance* can be carried out to eliminate this variability. For instance, the final weights of animals after completion of an experiment may be adjusted using their initial weights before the start of the experiment. In this manner, variability due to initial differences in size and, possibly, inherent ability to grow is eliminated and the accuracy of comparisons improved. It should however be noted that observations that are used in this fashion should not reflect treatment effects, since otherwise these might be eliminated with the other variability.

The method of carrying out an analysis of covariance is described in the next chapter.

One further important method of improving the sensitivity of a significance test should be noted, namely by restricting the field of possible or acceptable results. This cannot always be done, but where it can, fewer replications are needed to detect a difference of a given magnitude. Suppose that the possibility of treatment effects occurring in one direction can be ruled out. Then, when the coefficient of variation is, for example, 8 percent, only 15 replications are required to ensure (with 90 percent certainty) that a difference of 10 percent between two means in the given direction is significant at the 95 percent level. This compares with the 18 replications given in Table 1.7.2. A particular instance where such a method could be used would be in an experiment carried out to test the effect of a supplement on the growth of an animal, if it was known that any effect must necessarily increase the weight of the animal. Since the possibility of a negative effect could be ruled out, a *one-tailed* test of significance could be used, and a smaller experiment might be employed to achieve the same level of significance. However, it is implied that the experimenter is prepared to maintain his hypothesis, however detrimental the effect may appear from his results— the smaller experiment is achieved only by completely ruling out the possibility of a negative effect. Further, it should be noted that the improvement exists only in the sensitivity of the test of significance; with the same number of replications, the accuracy of the estimates remains unaltered. This device, then, is of limited advantage.

1.9 Choosing the design

There are three main steps in choosing the design—

(1) It has to be decided whether the design is unifactor or factorial.
(2) It has to be decided whether to group the observations to eliminate one, two or more causes of variation. For instance, it may be desired to eliminate simultaneously the effects of time and day of taking the observation. A Latin square design, e.g.—

Time	Day			
	1	2	3	4
1	A	B	D	C
2	B	A	C	D
3	D	C	B	A
4	C	D	A	B

illustrates one method of doing this, since each treatment is observed once on each day and once at each time of day.

(3) It has to be decided whether the number of treatments or treatment combinations is too large to allow a full replication to be fitted conveniently into one block. If so, the design will be referred to as an "incomplete block design" and, if not, as a "complete block design".

Table 1.9.1 indicates the types of design that might be used for unifactor or factorial experiments in complete or incomplete blocks eliminating one or two causes of variation. For the convenience of the experimenter, these designs are listed in Table 1.9.2, together with a list of properties relevant to their selection or rejection and of the pages of this text where reference is made to them.

Not all of the important properties nor all of the important designs are listed in this table, but it indicates those most frequently used. Particular omissions are designs for studying response surfaces, designs for long-term experiments, and designs for groups of experiments. These are dealt with in Chapters 9, 11 and 12, respectively.

Table 1.9.1 Classification of the main designs

		Unifactor	Factorial
Complete block	One grouping	Randomized blocks (1)	
	Two groupings	Latin squares (2)	
Incomplete block	One grouping	Balanced incomplete blocks (3) Partially balanced and cyclic designs (4)	Confounded designs (5) Fractional replications (6) Split-plot designs (7)
	Two groupings	Youden squares (8) Lattice squares (9)	Quasi-Latin squares (10)

1.10 Randomizing the design

The process of randomization is carried out in two main steps. First, a design of the type to be used has to be selected at random. The methods of doing this are described, where necessary, in the chapters relevant to these designs. Secondly, the design chosen has to be randomized.

The randomization may consist of any or all of four processes—

(1) the treatments may be allocated in random order to the treatment symbols;
(2) the treatment symbols may be arranged in random order in each block;

Table 1.9.2 Properties of main designs

Design	Pages	Properties
1 Randomized blocks	31–33	Easy to carry out. Easy to adjust for missing observations and other experimental complications. Any number of treatments and any number of replications can be used.
2 Latin squares	37–40	Relatively easy to carry out. Little difficulty in correcting for missing observations. Number of replications must be a multiple of the number of treatments, e.g. with 8 treatments, 8, 16, 24, . . . replications have to be used. This is often a disadvantage if the number of treatments is large. Useful for dealing with up to 10 treatments.
3 Balanced incomplete blocks	183–90	More difficult to carry out. Difficult to adjust for missing observations and other experimental complications. The number of replications needed is often large, although a number of designs exist which require few replications.
4 Partially balanced and cyclic designs	192–5	To be used when balanced incomplete blocks do not exist or when certain comparisons amongst the treatments are of special interest. Difficult to carry out and to adjust for missing observations and other experimental complications. The large number of designs that have been tabulated give considerable flexibility in the choice of the number of treatments and replications. Many of these designs can be used when there are two groupings.
5 Confounded designs	102–30	Can be used for any factorial arrangement but most useful for 2^m, 3^m, or 4^m designs when the number of treatments per block is 2^r, 3^r, or 4^r. Care is needed in applying the treatment combinations and if only one replicate is used, the design is more difficult to adjust for missing observations. Any number of replications may be used.

Table 1.9.2 Properties of main designs (*continued*)

	Design	Pages	Properties
6	Fractional replication	131–45	As for confounded designs. One-half, one-third or one-quarter replicates commonly used. Permits the experimenter to plan his investigation as a sequence of small experiments. Difficult to adjust for missing observations.
7	Split-plot designs	71–4 93–101 152–61	Allows some effects and interactions to be estimated with more accuracy at the expense of the accuracy of others. Particularly useful when some of the factors in the experiment require large quantities of experimental material whilst other factors can be economically used on small quantities of material.
8	Youden squares	190–1	Most useful for less than 40 treatments. More difficult to carry out. Difficult to adjust for missing observations and other experimental complications. Number of replications must equal the number of treatments per block. Number of treatments must equal the number of blocks. Limited number of suitable designs.
9	Lattice squares	191–2	Useful for dealing with 16–49 treatments. More difficult to carry out. Difficult to adjust for missing observations and other experimental complications. The number of treatments should be p^2 when the number of replications is $p + 1$, or if p is odd, possibly $\frac{1}{2}(p + 1)$.
10	Quasi-Latin squares	146–52	Most useful for 2^5, 2^6, 3^3, 3^4, 4^3 designs. More difficult to carry out. Difficult to adjust for missing observations and other experimental complications. The number of observations must be a perfect square or a multiple of a perfect square. The number of replications is usually small. Some care is usually needed in randomizing this design.

(3) the blocks may be arranged in random order;

(4) the rows and columns of the design may be arranged in random order.

Thus only process (2) is required in randomized block designs; processes (1) and (4) in Latin squares; processes (1), (2) and (3) in balanced incomplete block and other incomplete block designs; processes (1), (3) and (4) in Youden and lattice squares; processes (2) and (3) in factorial designs; and process (4) alone in quasi-Latin squares (with certain exceptions as indicated on pp. 148–51). In any case, the randomization process requires the arrangement of one or more series of quantities in random order, so that if random ordering can be carried out without allowing a personal or systematic element to intervene, the randomization can also be carried out.

To help with the process of placing a series of objects in random order, Appendix Tables A.7 to A.10 contain series of random orderings of the numbers 1–9, 1–16, 1–25, and 1–36. To obtain random orderings of any series of quantities, number them and look up the random orderings of the next higher number, rejecting numbers which are not needed. For instance, to find random orders of seven quantities, the random orderings of the numbers 1–9 should be used and the numbers 8 and 9 rejected.

To demonstrate the uses of this table, consider the randomization of the Latin square

A	B	C	D	E
B	D	E	C	A
C	E	B	A	D
D	C	A	E	B
E	A	D	B	C

The five treatments 1–5 may be assigned to the letters in the order in which they occur in Appendix Table A.7: A1, B2, C5, D4, E3. The design then becomes

1	2	5	4	3
2	4	3	5	1
5	3	2	1	4
4	5	1	3	2
3	1	4	2	5

Next, the rows of this design have to be arranged in random order. If this is done according to the second column of Appendix Table A.7, the five rows have to be rearranged in the order 4, 1, 3, 5, 2, thus—

4	5	1	3	2
1	2	5	4	3
5	3	2	1	4
3	1	4	2	5
2	4	3	5	1

Lastly, the columns may be arranged according to the order shown in the third column of Appendix Table A.7, i.e. 1, 3, 4, 5, 2, giving the final randomization—

4	1	3	2	5
1	5	4	3	2
5	2	1	4	3
3	4	2	5	1
2	3	5	1	4

The design should be applied in this form.

In the above illustration, the first three random orderings of Appendix Table A.7 have been used for convenience. In general, it is preferable to select, without inspection of the table, orderings from different sections. If this has to be done often, a larger random number table should be used to avoid re-using the same orderings.

Alternatively, if access to an electronic computer can be obtained, numerous methods are available for generating random permutations of numbers by computer.

1.11 Carrying out the analysis

The details of the analysis of specific designs will be given in the appropriate sections. Sometimes numerical examples will be provided; at other times the analysis will be formulated using the following notation—

$$\Sigma x = x_1 + x_2 + \ldots + x_n$$

$$\bar{x} = (x_1 + x_2 + \ldots + x_n)/n = \Sigma x/n$$

$$\Sigma(x - \bar{x})^2 = (x_1 - \bar{x})^2 + (x_2 - \bar{x})^2 + \ldots + (x_n - \bar{x})^2$$

$$= \Sigma x^2 - \frac{(\Sigma x)^2}{n}$$

$$\Sigma(x - \bar{x})(y - \bar{y}) = (x_1 - \bar{x})(y_1 - \bar{y}) + (x_2 - \bar{x})(y_2 - \bar{y}) + \ldots$$
$$+ (x_n - \bar{x})(y_n - \bar{y})$$

$$= \Sigma xy - \frac{(\Sigma x)(\Sigma y)}{n}$$

$$\text{s.s. } x = \frac{\Sigma(x - \bar{x})^2}{\text{Number of observations entering into each total } x}$$

$$\text{s.p. } xy = \frac{\Sigma(x - \bar{x})(y - \bar{y})}{\text{Number of observations entering into each total } x \text{ or } y}.$$

B_i $(i = 1, 2, \ldots, b)$, T_i $(i = 1, 2, \ldots, t)$, R_i $(i = 1, 2, \ldots, r)$ and C_i $(i = 1, 2, \ldots, c)$ will usually be used to denote block, treatment, row, and column totals respectively. G will be used to denote the overall total of all observations, and N the number of such observations. Thus, for instance, if each treatment total contains, say, n observations, we have

$$\text{s.s. } T = \frac{\Sigma T^2}{n} - \frac{(\Sigma T)^2}{N}$$

$$= \frac{T_1^2 + T_2^2 + \ldots + T_t^2}{n} - \frac{G^2}{N}.$$

If it is necessary to distinguish between the observations to which these totals refer, parentheses will be used. Thus $T_i(x)$ refers to treatment totals of the variable x, and $T_i(y)$ refers to treatment totals of the variable y, so that

$$\text{s.p. } T(x)T(y) = \frac{T_1(x)T_1(y) + \ldots + T_t(x)T_t(y)}{n} - \frac{G(x)G(y)}{N}.$$

Most of the analyses considered in this text can be carried out without too much difficulty on a desk calculator. In fact, the more sophisticated electronic calculating machines now available enable one to calculate the various sums, sums of squares and sums of cross-products in one operation; some will permit automatic calculation of more complex quantities such as standard errors; others can be programmed to carry out the entire analysis at one time. For other analyses the use of an electronic computer would be virtually essential. If a number of experiments are to be analysed then the use of a computer would be of considerable advantage even for the simplest type of experimental designs. General-purpose computer programs that enable any type of design to be analysed are available; see, for example, the papers on statistical programming in *Applied Statistics*, **16**, No. 2, 1967. Such programs can also be readily adapted to deal with unforeseen experimental complications such as missing observations. A further advantage of the computer is that it permits the estimated residuals from an analysis to be easily obtained. These would be tedious, and possibly difficult, to calculate on a desk calculator. An examination of the residuals is important in that it will often indicate whether the assumptions underlying the analysis have been violated or whether any observation, or set of observations, should be regarded as extreme, i.e. as outliers.

2 Randomized Blocks and Latin Squares

2.1 Randomized block design

The randomized block design is the simplest form of experimental design making use of the idea of stratification. The treatment material is first stratified into blocks, each block consisting of material as homogeneous as possible, and one replication of the treatment is then applied in random order to each block. Any number of replications may be used. Thus, for instance, with four treatments, replications may be set up using Appendix Table A.7: 1, 2, 4, 3; 4, 1, 3, 2; 1, 3, 4, 2; etc.

Since the treatments are applied at random on each block, treatment means give rise to unbiased estimates of treatment effects. The analysis of variance follows the lines shown in Table 2.1.1.

Table 2.1.1 Analysis of variance of randomized block experiment

	d.f.	s.s.	m.s.
Blocks	$b - 1$	s.s. B	
Treatments	$t - 1$	s.s. T	
Residual	$(b - 1)(t - 1)$	Obtained by differencing	s^2
Total	$bt - 1$	s.s. x	

The residual mean square may then be used to calculate standard errors of the means and differences between means in the manner described in **1.5**.

2.2 Examples of the analysis of a randomized block experiment

To illustrate the analysis of a randomized block experiment, we shall consider the results of a randomized block experiment using eight litters of five rats to test the effects of five diets on their weight gains in the four weeks after weaning. This experiment, conducted by Miss M. Chalmers, used litters as blocks, so that genetic variability in the weight gains could be eliminated. Its results are given in Table 2.2.1.

The means for the five diets are thus—

A	B	C	D	E
62·6	65·4	64·2	63·4	70·9

Table 2.2.1   Results of a randomized block experiment (weight gains in grams)

Litter	A	B	Diet C	D	E	Total
1	57·0	64·8	70·7	68·3	76·0	336·8
2	55·0	66·6	59·4	67·1	74·5	322·6
3	62·1	69·5	64·5	69·1	76·5	341·7
4	74·5	61·1	74·0	72·7	86·6	368·9
5	86·7	91·8	78·5	90·6	94·7	442·3
6	42·0	51·8	55·8	44·3	43·2	237·1
7	71·9	69·2	63·0	53·8	61·1	319·0
8	51·5	48·6	48·1	40·9	54·4	243·5
Total	500·7	523·4	514·0	506·8	567·0	2611·9

To estimate the standard errors of means and differences an analysis of variance has to be calculated. For this, we calculate

$$\text{s.s. } x = 57 \cdot 0^2 + 64 \cdot 8^2 + \ldots + 54 \cdot 4^2 - \frac{2611 \cdot 9^2}{40}$$

$$= 7584 \cdot 1$$

$$\text{s.s. } B = \frac{336 \cdot 8^2 + 322 \cdot 6^2 + \ldots + 243 \cdot 5^2}{5} - \frac{2611 \cdot 9^2}{40}$$

$$= 6099 \cdot 5$$

$$\text{s.s. } T = \frac{500 \cdot 7^2 + 523 \cdot 4^2 + \ldots + 567 \cdot 0^2}{8} - \frac{2611 \cdot 9^2}{40}$$

$$= 346 \cdot 9.$$

The analysis of variance is thus as shown in Table 2.2.2.

Table 2.2.2   Analysis of variance

	d.f.	s.s.	m.s.
Litters	7	6099·5	871·4
Diets	4	346·9	86·7
Residual	28	1137·7	40·6
Total	39	7584·1	

The variance ratio, $86{\cdot}7/40{\cdot}6 = 2{\cdot}14$, fails to reach the 5 percent level of significance, $2{\cdot}71$, and the differences between the treatments cannot be regarded as significant.

The standard error of the treatment means is

$$\sqrt{\left(\frac{40{\cdot}6}{8}\right)} = \pm\ 2{\cdot}25$$

and of the difference between treatment means is

$$\sqrt{\left[40{\cdot}6\left(\frac{1}{8}+\frac{1}{8}\right)\right]} = \pm\ 3{\cdot}19.$$

These should, in general, be used only for tests of significance of specific comparisons which the experiment was designed to test, and not for testing any large difference. The failure of the treatment variance-ratio to reach significance prohibits the general testing of comparisons between treatments.

2.3   Testing specific comparisons

If an experiment is carried out for the purpose of estimating and testing specific comparisons, these comparisons may be isolated and tested separately, irrespective of the significance of the general differences between treatments. For instance, in the experiment of the last section it was planned *before the start of the experiment* to compare diet 5, a herring-meal diet, with the remainder. It is therefore valid to make this comparison, even though an overall test of the differences between diets gives no significant results.

The overall mean of the weight increases on diets 1–4 is $63{\cdot}9$ as compared with the mean $70{\cdot}9$ for diet 5. The difference, $7{\cdot}0$, has a standard error

$$\sqrt{40{\cdot}6\left[\left(\frac{1}{8}+\frac{1}{32}\right)\right]} = \pm\ 2{\cdot}52.$$

The 99 percent confidence limits for this difference are thus $7{\cdot}0 \pm 2{\cdot}76 \times 2{\cdot}52 = 0{\cdot}04$ and $13{\cdot}96$, and it is consequently significant at the 1 percent level.

A component corresponding to this comparison may be isolated in the analysis of variance if so desired. The chief purpose of this is to allow the remainder to be examined rather than to test the specific comparison which may be more conveniently and directly tested as above.

To obtain the component corresponding to the comparison of the ith treatment with the remainder it is necessary to calculate

$$\frac{(G - tT_i)^2}{N(t - 1)}$$

as a sum of squares with 1 degree of freedom. Thus, for the data of the last section, the component corresponding to the comparison of diet 5 with the remainder is

$$\frac{(2611 \cdot 9 - 5 \times 567 \cdot 0)^2}{40 \times 4} = 311 \cdot 1,$$

and the full analysis of variance is as shown in Table 2.3.1.

Table 2.3.1 Full analysis of variance

	d.f.	s.s.	m.s.
Litters	7	6099·5	871·4
Diets ⎰ 5 — 1 to 4	1	311·1	311·1
⎱ Remainder	3	35·8	11·9
Residual	28	1137·7	40·6
Total	39	7584·1	

It is apparent that the comparison between diet 5 and the rest accounts for most of the treatments sum of squares; the variation between treatments 1 to 4 is negligible.

More complicated comparisons may be made, and correspondingly more complicated components may be removed in the analysis of variance. Thus, for instance, components may be required to test the average rate of change of treatment response with, say, amount or time of application. Such comparisons represent linear combinations of the observations of the type

$$a_1 x_1 + a_2 x_2 + \ldots + a_n x_n.$$

Their standard errors are given by

$$\sqrt{[s^2(a_1{}^2 + a_2{}^2 + \ldots + a_n{}^2)]}$$

and the corresponding sum of squares in the analysis of variance is

$$\frac{(a_1 x_1 + a_2 x_2 + \ldots + a_n x_n)^2}{a_1{}^2 + a_2{}^2 + \ldots + a_n{}^2}.$$

These rules will be used in subsequent sections.

Where two or more specific comparisons have to be made simultaneously, it is necessary for them to be independent or *orthogonal* if the corresponding components in the analysis of variance are also to be independent. The condition for two comparisons $\Sigma a_i x_i$ and $\Sigma b_i x_i$ to be orthogonal is $\Sigma a_i b_i = 0$. If this condition is not satisfied, then the two comparisons tend to be affected by each other, and the separation of their corresponding components in the analysis of variance is an invalid procedure. It is nevertheless possible to eliminate all effects of one component from the other and to use the resulting comparisons in the analysis of variance instead. Thus

$$\sum \left(b_i - a_i \frac{\Sigma a_i b_i}{\Sigma a_i^2} \right) x_i$$

is independent of $\Sigma a_i x_i$ and may be used instead of $\Sigma b_i x_i$. For example, the comparison of diet 4 with diets 1, 2, 3 and 5 is not independent of the comparison of diet 5 with the rest. This may be seen since the two comparisons may be represented by $4T_4 - T_1 - T_2 - T_3 - T_5$ and $4T_5 - T_1 - T_2 - T_3 - T_4$ and

$$(-1)^2 + (-1)^2 + (-1)^2 + (-1)(4) + (-1)(4) = -5 \neq 0.$$

However the comparison

$$4T_4 - T_1 - T_2 - T_3 - T_5 + (4T_5 - T_1 - T_2 - T_3 - T_4)/4$$
$$\equiv 5(3T_4 - T_1 - T_2 - T_3)/4$$

is independent of $4T_5 - T_1 - T_2 - T_3 - T_4$. Thus, if diet 5 has been compared with the rest, diet 4 should be compared with the rest *excluding* diet 5 to obtain an independent component.

This method of isolating and testing specific comparisons is of particular interest when the treatments represent an ordered series. For instance, the treatment might represent applications of differing amounts of fertilizer. In such cases it is useful to be able to isolate a component representing the average rate of change of treatment response with level of treatment—a linear component— and components representing the changes in the rate of change of treatment response, i.e. quadratic, cubic, etc., components.

In particular, when the treatment levels are equally spaced the components corresponding to linear, quadratic, . . . , effects can be estimated and tested using tables of orthogonal polynomials. (See, for example, Fisher and Yates' *Statistical Tables*.) The treatment totals need to be multiplied by the appropriate factors, added together and divided by the divisor given in these tables to give the sum of squares to be used in the analysis of variance. For instance, with four equally-space treatments, the linear component is tested using

$$\frac{(-3T_1 - T_2 + T_3 + 3T_4)^2}{20n},$$

the quadratic component using

$$\frac{(T_1 - T_2 - T_3 + T_4)^2}{4n},$$

and the cubic component using

$$\frac{(-T_1 + 3T_2 - 3T_3 + T_4)^2}{20n}.$$

These three components add up to give the total treatment sum of squares.

Table 2.3.2 gives values of the appropriate factors for testing linear, quadratic

Table 2.3.2 Coefficients of linear, quadratic and cubic components

Linear component

Number of treatments	3	4	5	6	7	8	9
Factors	-1	-3	-2	-5	-3	-7	-4
	0	-1	-1	-3	-2	-5	-3
	1	1	0	-1	-1	-3	-2
		3	1	1	0	-1	-1
			2	3	1	1	0
				5	2	3	1
					3	5	2
						7	3
							4
Divisor	$2n$	$20n$	$10n$	$70n$	$28n$	$168n$	$60n$

Quadratic component

Number of treatments	3	4	5	6	7	8	9
Factors	1	1	2	5	5	7	28
	-2	-1	-1	-1	0	1	7
	1	-1	-2	-4	-3	-3	-8
		1	-1	-4	-4	-5	-17
			2	-1	-3	-5	-20
				5	0	-3	-17
					5	1	-8
						7	7
							28
Divisor	$6n$	$4n$	$14n$	$84n$	$84n$	$168n$	$2772n$

Cubic component

Number of treatments	3	4	5	6	7	8	9
Factors		-1	-1	-5	-1	-7	-14
		3	2	7	1	5	7
		-3	0	4	1	7	13
		1	-2	-4	0	3	9
			1	-7	-1	-3	0
				5	-1	-7	-9
					1	-5	-13
						7	-7
							14
Divisor		$20n$	$10n$	$180n$	$6n$	$264n$	$990n$

and cubic components with up to nine treatments. For more than nine treatments, or for quartic and higher components, reference should be made to a full table of orthogonal polynomials.

2.4 Testing a series of treatments

The variance-ratio test in the analysis of variance provides an overall test of the differences between a series of treatments. If the variance-ratio is not significant, then only independent comparisons decided before the start of the experiment should be made. No other comparisons are valid.

If, alternatively, the variance-ratio is significant, it may be concluded that the treatment means differ significantly. To determine which treatments differ from which, the standard error of the difference between pairs of treatment means may be calculated and each tested in turn using a t-test. This procedure will undoubtedly give a larger number of significant differences than actually exist. One way around this problem is to modify the significance level at which each pair is tested. Suppose a variance-ratio shows a significant overall difference between treatment means at the 5 percent level. Since there are $\frac{1}{2}t(t-1) = t^{\star}$, say, possible differences between these means, then each t-test should be conducted at the $(5/t^{\star})$ percent level. This ensures that the *overall* significance level for testing all the differences is approximately 5 percent.

If we are only concerned with differences between pairs of means, and if all means are based on the same number of observations, a more conservative method would be to use Tukey's studentized range test. This involves comparing the difference between the pair of means with a multiple of the standard error of a single mean, where the multiple is given by the upper percentage point of the studentized range distribution, using the same level of significance as that used for the variance-ratio test. This distribution has two parameters, namely t and f, where t is the number of treatments and f represents the degrees of freedom of the residual mean square. Tables of the 5 percent and 1 percent points for this distribution are given for various values of t and f in Appendix Tables A.5 and A.6.

Further details of these and other *multiple comparison* procedures can be found in the excellent book by Miller (1966).

2.5 Latin square design

With randomized block designs the grouping of experimental units into blocks is used to reduce the error of an experiment. In the Latin square design, the grouping of replications in two directions is employed. Each treatment occurs once in each row and once in each column. The number of replications is thus equal to the number of treatments. A typical example is the Latin square shown in **1.10**.

The design may be set out spatially, e.g. in a field, to eliminate differences arising from the positioning of the treatments, but the rows and columns may alternatively be taken to represent quantities such as different times or methods of application of treatments, different batches of treatment material, or possibly different observers. Sometimes, therefore, it is simply desired to eliminate the effects of rows and columns, and on other occasions to estimate them.

The analysis of the Latin square design is quite simple. The treatment means may be used directly to estimate treatment effects, and similarly row and column effects can be estimated, if desired, from row and column means.

The analysis of variance follows lines similar to that for randomized blocks, row and column sums of squares being calculated in the same way as blocks sums of squares are calculated in the latter instance. The analysis is formulated in Table 2.5.1. The residual mean square from this analysis may be used in the usual way to estimate standard errors of means and differences.

Table 2.5.1   Analysis of variance of Latin square experiment

	d.f.	s.s.	m.s.
Rows	$t - 1$	s.s. R	
Columns	$t - 1$	s.s. C	
Treatments	$t - 1$	s.s. T	
Residual	$(t - 1)(t - 2)$	Obtained by differencing	s^2
Total	$t^2 - 1$	s.s. x	

From a given Latin square many different squares can be generated by permuting the rows, columns and treatments. There are four basic, or *standard*, 4×4 Latin squares and 576 different squares in all. Table 2.5.2 gives these four standard squares. Each square has ABCD in the first row and column.

Table 2.5.2   Standard 4×4 Latin squares

I				II				III				IV			
A	B	C	D	A	B	C	D	A	B	C	D	A	B	C	D
B	A	D	C	B	C	D	A	B	D	A	C	B	A	D	C
C	D	B	A	C	D	A	B	C	A	D	B	C	D	A	B
D	C	A	B	D	A	B	C	D	C	B	A	D	C	B	A

To randomize a 4×4 Latin square we would choose at random one of the 576 squares. Alternatively, we could select at random one of the standard squares and then randomize rows, columns and treatments, as shown in **1.10**.

For a 5 × 5 Latin square there are 56 standard squares and 161 280 arrangements. For 6 × 6 and 7 × 7 squares there are 9408 and 16 942 080 standard squares respectively. A restricted randomization is normally used for 5 × 5 and larger squares. The procedure is to select one square, either tabulated or constructed, and then randomize rows, columns and treatments. This procedure is suitable for practical purposes.

2.6 Example of the analysis of a Latin square experiment

In an experiment carried out by K. M. Henry and H. W. Kosterlitz, seven diets were fed to litters of seven male rats. The diets were tested in a 7 × 7

Table 2.6.1 Results of Latin square experiment

Litter	Weight order							Total
	1	2	3	4	5	6	7	
1	E 736·6	A 587·8	G 811·8	B 724·7	F 762·4	D 644·3	C 665·2	4932·8
2	F 757·0	D 737·1	A 578·3	G 826·5	B 809·7	C 662·6	E 794·0	5165·2
3	A 573·2	G 789·8	C 577·0	F 751·0	E 822·5	B 628·3	D 617·1	4758·9
4	C 686·3	E 761·0	B 667·9	D 683·2	A 563·9	F 758·3	G 732·7	4853·3
5	G 942·1	F 802·0	E 920·0	C 635·0	D 725·5	A 550·0	B 667·9	5242·5
6	D 740·0	B 761·6	F 757·8	E 896·6	C 652·9	G 694·1	A 565·8	5068·8
7	B 634·5	C 690·9	D 616·9	A 548·4	G 758·3	E 823·6	F 738·5	4811·1
Total	5069·7	5130·2	4929·7	5065·4	5095·2	4761·2	4781·2	34832·6

Latin square in which the rows represented litters and the columns represented the order of the rats in each litter by weight. Thus the rats on each diet were arranged to eliminate weight and litter differences from treatment comparisons. Measurements were taken of the liver protein in mg per 100 g body weight. The results of this experiment are shown in Table 2.6.1.

Treatment totals

A	B	C	D	E	F	G
3967·4	4894·6	4569·9	4764·1	5754·3	5327·0	5555·3

The treatment means are thus

A	B	C	D	E	F	G
566·8	699·2	652·8	680·6	822·0	761·0	793·6

To estimate their standard errors and to test the differences between them, an analysis of variance is carried out as in Table 2.6.2.

Table 2.6.2   Analysis of variance of Latin square experiment

	d.f.	s.s.	m.s.
Litters	6	29 525	4 921
Weight order	6	20 141	3 357
Diets	6	328 323	54 720
Residual	30	74 170	2 472
Total	48	452 159	

The differences between diets give rise to a variance ratio of 22·1, which is highly significant. The standard error of a treatment mean is $\sqrt{(2472/7)} = \pm 18\cdot79$, and the standard error of the difference between treatment means is

$$\sqrt{[2472(\tfrac{1}{7} + \tfrac{1}{7})]} = \pm 26\cdot6.$$

In this instance, specific comparisons were of interest, and the analysis was concluded as shown in **4.5**. However, if this had not been so, it would have been necessary to carry out one of the procedures indicated in **2.4**. For instance, using Tukey's studentized range test, the 5 percent point from Appendix Table A.5 with parameters $t = 7$ and $f = 30$ is 4·46. Hence mean differences exceeding $18\cdot79 \times 4\cdot46 = 83\cdot81$ would be significant at the 5 percent level.

Hence, employing the studentized range test, it would be concluded that diet A was significantly different from the other diets, that diet C was different from F, G, and E, and that both D and B were significantly different from G and E. Another way of presenting this result would be to arrange the diet means in order and underline those diets *not* significantly different from each other. This gives

A   C   D   B   F   G   E

Of course, the conclusions would be much clearer if these lines were non-overlapping. The availability of further information about the nature of the diets is used in **4.5**.

2.7 Graeco-Latin square design

Graeco-Latin square designs simply carry one step further the process of stratifying the treatments. In designs of this type, the effects of three or more groupings can be removed from all treatment comparisons. An illustration of the type of design is shown in Table 2.7.1.

Table 2.7.1 Graeco-Latin square design

A α	B β	C γ	D δ	E ϵ
C ϵ	D α	E β	A γ	B δ
E δ	A ϵ	B α	C β	D γ
B γ	C δ	D ϵ	E α	A β
D β	E γ	A δ	B ϵ	C α

It will be seen that both the Latin and the Greek Letters occur once in each row and once in each column, and further that each Latin letter occurs once with each Greek letter. In this manner, row, column, Latin letter, and Greek letter effects can be estimated independently, and the sum of squares in the analysis of variance partitioned accordingly.

The Greek letters in this design may be taken to represent either treatments which are completely independent of the Latin letter treatments and which it is desired to test simultaneously, or effects such as source of treatment material, which it is desired to eliminate in making treatment comparisons.

Graeco-Latin squares and squares involving still more groupings may be constructed using sets of orthogonal Latin squares to be found in Fisher and Yates' *Statistical Tables*. No designs of this type exist for dealing with six treatments.

2.8 Efficiency of randomized blocks and Latin squares

In order to estimate the advantage of using blocks in randomized block designs, or rows and columns in Latin square designs, it is necessary to replace the treatment mean square by the residual mean square and to estimate what the mean square would be if blocks or rows or columns had not been used. The advantage is then measured by the gain in efficiency, i.e. the proportional reduction in the residual mean square. Two examples will clarify the procedure.

First, consider the gain in efficiency resulting from the use of litter-mates in the experiment of **2.2** as compared with a completely randomized arrangement. To estimate what the residual mean square would be in such an arrangement, the diets mean square is replaced by the residual mean square in Table 2.2.2, and an overall mean square is calculated, as shown in Table 2.8.1.

The relative efficiencies of the two designs in this instance are thus 189·7 : 40·6 or 467 : 100. A 367 percent increase in efficiency has arisen here from the use of litters as blocks in the randomized block design.

As a second illustration, consider the gain in efficiency resulting from the use of litter-mates as rows in the experiment of **2.6** as compared with a randomized

Table 2.8.1   Estimation of residual mean square for a completely randomized arrangement

	d.f.	s.s.	m.s.
Litters	7	6099·5	871·4
Diets	4	162·4 ←—— 40·6	40·6
Residual	28	1137·7	40·6
Total	39	7398·6 ——→ 189·7	

block design in which only the weight groups were eliminated. The analysis follows the lines shown in Table 2.8.2.

The relative efficiencies of the Latin square and randomized block designs are here 2822 : 2472 or 114 : 100, so that a 14 percent increase in efficiency arises from the use of litter-mates as rows in this design. Similarly, it may be shown that the use of weight ordering as columns gives a 5 percent increase in efficiency.

Table 2.8.2   Estimation of residual mean square for a randomized block arrangement

	d.f.	s.s.	m.s.
Litters	6	29525	4921
Diets	6	14832 ←—— 2472	2472
Residual	30	74170	2472
Total	42	118527 ——→ 2822	

The methods used here for randomized block and Latin square designs can of course be applied to other designs, and they form the basis of most methods of estimating efficiency.

2.9   Covariance analysis for the adjustment of treatment means

It was pointed out in **1.8** that it is often possible to carry out an analysis of covariance to adjust for and eliminate the effects of supplementary measurements, say $x_1, x_2, \ldots$, which can be used to account for some of the variability in the main measurements, $y_1, y_2, \ldots$. A main condition for this to be a valid technique is that the supplementary or *concomitant* observations, x, should not reflect treatment effects, so that the estimates of treatment effects in the dependent measurements, y, should not be biased by the adjustment.

The process of adjustment is carried out in two steps. First, the average amount by which y changes for a unit change in x is estimated. This is

$$b = \frac{\text{Residual sum of products of } x \text{ and } y}{\text{Residual sum of squares of } x}$$

and is calculated by repeating the analysis of variance using x and carrying out and *analysis of covariance* using x and y. Thus, for a randomized block design, the calculation would follow the lines shown in Table 2.9.1.

Table 2.9.1 Analyses of variance and covariance for randomized block experiment

	d.f.	s.s. (y)	s.p. (xy)	s.s. (x)
Blocks	$b-1$	s.s. $B(y)$	s.p. $B(x)B(y)$	s.s. $B(x)$
Treatments	$t-1$	s.s. $T(y)$	s.p. $T(x)T(y)$	s.s. $T(x)$
Residual	$(b-1)(t-1)$		(obtained by differencing)	
Total	$bt-1$	s.s. y	s.p. xy	s.s. x

Note that in doing this it is possible to test whether x is significantly affected by the treatments.

Secondly, the differences of the treatment means of x from a suitable arbitrary value are calculated, and b times these differences are taken from the treatment means for y. This gives the adjusted treatment means for y, the mean values obtained when differences in x are eliminated.

The methods of adjustment will be demonstrated using an example due to Bliss and Marks (1939).

Table 2.9.2 gives the design of an experiment measuring the response of Himalayan rabbits to four doses of insulin. In this experiment, each of the four

Table 2.9.2 Design of an insulin-response experiment

Phase	Rabbit							
	1	2	3	4	5	6	7	8
1	C	A	B	D	C	A	D	B
2	B	D	C	A	D	B	C	A
3	A	C	D	B	A	C	B	D
4	D	B	A	C	B	D	A	C

doses A–D (equally spaced on a logarithmic scale) was given at intervals of 10–20 days to each of eight rabbits. The design was two simultaneous Latin squares in which columns eliminated the differences between rabbits, and rows the differences between phases of the experiment.

Two series of measurements were taken in this experiment. First, the percentage fall in blood-sugar in the animals in the five hours after treatment with insulin was used as a measure of the response to the insulin. Secondly, the initial blood-sugar before the insulin was injected was used as a concomitant observation, since it was believed that the higher initial sugars might give the higher percentage falls in sugar and that a knowledge of this might be used to reduce the variability in the design. Table 2.9.3 gives the results of these two measurements.

Table 2.9.3 Results of an insulin-response experiment

Percentage fall in blood-sugar, f

Phase	Rabbit 1	2	3	4	5	6	7	8	Total
1	32·7	11·2	23·2	48·1	35·1	27·2	36·0	40·0	253·5
2	26·2	31·8	28·9	18·7	37·2	39·8	37·8	25·8	246·2
3	−4.0	14·0	27·5	25·6	2·8	36·2	28·4	50·7	181·2
4	33·2	16·5	21·2	40·2	12·7	47·7	25·1	39·4	236·0
Total	88·1	73·5	100·8	132·6	87·8	150·9	127·3	155·9	916·9

Dosage	A	B	C	D
Total	128·0	212·4	264·3	312·2
Mean	16·00	26·55	33·04	39·02

Initial blood-sugar, i

Phase	Rabbit 1	2	3	4	5	6	7	8	Total
1	107	91	99	93	103	88	94	89	764
2	94	93	90	77	94	85	91	89	713
3	75	83	91	78	87	79	81	84	658
4	94	86	97	87	101	81	87	95	728
Total	370	353	377	335	385	333	353	357	2863

Dosage	A	B	C	D
Total	691	713	735	724
Mean	86·4	89·1	91·9	90·5

To estimate the effect of initial blood-sugar on the percentage fall, it is necessary to calculate analyses of variance and covariance. These follow similar lines to the analyses for a single Latin square. Thus, for instance, for the differences between phases, we have

Sum of squares for mean fall

$$= \frac{1}{8} \left[(253 \cdot 5)^2 + (246 \cdot 2)^2 + (181 \cdot 2)^2 + (236 \cdot 0)^2 - \frac{(916 \cdot 9)^2}{4} \right]$$
$$= 403 \cdot 7.$$

Sum of squares for initial blood-sugar

$$= \frac{1}{8} \left[(764)^2 + (713)^2 + (658)^2 + (728)^2 - \frac{(2863)^2}{4} \right]$$
$$= 727 \cdot 6.$$

Sum of products for mean fall with initial blood-sugar

$$= \frac{1}{8} \left[(253 \cdot 5)(764) + (246 \cdot 2)(713) + (181 \cdot 2)(658) + (236 \cdot 0)(728) \right. $$
$$\left. - \frac{(916 \cdot 9)(2863)}{4} \right]$$
$$= 497 \cdot 6.$$

The completed analyses are thus as shown in Table 2.9.4.

Table 2.9.4 Analyses of variance and covariance

	d.f.	s.s. (f)	s.p. (fi)	s.s. (i)
Rabbits	7	1702·2	−631·2	609·7
Phases	3	403·7	497·6	727·6
Dosages	3	2330·6	488·9	132·4
Residual	18	528·7	119·4	320·3
Total	31	4965·2	474·7	1790·0

It should be noted that the initial blood-sugars do not, of course, reflect differences between dosages.

This analysis may now be used to estimate the effect on fall in blood-sugar of a unit change in initial blood-sugar. This is

$$b = \frac{119 \cdot 4}{320 \cdot 3} = 0 \cdot 373,$$

indicating that higher initial blood-sugars give higher percentage falls in blood-sugar. This might now be used to adjust the mean falls in blood-sugar to initial blood-sugars of 90 exactly. Thus, for instance, dosage A had an initial blood-sugar of 86·4, or 3·6 below the level to which adjustment is to be made. The corresponding adjustment is thus $3 \cdot 6 \times 0 \cdot 373 = 1 \cdot 34$, and the adjusted mean is 17·34. Other adjusted means are given in Table 2.9.5.

Table 2.9.5 Adjusted means

Dosage	A	B	C	D
Mean	17·3	26·9	32·3	38·8

If it is desired to test whether initial blood-sugar accounts for a significant proportion of the residual sum of squares and whether comparisons between adjusted means are more accurate, it should be noted that the sum of squares due to the concomitant observation is b times the residual sum of products. Here this is

$$0·373 \times 119·4 = 44·5,$$

so that an analysis of variance to test the effect of the initial blood-sugar may be set up as in Table 2.9.6.

Table 2.9.6 Analysis of variance testing effect of concomitant observation

	d.f.	s.s. (f)	m.s.
Initial blood-sugar	1	44·5	44·5
New residual	17	484·2	28·5
Old residual	18	528·7	29·4

It may be seen that the adjustment does not account for a significant proportion of the residual sum of squares and that the reduction in the residual mean square due to taking initial blood-sugar into account is very small. Usually in such circumstances the correction for the concomitant observation would not be made, since any gain in accuracy would be too small.

2.10 Standard errors of adjusted means

The standard errors of adjusted means and differences between adjusted means may be calculated from the analysis of covariance. Extra terms need to be included in the standard errors to account for the adjustments.

If the means are adjusted to a value x_0, the ith adjusted mean becomes $\bar{y}_i - b(\bar{x}_i - x_0)$, and its standard error is

$$\sqrt{\left[s^2\left(\frac{1}{n} + \frac{(\bar{x}_i - x_0)^2}{\text{Residual sum of squares for } x}\right)\right]},$$

where the means are based upon n observations. Correspondingly the standard error of the difference between the ith and jth adjusted means is

$$\sqrt{\left[s^2\left(\frac{1}{n_i} + \frac{1}{n_j} + \frac{(\bar{x}_i - \bar{x}_j)^2}{\text{Residual sum of squares for } x}\right)\right]},$$

where the two means are based upon n_i and n_j observations respectively.

For example, for the adjusted mean A of the last section, the appropriate standard error is

$$\sqrt{\left[28{\cdot}5\left(\frac{1}{8}+\frac{(3{\cdot}6)^2}{320{\cdot}3}\right)\right]} = \pm\, 2{\cdot}17,$$

while for the difference between adjusted means A and B, the standard error is

$$\sqrt{\left[28{\cdot}5\left(\frac{1}{8}+\frac{1}{8}+\frac{(2{\cdot}7)^2}{320{\cdot}3}\right)\right]} = \pm\, 2{\cdot}79.$$

It should be noted that this approach means that each difference has a different standard error and therefore may be very lengthy if a number of comparisons have to be made. Finney (1946) has shown how an average value for the standard errors of differences can be calculated using

$$\sqrt{\left[s^2\left(\frac{1}{n_1}+\frac{1}{n_2}\right)\left(1+\frac{\text{Treatment mean square for } x}{\text{Residual sum of squares for } x}\right)\right]}.$$

In this instance, this gives the value

$$\sqrt{\left[28{\cdot}5\left(\frac{1}{8}+\frac{1}{8}\right)\left(1+\frac{44{\cdot}1}{320{\cdot}3}\right)\right]} = \pm\, 2{\cdot}85,$$

compared with $\pm\, 2{\cdot}70$ for the smallest standard error of a difference and $\pm\, 3{\cdot}13$ for the largest.

To attach a standard error to b, it is necessary to use the formula

$$\sqrt{\left(\frac{s^2}{\text{Residual sum of squares for } x}\right)}.$$

Here this gives a value $\pm\, 0{\cdot}298$.

2.11 Significance tests in covariance analysis

Tests of the difference between any pair of means or of any specific comparison may be made using standard errors, calculated as above, and the t table. However, to carry out an overall test of significance on a series of adjusted means, a more lengthy analysis is needed. The example of 2.9 will serve to demonstrate the procedure, although, of course, adjustment would not normally be made for an insignificant concomitant observation.

The first step is to total the sum of squares for the residuals and treatments. Here these are as shown in Table 2.11.1.

Table 2.11.1 Totals for sums of squares

	d.f.	s.s. (f)	s.p. (fi)	s.s. (i)
Dosages and residual	21	2859·3	608·3	452·7

These totals should then be used to calculate the regression coefficient $b = 608{\cdot}3/452{\cdot}7 = 1{\cdot}3437$, the sum of squares attributable to the concomitant observation, $1\cdot3437 \times 608\cdot3 = 817\cdot4$, and the remainder when this has been removed, $2859\cdot3 - 817\cdot4 = 2041\cdot9$. Using this value and the residual of Table 2.9.6, an analysis of variance can now be set up to show the differences between treatments when the effect of initial blood-sugar has been eliminated, the treatment sum of squares being obtained by subtraction. This is done in Table 2.11.2.

Table 2.11.2 Analysis of variance when effect of initial blood-sugar is removed

	d.f.	s.s. (f)	m.s.	Variance ratio
Dosages	3	1557·7	519·2	18·21
Residual	17	484·2	28·5	
Dosages and residual	20	2041·9		

The differences between the adjusted dosage means are obviously very significant, but it might be noted that since in this instance the concomitant variable does not account for a significant amount of the total variation, the variance ratio here is only $18\cdot21$, compared with $26\cdot45$ for the original observations.

To test particular sets of comparisons, it is necessary to employ separate analyses similar to that above to test each set in turn.

2.12 Missing observations in a randomized block design

It may happen that in one of the blocks of the randomized block design one treatment is not tested, or more generally, the results of one or more treatments in one or more blocks are not available. A test-tube may be broken, an animal may die, or a field-plot may be trampled. When this happens, the missing observations make the interpretation of the experiment more difficult, and, of course, the estimates of treatment effects are less accurate. It sometimes happens that all the treatments in one or more blocks of an experiment fail. For randomized blocks this presents no difficulty, since the failed blocks may be ignored in carrying out the analysis.

If a limited number of observations are missing and if we can assume that the loss of the observations is not caused or influenced by the treatments, we can use one of the following two methods for estimating the missing observations. In the first method, we estimate the missing observations by minimizing the residual sum of squares. In the second method, rough values are taken for the missing observations, and an analysis of covariance is then carried out on dummy variables to adjust for the missing values.

First, let us consider a randomized block design with b blocks and t treatments and with one missing value. Let the sum of the observations in the same block as the missing value be B, let the sum of the other observations on the same treatment as the missing value be T, and let the grand sum of all observations not missing be G. Finally, let the missing value be denoted by y. In the analysis of variance table we can show that the residual sum of squares is given by

$$y^2 - \frac{1}{b}(T + y)^2 - \frac{1}{t}(B + y)^2 + \frac{1}{bt}(G + y)^2 + \text{terms not involving } y.$$

The value of y which minimizes this sum of squares is given by

$$y = \frac{tT + bB - G}{(t - 1)(b - 1)}.$$

This value of y takes the place of the missing value in the table, and an analysis of variance is carried out as usual except that one degree of freedom is subtracted from the residual sum of squares. If more than one observation is missing, an iterative procedure can be used. Rough values are given to all the missing values except one. The above formula is used to give this value. This new value can then be used to obtain an estimate of another missing value, and so on. This process proceeds until accurate estimates of the missing values are obtained. The degrees of freedom of the residual sum of squares in the analysis of variance are then reduced by the number of estimated values. Approximate standard errors for the means of sets of observations should be calculated using the actual number of observations. Thus a mean based on ten observations and two estimated observations would be treated as if it were based upon ten observations.

As an example of the analysis of missing observations, we shall consider the randomized block experiment summarized in Table 2.12.1. This table gives

Table 2.12.1 Weight increase of rats on three diets

Litter	Diet A	Diet B	Diet C	Total
1	175·4	176·4	147·8	499·6
2	(x)	134·4	152·4	286·8
3	124·4	155·2	114·2	393·8
4	90·4	111·8	88·2	290·4
5	74·6	99·4	98·4	272·4
6	(y)	136·6	92·6	229·2
7	144·2	133·0	(z)	277·2
8	128·6	151·0	130·4	410·0
Total	737·6	1097·8	824·0	2659·4

Approximations to missing values

	Initial	1st	2nd	3rd
x		138·59	138·58	138·58
y	110·9	109·63	109·80	109·78
z	129·7	127·31	127·30	127·27

the weight increases of rats fed on three diets during seven weeks after weaning. Eight litters of three rats were randomized between the diets in this experiment. Three animals died or gave rise to extreme values which had to be rejected.

Treatment and litter means are first constructed. These, together with the overall mean, can be used to provide initial rough estimates of the missing values. For instance, an initial estimate for y is given by the sum of the mean of litter 6 and the mean of diet A less the overall mean, i.e. $y = 114 \cdot 6 + 122 \cdot 9 - 126 \cdot 6 = 110 \cdot 9$. Similarly, the initial estimate of z is $129 \cdot 7$. These two initial estimates can be used to obtain the first estimate of x, using the above formula, i.e.

$$x = \frac{3(737 \cdot 6 + 110 \cdot 9) + 8(286 \cdot 8) - (2659 \cdot 4 + 110 \cdot 9 + 129 \cdot 7)}{14} = 138 \cdot 59.$$

Using this estimate of x and the initial value of z, a new estimate of y can be calculated by this formula. In Table 2.12.1 the change between the second and third estimates is not very large, and we would accept the third estimates.

The estimated missing values should then be used in the final analysis. Using $138 \cdot 6$, $109 \cdot 8$ and $127 \cdot 3$ for x, y and z respectively, the analysis of variance and table of means is completed in Table 2.12.2. The degrees of freedom of the total and residual sums of squares are reduced by three to give an unbiased estimate of error, but the variance-ratio test is now only approximate.

Table 2.12.2   Analysis of variance and table of means

	d.f.	s.s.	m.s.	Variance ratio
Litters	7	13113·31	1873·33	8·86
Treatments	2	1465·23	732·62	3·47
Residual	11	2325·34	211·39	
Total	20	16903·88		

Diet	A	B	C
Mean	123·3	137·2	118·9

Approximate standard errors of the differences between any two means can easily be constructed. For instance, the standard error of the difference between diets A and B is approximately

$$\sqrt{\left[211 \cdot 39 \left(\frac{1}{6} + \frac{1}{8}\right)\right]} = \pm 7 \cdot 85.$$

In general, if there are a number of comparisons to be tested, the standard error of the difference between groups of about average size might be used as an indicator of the magnitude of error. More exact values may then be calculated in cases of doubtful significance.

If exact tests of significance were required in this experiment, it would be necessary to carry out an analysis of covariance of the weight increases w on dummy variables d_x, d_y and d_z. For each missing value a dummy variable is created. This variable takes the value 1 when it corresponds to the missing observation and zero otherwise. For instance, in our example, $d_x = 1$ for diet A and litter 2 and $d_x = 0$ elsewhere. If each of the missing values is replaced initially by, say, 130·0 the covariance analysis will proceed as in Table 2.12.3.

Table 2.12.3 Analysis of covariance

	d.f.	s.s. (d_x)	s.p. $(d_x d_y)$	s.p. $(d_x d_z)$	s.p. $(d_x w)$
Litters	7	$\frac{7}{24}$	$-\frac{1}{24}$	$-\frac{1}{24}$	11·875
Treatments	2	$\frac{2}{24}$	$\frac{2}{24}$	$-\frac{1}{24}$	−2·358
Residual	14	$\frac{14}{24}$	$-\frac{2}{24}$	$\frac{1}{24}$	−6·575
Total	23	$\frac{23}{24}$	$-\frac{1}{24}$	$-\frac{1}{24}$	2·942

			s.s. (d_y)	s.p. $(d_y d_z)$	s.p. $(d_y w)$
Litters	7		$\frac{7}{24}$	$-\frac{1}{24}$	−7·325
Treatments	2		$\frac{2}{24}$	$-\frac{1}{24}$	−2·358
Residual	14		$\frac{14}{24}$	$\frac{1}{24}$	12·625
Total	23		$\frac{23}{24}$	$-\frac{1}{24}$	2·942

				s.s. (d_z)	s.p. $(d_z w)$
Litters	7			$\frac{7}{24}$	8·675
Treatments	2			$\frac{2}{24}$	−7·808
Residual	14			$\frac{14}{24}$	2·075
Total	23			$\frac{23}{24}$	2·942

					s.s. (w)
Litters	7				12505·40
Treatments	2				1359·14
Residual	14				2642·70
Total	23				16507·24

The corrections to be subtracted from the initial estimates of the missing values are given by the solutions of the equations

$$\tfrac{14}{24}x - \tfrac{2}{24}y + \tfrac{1}{24}z = -6\cdot575$$
$$-\tfrac{2}{24}x + \tfrac{14}{24}y + \tfrac{1}{24}z = 12\cdot625$$
$$\tfrac{1}{24}x + \tfrac{1}{24}y + \tfrac{14}{24}z = 2\cdot075$$

i.e.　$x = -8\cdot58, \quad y = 20\cdot22, \quad z = 2\cdot73.$

The most accurate estimates of the missing values are thus 138·58, 109·78 and 127·27. In this case, the values are the same as those obtained previously.

The analysis of covariance may be completed without much difficulty and tables of means constructed as in Table 2.12.4. The variance-ratio tests are now exact.

Table 2.12.4　Analysis of variance and table of means

	d.f.	s.s.	m.s.	Variance ratio
Litters	7	12615·80	1802·26	8·53
Treatments	2	1349·49	674·75	3·19
Residual	11	2325·33	211·39	
Total	20	16290·62		

Diet	A	B	C
Mean	123·2	137·2	118·9

Approximate standard errors may be attached to the difference between means in the same manner as before. If exact values are required, it is necessary to calculate the inverse matrix of the coefficients of the equations. Methods for inverting matrices are given in most books on matrix algebra; see, for example, Graybill (1969). This gives the matrix

$$\begin{bmatrix} 1\cdot7620 & 0\cdot2620 & -0\cdot1446 \\ 0\cdot2620 & 1\cdot7620 & -0\cdot1446 \\ -0\cdot1446 & -0\cdot1446 & 1\cdot7349 \end{bmatrix}$$

From this we can see, for example, that the variance of the adjustment to x is $1\cdot762\sigma^2$ and of the adjustment to $x + y$ is $4\cdot048\sigma^2$. The standard error of the difference between the treatment means for A and B is thus

$$\sqrt{\left[211\cdot39\left(\frac{1}{8} + \frac{1}{8} + \frac{4\cdot048}{64}\right)\right]} = \pm\, 8\cdot14$$

or about 4 percent greater than the previous value.

Normally, the main need will be for unbiased estimates of treatment effects, and rough estimates of standard errors will suffice. Hence, unless a large number of observations are missing, the successive approximation method is usually preferable.

If a large number of observations are missing, the standard errors derived by this method will be inaccurate. However, in this case, the treatment effects will usually be inaccurately estimated, and an extensive analysis will not generally be worthwhile.

The successive approximation method is not particularly useful for analysing experiments using digital computers. Since the method is algebraic rather than arithmetical, different formulae would be required for the different types of block designs. Healy and Westmacott (1956) proposed an alternative method suitable for use on computers. Its main attraction is that it involves repeated use of the analysis routines needed when there are no missing values. As before, the procedure estimates the missing observations so as to minimize the residual variance. With initial estimates replacing the missing observations, the first step is to calculate the residuals for all plots containing missing observations. These residuals measure the deviations from the general mean, corrected for treatment and block effects. They can easily be obtained in a routine analysis on a computer. For a randomized block design, the residuals are given by expressions of the form $y_{ij} - t_i - b_j + m$, where y_{ij} is the observation on the ith treatment in the jth block, t_i is the ith treatment mean, b_j the jth block mean and m the overall mean. New estimates of the missing observations are then obtained by subtracting their residuals from the initial estimates. New residuals are then calculated and used to obtain new estimates. The process is continued until the residuals of the missing plots are sufficiently close to zero or, alternatively, until there is little difference between two successive residual sums of squares. Applying this technique to the data in Table 2.12.1, using the same initial estimates, gave the estimates $x = 138·58, y = 109·78$ and $z = 127·27$ after six iterations.

Pearce (1965) suggested a refinement to this technique aimed at reducing the number of iterations. This involves multiplying the residuals by N/f before re-estimating the missing observations, where N is the total number of plots and f the number of degrees of freedom for error in the complete design. For a randomized block design, $N = bt$ and $f = (t - 1)(b - 1)$. For the data of Table 2.12.1, the same estimates as above are obtained, using Pearce's refinement, after three iterations. A further modification of the procedure has been proposed by Pearce and Jeffers (1971); see also Preece (1971).

The analysis of covariance technique is particularly well suited for use on computers. As for the Healy–Westmacott procedure, it makes repeated use of the analysis routines that are needed when there are no missing values. The residuals from such an analysis are again required. The first steps are to compute the residuals from a standard analysis of the observations *and* of each of the dummy variables. They will then provide the equations required to obtain the estimates. Any values can be used to replace the missing observations initially. Table 2.12.5 gives the residuals for the plots containing the missing observations for the weight increases w and the dummy variables d_x, d_y and d_z. Initial values of 130·0 are again used.

The values given in Table 2.12.5 are, in fact, the quantities in the equations on page 52. To complete the analysis, therefore, all that is now required is a

Table 2.12.5 Residuals for the missing plots from a randomized block analysis of weight increases and dummy variables

Diet	Litter	w	d_x	d_y	d_z
A	2	−6·575	0·5833	−0·0833	0·0417
A	6	12·625	−0·0833	0·5833	0·0417
C	7	2·075	0·0417	0·0417	0·5833

routine to invert the matrix of coefficients and hence solve the equations. Apart from providing exact estimates and standard errors, the method has the additional advantage that it is non-iterative; further details can be found in Rubin (1972).

2.13 Missing observations in a Latin square design

The methods given in **2.12** for estimating missing observations can also be used in Latin square experiments. If one observation is missing then the estimate which minimizes the residual sum of squares is

$$y = \frac{t(R + C + T) - 2G}{(t - 1)(t - 2)},$$

where R, C and T are respectively the totals for the row, column and treatment which contain the missing observation, and where G is the overall total. An iterative procedure, using the above formula, can be used if more than one observation is missing. Alternatively, a covariance analysis with dummy covariates can be adopted. Healy–Westmacott's procedure, a suitable modification of it, or a covariance analysis could be used in a computer analysis, where residuals now measure the deviations from the general mean, corrected for treatment, row, and column effects.

For Latin squares with missing rows (or columns) the orthogonality between treatments and columns (or rows) will have been destroyed. In this situation, the columns (or rows) form incomplete blocks and the design can be analysed along the lines indicated in Chapter 10. Alternatively, the method given below for a missing treatment can be used.

Where a treatment has failed or almost failed, it is usually necessary to ignore the measurements from that treatment. Otherwise, the inclusion of these values in the analysis would often give a heterogeneous error. For a randomized block design, the failed treatment can be ignored and the remaining treatments analysed as a randomized block design. If, however, the design is more complicated, then the rejection of the observations from one treatment destroys the orthogonality of the various comparisons.

Yates (1936) has given a simple procedure for fitting values for the rejected treatment. The method, which is basically the same as the Healy–Westmacott procedure, will be demonstrated by means of an example. Table 2.13.1 gives

Table 2.13.1 Hay yields in a 6 × 6 Latin square

														Total	Deviations
E	42·6	A	—	F	28·5	C	32·2	B	32·2	D	25·7	161·2	−1·77
C	41·5	E	40·2	B	34·4	F	32·6	D	33·9	A	—	182·6	2·51
F	32·2	C	33·3	D	25·7	B	32·6	A	—	E	30·2	154·0	−3·21
B	35·0	F	39·1	A	—	D	35·0	E	34·4	C	35·6	179·1	1·81
D	33·9	B	36·1	E	35·0	A	—	C	40·8	F	41·9	187·7	3·53
A	—	D	28·5	C	31·6	E	23·3	F	32·6	B	39·8	155·8	−2·85
Total	185·2		177·2		155·2		155·7		173·9		173·2	1020·4	0·02
Deviations	3·03		1·43		−2·97		−2·87		0·77		0·63	0·02	

Overall mean = 34·01

the yields of hay in a 6×6 Latin square to which six liming treatments were applied. The zero level, A, gave yields of about one-half the other yields, and we might therefore reject it in carrying out the analysis.

The first step is to form the row and column means and to determine their deviations from the overall mean. These are shown in Table 2.13.1.

These deviations are then used to derive first estimates for the missing values. Thus, in the first column the estimate of the missing value is $34·01 + 3·03 - 2·85 = 34·19$, and the estimates in the other columns are 33·67, 32·85, 34·67, 31·57, 37·15. These estimates should now be substituted in the Latin square, and the deviations of the row and column means from the overall means recalculated. These can then be used to derive second estimates for the missing values. Here these are 34·21, 33·60, 32·65, 34·77, 31·15, 37·66.

This process can now be repeated until fairly stable estimates are obtained. It is unnecessary to recalculate the row and column deviations each time, and only the changes in these need be recorded. For instance, for the plot in the sixth column, with 37·66 instead of 37·15 the row and column deviations increase by $\frac{1}{6}(37·66 - 37·15) = 0·085$. The next estimate is thus $37·66 + 0·085 + 0·085 = 37·83$.

The final values so derived are 34·2, 33·6, 32·6, 34·8, 31·0, 37·9. These should now be substituted in the Latin square, and the analysis completed as in Table 2.13.2. Of course, the comparison of the estimated treatment with the others is of no importance and should be isolated and treated as error. Here, the sum of squares for the comparison of A with the other treatments is zero.

Table 2.13.2 Analysis for incomplete Latin square

	d.f.	s.s.	m.s.	Variance ratio
Rows	5	219·23		
Columns	5	129·87		
Treatments	4	103·86	25·96	1·44
Residual	15	270·36	18·02	
Total	29	723·32		

Treatment means ($\pm$ 1·73)

B	C	D	E	F
35·0	35·8	30·4	34·3	34·5

The row and column sums of squares in this table are not independent, but their total gives the sum of squares due to rows and columns. To derive a test for, say, rows, it is necessary to subtract the sum of squares for columns, calculated directly from Table 2.13.1, from this total.

A similar procedure to that above can be applied for any number of missing treatments.

It should be noted that it is sometimes possible to avoid a great deal of extra calculation if the row-to-row or column-to-column variation is not very large. It is then often possible to ignore either rows or columns and to treat the experiment as randomized blocks in order to derive an approximate estimate of the residual mean square. In this instance, if rows are ignored, the mean square becomes 18·72, and if columns are ignored it becomes 22·30. Either of these might be used to provide approximate standard errors.

3 Simple Factorial and Split-plot Designs

3.1 Purposes of factorial experiments

In setting up experiments of the type described in the last chapter, it is common to estimate and compare treatment effects under a broad set of conditions. The results from such experiments apply only to the conditions under which they are carried out, and if these are changed, the results may be completely altered. Only by varying the basic conditions or treatments within the experiment can wider results be obtained. The factorial experiment does this by testing the treatments under a series of different conditions.

For instance, in comparing weight increases of animals kept on different diets, animals of both sexes from several breeds fed by different methods may be used in a factorial design. By using every method of feeding each diet to both sexes of each breed, i.e. a factorial design, it is possible to determine the best methods, diets, and breeds. It is also possible to study whether the best method of feeding varies from diet to diet, or whether the optimum method and diet depend upon the sex and breed of animal. Consequently, by using a factorial design we can study the manner in which the effects may vary with changes in other experimental factors, i.e. the *interaction* of the experimental factors.

The factorial design, by using every combination of a series of treatments and experimental conditions, allows the average effects and, more important, their interactions with one another to be estimated simultaneously. By this approach, the constancy of each effect may be tested, and where it is shown to be dependent on the other treatments, any interrelation may be studied. If the set of factors do not interact, all the observations may be used in making treatment comparisons. If, however, they do interact, then attention may have to be restricted to particular combinations. The existence of interactions can only be verified by the use of a factorial experiment, and the simultaneous determination of significant interactions is greatly facilitated. The recognition of which interactions are relevant then allows attention to be focused on these. For example, if we find that the best method of feeding depends upon the diet but not upon the breed or sex of the animal, we may consider the different methods of feeding for each diet separately, but averaged over both sexes and all breeds.

A factorial experiment, therefore, is concerned with examining simultaneously a number of basic treatments or *factors*, each of which take a number of possible forms or *levels*. A particular combination of the levels of the factors determines a treatment. The term "factor" is used here to indicate any feature that is under the control of the experimenter and can be varied at will from trial to trial. Factors of this kind should be distinguished from classification factors which are used to increase the precision of the experiment by stratifying the experimental units into relatively homogeneous groups. The methods considered in the last chapter for grouping units and for controlling the remaining variation by randomization also apply in factorial experiments.

3.2 Example of a simple factorial experiment

Table 3.2.1 gives the results of a simple factorial design carried out by S. Jamieson to test suspected copper and cobalt deficiencies of pasture. Four groups of twenty-five sheep were chosen at random in this experiment. The first group was left untreated, the second group was given copper salts by mouth, the third group was similarly given cobalt salts, and the last group both copper and cobalt salts. The figures in Table 3.2.1 give the weight gains in the first six weeks of the experiment.

Table 3.2.1   Weight increases of sheep in factorial experiment

Treatment

Neither	Copper	Cobalt	Copper and Cobalt
18	13	18	19
17	20	25	13
34	12	18	22
12	18	22	22
8	16	28	22
9	19	20	20
22	15	22	23
14	14	17	23
20	6	14	26
14	20	22	21
14	25	27	4
22	18	24	20
21	11	23	20
21	18	18	16
13	18	28	15
6	15	25	20
26	14	16	12
17	17	20	10
14	18	19	24
26	7	26	22
22	8	20	22
14	18	19	16
16	22	21	19
18	22	13	2
16	29	14	20

	Neither	Copper	Cobalt	Copper and Cobalt
Total	434	413	519	453
Mean	17·4	16·5	20·8	18·1

There is apparently a positive effect of cobalt and a negative effect of copper. To obtain standard errors for these means, an analysis of variance has to be carried out as shown in Table 3.2.2. The variance ratio, 2·78, just reaches significance at the 5 percent level, but this is of no particular interest here since the experiment is designed to test specific comparisons.

Table 3.2.2   Analysis of variance

	d.f.	s.s.	m.s.
Treatments	3	252·2	84·1
Residual	96	2907·2	30·3
Total	99	3159·4	

First, the mean weight-increase of animals receiving copper (Cu) may be compared with those not receiving it. Secondly, the mean weight-increase of animals receiving cobalt (Co) may be compared with the weight-increases of animals not receiving cobalt. Thirdly, the effects of the copper treatment may be compared for the animals receiving cobalt with those not receiving it, or conversely. This latter comparison tests the constancy of either effect when the other treatment is altered. It measures what is called the "interaction" of the two treatments. These three effects are measured by

$$Cu = \tfrac{1}{2}(18\cdot1 + 16\cdot5) - \tfrac{1}{2}(20\cdot8 + 17\cdot4) = -1\cdot8$$

$$Co = \tfrac{1}{2}(18\cdot1 + 20\cdot8) - \tfrac{1}{2}(16\cdot5 + 17\cdot4) = 2\cdot5$$

$$\text{Interaction } Cu.Co = \tfrac{1}{2}[(18\cdot1 - 20\cdot8) - (16\cdot5 - 17\cdot4)]$$

$$\text{or } \tfrac{1}{2}[(18\cdot1 - 16\cdot5) - (20\cdot8 - 17\cdot4)] = -0\cdot9.$$

It should be noted that the interaction of Cu and Co is defined as *half* the difference between the effects of either treatment in the presence and absence of the other. The factor $\tfrac{1}{2}$ is introduced for two purposes. By its introduction, the interaction is estimated with the same accuracy as the main effects, and all can be tested with the same standard error. Since each represents the difference between the two means of fifty observations, the standard error is

$$\sqrt{\left[30\cdot3\left(\frac{1}{50} + \frac{1}{50}\right)\right]} = \pm\, 1\cdot10.$$

Evidently, only the Co effect is significant, and this is not significantly affected by the presence or absence of Cu.

A further consequence of the use of the additional factor $\tfrac{1}{2}$ is that the average effects and interactions may easily be used to calculate the effects under any conditions. For instance, the effect of Co in the presence of Cu is

$$Co + Cu.Co = 2\cdot5 - 0\cdot9 = 1\cdot6$$

and its effect in the absence of Cu is

$$Co - Cu.Co = 2\cdot5 + 0\cdot9 = 3\cdot4.$$

The interaction Cu.Co may thus be regarded as an adjustment to the average effects to derive effects under given fixed conditions. It serves to indicate the extent to which the effects act independently. For absolute independence, the interaction would be zero.

The treatment sum of squares in the analysis of variance can, of course, be partitioned to indicate the variability arising from each of these three components. The appropriate coefficients for these effects are given in Table 3.2.3.

Table 3.2.3 Coefficients of the factorial effects

Effect	Copper and Cobalt	Cobalt	Copper	Neither	Divisor
	Treatment				
Cu	+1	−1	+1	−1	$4n$
Co	+1	+1	−1	−1	$4n$
Cu.Co	+1	−1	−1	+1	$4n$

We see that these components are orthogonal to each other and account for the three degrees of freedom for treatments. Using the method indicated in **2.3**, the sums of squares for these components are

$$Cu : \frac{(453 - 519 + 413 - 434)^2}{100} = 75\cdot69$$

$$Co : \frac{(453 + 519 - 413 - 434)^2}{100} = 156\cdot25$$

$$Cu.Co : \frac{(453 - 519 - 413 + 434)^2}{100} = 20\cdot25.$$

These total to give the treatments sum of squares. The analysis of variance may thus be used, if so desired, to test the significance of the main effects and interaction.

The main ideas involved in this experiment should be noted. The specification of the results of the experiment using main effects and interactions (which are estimated independently of one another, but with equal accuracy) allows the central characteristics of the results to be readily appreciated. Further, since all observations enter into the estimation of each main effect and interaction, there is little doubt that the factorial arrangement makes use of all available information in the measurements taken. It will be seen in later sections that these properties are characteristic of the factorial design.

3.3   The 2^3 factorial design

As an extension of the analysis let us now consider the 2^3 factorial design, i.e. the design in which all combinations of three factors each at two levels is employed. Suppose the three treatments are nitrate, potash and phosphate, and the higher levels of these treatments are denoted by n, k and p respectively, the lower levels being indicated by the absence of these letters. There are $2^3 = 8$ treatment combinations:

$$(1), n, p, np, k, nk, pk, npk,$$

where (1) represents the combination of the three lower levels, i.e. the absence of the letters n, k and p.

From any such set of treatment combinations, the main effects and interactions may be estimated from the comparison of half the observations with the other half. Thus, in the above example, comparison of the mean of the four treatment combinations with the higher level of nitrate, n, np, nk, npk, with the mean of those with the lower level, (1), p, k and pk, measures the average effect of nitrate. This is usually denoted by N. Thus

$$N = \tfrac{1}{4}[(npk + nk + np + n) - (pk + p + k + (1))],$$

where the mean yield of each treatment combination is used.

Similarly,

$$P = \tfrac{1}{4}[(npk + np + pk + p) - (nk + n + k + (1))]$$

$$K = \tfrac{1}{4}[(npk + nk + pk + k) - (np + n + p + (1))].$$

The interaction of any two factors, the *first-order* interaction, may now be found. Consider the interaction between nitrate and phosphate, denoted by NP. It is first measured separately at each level of potash:

$$NP \text{ (higher level of potash)} = \tfrac{1}{2}[(npk - pk) - (nk - k)]$$

$$NP \text{ (lower level of potash)} = \tfrac{1}{2}[(np - p) - (n - (1))].$$

With potash at the higher level, $npk - pk$ measures the effect of changing the level of nitrate in the presence of phosphate, whilst $nk - k$ measures the effect of changing the level of nitrate in the absence of phosphate. In the absence of interaction these two quantities would be the same, and hence the mean difference of these quantities is a measure of interaction; similarly for potash at the lower level. The NP interaction is taken as the mean of these two effects, i.e.

$$NP = \tfrac{1}{4}[(npk + np + k + (1)) - (nk + pk + n + p)].$$

Similarly, expressions for the other two first-order interactions are given by

$$NK = \tfrac{1}{4}[(npk + nk + p + (1)) - (np + pk + n + k)]$$

$$PK = \tfrac{1}{4}[(npk + pk + n + (1)) - (np + nk + p + k)].$$

A further interaction may be calculated—the second-order interaction. This interaction, denoted by NPK, will be non-existent if the NP interaction is the same at each level of K (or, equivalently, the NK interaction at each level of P, etc.). The mean difference of these two effects therefore provides a measure of the NPK interaction, i.e.

$$NPK = \tfrac{1}{4}[(npk + n + p + k) - (np + pk + nk + (1))].$$

The importance of these seven possible comparisons between the eight treatment combinations lies in that they provide a concise summary of the situation, are independent of one another, and are of equal accuracy. They may in consequence be used to determine the important features of any 2^3 factorial design.

3.4 Example of the analysis of a 2^3 experiment

The calculation and testing of treatment comparisons suggested in the last section is, of course, carried out as a routine procedure, and the form of analysis is in consequence much shorter. The steps to be followed are best demonstrated by an example.

Table 3.4.1 gives the yields of experimental hay plots receiving fertilizer

Table 3.4.1 Experimental plan and yields

pk	k	nk	n	
36·9	31·4	43·6	33·8	Block totals
np	(1)	p	npk	
43·3	28·1	31·9	41·8	290·8
npk	(1)	pk	p	
41·0	31·8	36·5	33·0	
nk	np	k	n	
42·8	35·2	35·9	35·4	291·6
np	k	pk	nk	
35·0	29·6	38·0	36·5	
p	n	(1)	npk	
32·1	38·3	34·2	41·5	285·2

Overall total = 867·6

Treatment totals

(1)	n	p	np	k	nk	pk	npk
94·1	107·5	97·0	113·5	96·9	122·9	111·4	124·3

dressings of nitrate n, phosphate p, and potash k. There are three replications of the eight treatment combinations, making twenty-four plots in all.

The first step is to estimate the treatment effects from the treatment totals. This is best carried out systematically by arranging the treatment totals in a column in a standard order as shown in Table 3.4.2. Each factor is introduced in turn and is followed by all combinations of itself and the factors previously introduced. Thus, if a further factor d were introduced, it would be followed in turn by $nd, pd, npd, kd, nkd, pkd, npkd$.

Table 3.4.2   Calculation of treatment effects

Treatment	Yield	(1)	(2)	(3)	Effect	Mean
(1)	94·1	201·6	412·1	867·6	Total	
n	107·5	210·5	455·5	68·8	N	5·73
p	97·0	219·8	29·9	24·8	P	2·07
np	113·5	235·7	38·9	−10·0	NP	−0·83
k	96·9	13·4	8·9	43·4	K	3·62
nk	122·9	16·5	15·9	9·0	NK	0·75
pk	111·4	26·0	3·1	7·0	PK	0·58
npk	124·3	12·9	−13·1	−16·2	NPK	−1·35

The column of total yields is then used to calculate column (1) in Table 3.4.2. The first four numbers are the sums in pairs of the total yields, and the last four numbers are the differences in pairs of these yields; the upper number is subtracted from the lower in each case. For example, $201·6 = 94·1 + 107·5$, and $13·4 = 107·5 − 94·1$. In the same way, column (2) is derived from column (1), and column (3) from column (2). Since there are three factors, only three columns need be calculated in this manner.

A number of checks are available on the calculations. First, the sum of column (i) will be equal to $2i$ times the total yield of the treatment combinations having the first i factors at the higher level. For instance, the sum of column (3) is eight times the total yield of npk, i.e. $8 \times 124·3 = 1094·4$. Secondly, the leading element in column (3) is the overall total of all plots. Finally, the sum of squares of the other figures in column (3) divided by 24 (the number of plots) gives the treatment sum of squares, i.e.

$$[68·8^2 + 24·8^2 + \ldots (− 16·2)^2]/24 = 321·9,$$

which corresponds to the value s.s. $T = 321·9$ calculated directly. Only the first method, carried out on each column, provides a check on the accuracy of *all* the calculations.

The main effects and interactions may then be directly calculated from column (3) by dividing by half the number of plots, i.e. 12. These are shown in the last column.

It can be seen that the N, P and K effects are all positive. The NK and PK effects are positive, indicating that application of potash tends to increase the effects of nitrate and phosphate. The NP effect is negative, showing that the presence of nitrate reduces the effect of phosphate. In fact, in the presence of nitrate, the average effect of phosphate is reduced to $2\cdot07 - 0\cdot83 = 1\cdot24$. Lastly, the NPK interaction is negative, indicating that, when potash is present, the NP interaction is reduced and that the average effect of phosphate is reduced still further. The effect of phosphate in the presence of nitrate and potash is, in fact,

$$2\cdot07 - 0\cdot83 + 0\cdot58 - 1\cdot35 = 0\cdot47.$$

The overall conclusion is, thus, that nitrate and potash give beneficial effects, especially when applied together. Little is to be gained from the application of phosphate if nitrate is present, especially if potash is also present.

These conclusions might also have been reached from an inspection of the mean yields, but with more than three factors this becomes too difficult and lengthy to carry out, although inspection of the main effects and interactions is still possible.

The above comments are true irrespective of the errors attached to the estimates. It is, however, relevant to inquire which of the main effects and inter-actions are significant, i.e. how reliable these characteristics of the experiment are. For this purpose, standard errors are needed (although the relative magnitude of the effects and interactions often gives a good guide to their reliability), and an analysis of variance needs to be calculated as in Table 3.4.3. This is a randomized block type of analysis.

Table 3.4.3 Analysis of variance

	d.f.	s.s.	m.s.
Blocks	2	$3\cdot0$	
Treatments	7	$321\cdot9$	
Error	14	$124\cdot6$	$8\cdot90$
Total	23	$449\cdot5$	

The standard errors of the treatment effects may then be calculated from $\sqrt{(4s^2/N)}$, N being the total number of observations. Here, this gives

$$\sqrt{\left(\frac{4 \times 8\cdot90}{24}\right)} = \pm\, 1\cdot22,$$

and, using t with 14 degrees of freedom, gives 5 percent and 1 percent levels of significance as $2\cdot61$ and $3\cdot63$ respectively. Evidently both N and K are significant at, roughly, the 1 percent level and nothing else is significant.

The same conclusions could be reached by calculating the sum of squares for each component separately. This is done by squaring the items in column (3) of Table 3.4.2 and then dividing by the total number of observations, i.e. 24. This gives the partition of the treatment sum of squares shown in Table 3.4.4. There is a difference in the total due to rounding off.

Table 3.4.4 Partition of treatment sum of squares

	d.f.	s.s.
N	1	197·2
P	1	25·6
NP	1	4·2
K	1	78·5
NK	1	3·4
PK	1	2·0
NPK	1	10·9
Treatments	7	321·8

In general, however, a partition of this type is unnecessary and would not be calculated since it is easier to test the effects directly.

As a final step in the presentation of the results, tables of means and their standard errors must be prepared. Often only the significant differences are of interest, but where the experiment is one of a series, other tables may be required. These tables of means may be constructed directly from the yields or may be derived from the calculated effects, the latter approach being preferable when a large number of factors is involved. Thus, in this example, the overall mean yield, $\bar{x}$, is $867 \cdot 6/24 = 36 \cdot 15$. Using this, we get the mean yields of plots with and without nitrate—

Mean yield with n $\quad = \bar{x} + \frac{1}{2}N = 39 \cdot 02$

Mean yield without $n = \bar{x} - \frac{1}{2}N = 33 \cdot 28$.

Correspondingly, in constructing a two-way table to demonstrate the interaction of nitrate and potash, we get

Mean yield with n and k $\quad = \bar{x} + \frac{1}{2}(N + K + NK) = 41 \cdot 20$

Mean yield with n and without $k = \bar{x} + \frac{1}{2}(N - K - NK) = 36 \cdot 83$

Mean yield without n and with $k = \bar{x} + \frac{1}{2}(-N + K - NK) = 34 \cdot 72$

Mean yield without n or k $\quad = \bar{x} + \frac{1}{2}(-N - K + NK) = 31 \cdot 85$

or briefly as in Table 3.4.5.

Where, as in this experiment, the number of factors is small, such tables would usually be constructed directly from the treatment totals.

Table 3.4.5 Two-way table of means for nitrate and potash

	Without n	With n	Mean
Without k	31·85	36·83	34·34
With k	34·72	41·20	37·96
Mean	33·29	39·02	36·15

Standard error of means in body of table $= \pm\ 1\cdot22$
= Standard error of differences between marginal means.

3.5 The 2^m factorial design

The general factorial design testing m factors each at two levels has 2^m treatment combinations, and corresponding to these, $2^m - 1$ comparisons may be made in the form of main effects and interactions. For instance, with five factors, A, B, C, D, E, $2^5 = 32$ treatment combinations are required, and 31 comparisons may be made as shown in Table 3.5.1.

Table 3.5.1 Treatment comparisons for 2^5 experiments

	Number
Main effects, A, B, C, D, E	5
First-order interactions, AB, AC, AD, etc.	10
Second-order interactions, ABC, ABD, etc.	10
Third-order interactions, ABCD, ABCE, etc.	5
Fourth-order interactions, ABCDE	1
Total	31

The interpretation of third- and higher-order interactions is complicated and needs to be considered carefully in the light of what other interactions appear to be important. Usually such high interactions do not reflect real effects.

The comments of Yates (1937) might be noted in this connection: "The experimenter . . . should avoid giving exaggerated emphasis to some statistically significant but isolated high-order interaction which has no apparent physical meaning. If we are using a 1 in 20 level of significance, one out of every twenty of the main effects and interactions will on the average be judged statistically significant, even when the treatments produce no effects at all. Such anomalous results, therefore, together with non-significant effects, should be placed on record and judgment reserved until further information has accumulated."

The analysis of the general 2^m factorial experiment follows very similar lines to those indicated in the previous section. The main steps are—

(1) The plus-and-minus technique is carried through m steps, the final values

being divided by half the number of observations, i.e. $\frac{1}{2}N$, to give the treatment effects and interactions. These may be directly examined.

(2) The standard error of the effects and interactions is calculated from $\sqrt{(4s^2/N)}$, where s^2 is derived from an analysis of variance of the experiment results. This may be used to test the significance of the effects. Alternatively, if desired, the treatment sum of squares may be partitioned into components corresponding to the main effects and interactions.

(3) The analysis is completed by the construction of tables of means. These may be constructed either directly or by using the estimated effects. With a large number of factors, the latter is usually simpler.

For a large number of factors, it is advisable to check (1) by applying the rule given in the previous section to each column sum.

For dealing with missing observations in 2^m experiments the methods given in **2.12**, based on minimizing the error sum of squares, can be used. If the design has not been replicated, as is often the case with factorial experiments, the problem arises how to estimate error. It can no longer be estimated by comparing replications. Instead it must be estimated from some of the high-order interactions. The uses of single replicate factorial experiments and of high-order interactions for error are discussed more fully in **5.5**. It may be difficult, however, for the experimenter to decide at the outset of the experiment which interactions should be used for error. This would be especially true for some of the fractional designs discussed in Chapter 7. An alternative approach in such situations has been suggested by Draper and Stoneman (1964). With one observation missing, their procedure is to estimate the missing value by setting to zero one of the factorial effects, such as the highest-order interaction, thought to be of no importance. If, however, this effect were important, the estimate of the missing value would be unsatisfactory, and consequently serious bias would result in the estimates of those effects retained. The existence of such bias, which can be detected by examining the retained effects using the half-normal plot described in **14.7**, would lead to a different effect being used to estimate the missing value. In turn, its bias would be examined. Similarly, p missing values can be estimated by setting to zero p factorial effects thought to be unimportant.

3.6 Designs involving factors at two levels

The analysis of designs involving factors at two levels may be shortened using the methods devised for the 2^m experiment. If the plusing and minusing procedure is carried out for the factors at two levels for each combination of the other factors, the resulting totals and differences may be used to calculate the components of interaction. Alternatively, it is often convenient to carry out the plusing and minusing procedure when the summary tables are constructed. The totals and differences of the two levels of each factor may then be calculated simultaneously. An example will demonstrate the method.

Table 3.6.1 gives the total weights of six-week-old chickens used in an experiment by J. Duckworth and K. Carpenter.

Table 3.6.1 Total weights of groups of sixteen chickens (in grams)

Protein	Protein level	Level of fish solubles	House I	House II	Total	Difference
	0	0	6559	6292	12851	267
		1	7075	6779	13854	296
Groundnut	1	0	6564	6622	13186	−58
		1	7528	6856	14384	672
	2	0	6738	6444	13182	294
		1	7333	6361	13694	972
	0	0	7094	7053	14147	41
		1	8005	7657	15662	348
Soya bean	1	0	6943	6249	13192	694
		1	7359	7292	14651	67
	2	0	6748	6422	13170	326
		1	6764	6560	13324	204
Total			84710	80587	165297	4123

The birds were raised on twelve different diets in a $3 \times 2 \times 2$ design. The treatment factors were

$$\left\{ \begin{array}{c} \text{Form of protein,} \\ \text{groundnut or soyabean} \end{array} \right\} \times \left\{ \begin{array}{c} \text{Level of protein,} \\ \text{0, 1 or 2} \end{array} \right\} \times \left\{ \begin{array}{c} \text{Level of fish solubles,} \\ \text{0 or 1} \end{array} \right\}$$
$$\qquad\quad P \qquad\qquad\qquad\qquad L \qquad\qquad\qquad\qquad F$$

Two replicates were carried out in different houses. There were, thus, two sets of twelve pens each of sixteen birds arranged in two houses.

The first step in the analysis is to calculate treatment totals and differences. This has been done in Table 3.6.2.

The treatment totals are calculated in the usual manner. The differences, indicated in italics, are calculated at the same time. Thus, while L indicates the totals at the three levels of protein, FL indicates the differences between the fish soluble totals at the different levels of protein, etc.

The components in the analysis of variance may now be directly constructed. For instance, the sum of squares for F is

$$\frac{(5841)^2}{24} = 1\,421\,550 \text{ (to the nearest ten)}$$

and for FL it is

$$\frac{(2518)^2 + (2657)^2 + (666)^2}{8} - \frac{(5841)^2}{24} = 308\,890.$$

Table 3.6.2   Treatment totals and differences

Protein	Protein level	Level of fish solubles 0	1	Total	Difference between fish solubles, F
Groundnut	0	12851	13854	26705	*1003*
	1	13186	14384	27570	*1198*
	2	13182	13694	26876	*512*
	Total	39219	41932	81151	*2713*
Soya bean	0	14147	15662	29809	*1515*
	1	13192	14651	27843	*1459*
	2	13170	13324	26494	*154*
	Total	40509	43637	84146	*3128*
Totals	0	26998	29516	56514 ⎫	*2518* ⎫
	1	26378	29035	55413 ⎬ L	*2657* ⎬ *FL*
	2	26352	27018	53370 ⎭	*666* ⎭
	Total	79728	85569	165297	*5841* F
Difference between protein forms, P	0	*1296*	*1808*	*3104* ⎫	*512* ⎫
	1	*6*	*267*	*273* ⎬ *PL*	*261* ⎬ *FPL*
	2	*−12*	*−570*	*−382* ⎭	*−358* ⎭
	Total	*1290*	*1705*	*2995* P	*415* *FP*

The linear and quadratic components may also be easily extracted. Thus the linear and quadratic components for *FL* are

$$\frac{(666 - 2518)^2}{2 \times 8} = 214370$$

and

$$\frac{(666 - 2 \times 2657 + 2518)^2}{6 \times 8} = 94520.$$

The analysis of variance may be constructed as in Table 3.6.3.

The error term in this analysis may be checked by direct calculation from Table 3.6.1. If the differences between replicates are calculated as in the last column, the error sum of squares may then be calculated from

$$\frac{(267)^2 + (296)^2 + \ldots + (204)^2}{2} - \frac{(4123)^2}{24} = 492\,640.$$

Tables of means might now be constructed directly from Table 3.6.1. Table 3.6.4 gives tables demonstrating the *FL* and *PL* interactions. In this experiment, the lowest level of soya bean has given the heaviest birds, while the addition of fishmeal has further increased the weights of the birds.

Table 3.6.3 Completed analysis of variance

		d.f.	s.s.	m.s.	Variance ratio
F		1	1421550		31·74***
P		1	373750		8·34*
FP		1	7180		0·16
L	Linear	1	617800		13·79**
	Quadratic	1	18490		0·41
FL	Linear	1	214370		4·79(?)
	Quadratic	1	94520		2·11
PL	Linear	1	759510		16·96**
	Quadratic	1	98640		2·20
FPL	Linear	1	47310		1·06
	Quadratic	1	2820		0·06
Treatments		11	3655940		
Houses		1	708300		
Residual		11	492640	44790	
Total		23	4856870		

***Significant at 0·1 percent level
**Significant at 1 percent level
*Significant at 5 percent level
(?) Doubtful significance.

Table 3.6.4 Table of means (groups of 16)

Protein level	Form of protein		Level of fish solubles		Mean
	Ground-nut	Soya bean	0	1	
0	6676	7452	6750	7379	7064
1	6892	6961	6594	7259	6927
2	6719	6624	6588	6754	6671
Mean	6763	7012	6644	7131	6887

Standard error of means in body of table = ± 106
Standard error of protein-level means = ± 75
Standard error of protein and fish soluble means = ± 61

3.7 Halved-plot designs

The split-plot design is used to test two or more sets of factors. Usually, one set of factors is applied to the main plots of the experiment, and a second set is applied to sub-plots within each plot. As a consequence, the second set of factors and their interactions with the first set give rise to comparisons which are made within plots. These comparisons are therefore made more accurately than comparisons between plots.

In its simplest form, the design uses plots split into halves to which two treatments are applied in random order. For instance, a randomized block design testing different varieties may have each plot split in half, with nitrate applied to one randomly chosen half and no nitrate to the other. The comparisons of the varieties are then made between plots, while the nitrate effect and the interaction of nitrate with varieties is estimated within plots.

The analysis of halved-plot designs is particularly simple. Treatment means may be calculated directly. The totals of each plot may be used to calculate the normal analysis of the plot comparisons, while the differences between the halves of each plot may be used to calculate the analysis of the within-plot comparisons. Two errors are therefore used in the analysis of variance: one, s^2, being a within-plot error, the other, s_1^2, being a between-plot error.

If treatment A is applied to one half of each plot and x and x' are used to denote the yields of the half-plots receiving and not receiving A, the analysis of variance follows lines similar to those shown in Table 3.7.1. Here N represents the total number of whole plots, and n the number of half-plots per treatment.

Table 3.7.1   Analysis of variance of a halved-plot design

	d.f.	s.s.	m.s.
Blocks	$b-1$	$\frac{1}{2}$ s.s. $B(x+x')$	
Treatments	$t-1$	$\frac{1}{2}$ s.s. $T(x+x')$	
Between-plot residual	$(b-1)(t-1)$	Obtained by differencing	s_1^2
Between plots	$N-1$	$\frac{1}{2}$ s.s. $(x+x')$	
A	1	$[\Sigma(x-x')]^2/2N$	
A $\times$ treatments	$t-1$	$\frac{1}{2}$ s.s. $T(x-x')$	
Within-plot residual	$N-t$	Obtained by differencing	s^2
Total	$2N-1$	s.s. $(x$ and $x')$	

It should be noted that this analysis is carried out treating the halved plot as the unit throughout. In consequence, the mean square per plot is really $2s_1^2$ and not s_1^2. No difficulty should be encountered, however, provided the halved-plot basis is used throughout.

The standard error of the effect A is $\sqrt{(2s^2/N)}$ and of the difference between any pair of main-plot treatment means (on a halved-plot basis, of course) is

$\sqrt{(s_1^2/n)}$. The standard error of the effect A for any individual treatment is $\sqrt{(2s^2/n)}$, while the standard error of the difference between any pair of treatment means in the presence or absence of A is $\sqrt{[(s^2 + s_1^2)/n]}$. These errors may be used to test the significance of any treatment comparison.

3.8 Example of a halved-plot design

To illustrate the halved-plot design, we shall consider the results of a trawling trial carried out by the Scottish Marine Laboratory. Here the main-plot comparisons were sampling times of trawling, and three two-hour trawls, t_1, t_2, t_2, were carried out in three different areas. This is a randomized block design, the areas corresponding to blocks, the two-hour trawls to plots, and the time of trawling to treatments. During half of each two-hour period, chosen at random, trawling was carried out with a small mesh s, so that the design corresponded to a split-plot arrangement. Table 3.8.1 gives the logarithms of the numbers of haddock caught in each hour's haul.

Table 3.8.1 Results of trawling trial

		s	—
	t_1	2·02	2·12
Area I	t_2	2·48	2·26
	t_3	2·32	2·11
	t_1	2·22	2·00
Area II	t_2	2·49	2·26
	t_3	2·43	2·36
	t_1	2·12	2·21
Area III	t_2	2·41	2·21
	t_3	2·46	2·36

A table of means may be directly constructed to show the effects. This is done in Table 3.8.2.

Table 3.8.2 Table of means

	s	—	Mean
t_1	2·12	2·11	2·12
t_2	2·46	2·24	2·35
t_3	2·41	2·28	2·34
Mean	2·33	2·21	2·27

4—EDA   *   *

To carry out overall tests of significance and to assign standard errors to the differences between these means, an analysis of variance has to be carried out. This gives the analysis shown in Table 3.8.3.

Table 3.8.3   Analysis of variance of halved-plot experiment

	d.f.	s.s.	m.s.
Areas	2	0·0230	
T	2	0·2136	0·1068
Residual	4	0·0388	0·0097
Between two-hour periods	8	0·2754	
S	1	0·0624	0·0624
S × T	2	0·0322	0·0161
Residual	6	0·0384	0·0064
Total	17	0·4084	

The differences between trawling times are tested by the variance ratio $0.1068/0.0097 = 11.01$, which is significant at the 5 percent level. The effect of the small mesh is tested by the variance ratio $0.0624/0.0064 = 9.75$, which is also significant at the 5 percent level. The interaction ST, i.e. the variation between the effect of the small mesh at different times, is tested by the variance ratio $0.0161/0.0064 = 2.52$, and is not significant.

Standard errors of differences may now be calculated to complete the presentation of the experimental results. The following standard errors of differences may be required—

Between means of different times $= \sqrt{\left(\dfrac{0.0097}{3}\right)} = \pm\, 0.057,$

Between means of different meshes $= \sqrt{\left(\dfrac{2 \times 0.0064}{9}\right)} = \pm\, 0.038,$

Between means of different times for any particular mesh $= \sqrt{\left(\dfrac{0.0097 + 0.0064}{3}\right)} = \pm\, 0.073,$

Between means of different meshes at any particular time $= \sqrt{\left(\dfrac{2 \times 0.0064}{3}\right)} = \pm\, 0.065.$

The use of errors of this type in testing significance will be further considered in **4.8**.

4 General Factorial and Split-plot Designs

4.1 Factorial designs with two sets of factors

The factorial principle may also be applied when factors are to be tested at more than two levels. In principle, this involves nothing new, but the methods of analysis differ from those when each of the factors is at two levels. In the following sections we shall consider the appropriate methods.

As for the 2^m factorial experiment, it is convenient to denote the treatments by small letters, a, b, c, etc., and suffixes may be used to denote the level of the treatment. Thus a_0, a_1, a_2 are used to denote three levels of the treatment A; b_0, b_1, b_2, three levels of treatment B, and so on. With two sets of factors, each at three levels, we shall therefore have the nine treatment combinations

$$a_0b_0, \ a_1b_0, \ a_2b_0, \ a_0b_1, \ a_1b_1, \ a_2b_1, \ a_0b_2, \ a_1b_2, \ a_2b_2.$$

These may be conveniently compiled in the two-way table

Table 4.1.1 Arrangement of yields in two-way table

a_0b_0	a_0b_1	a_0b_2	a_0
a_1b_0	a_1b_1	a_1b_2	a_1
a_2b_0	a_2b_1	a_2b_2	a_2
b_0	b_1	b_2	

This provides the method of presenting the results from factorial experiments of this type.

For any experiment involving several sets of factors, the first step in the analysis is to construct tables giving the total yields for each treatment combination. For instance, Table 4.1.2 gives the yields of grain from an experiment on oats in which two factors, nitrate and phosphate, were each tested at three levels. Here the lowest levels, n_0 and p_0. represent no application; n_1 and p_1 represent *drilled* dressings of 110 kg sulphate of ammonia and 190 kg superphosphate per ha, respectively; n_2 and p_2 represent *broadcast* dressings of 110 kg sulphate of ammonia and 380 kg superphosphate per ha, respectively. There are three replications, each in one block of nine plots.

Table 4.1.2 Plan and yields of grain

n_0p_2	23·3	n_0p_0	15·3	n_2p_0	13·7
n_1p_2	17·4	n_0p_1	22·7	n_2p_2	15·2
n_1p_1	24·2	n_2p_0	16·5	n_1p_1	14·8
n_2p_2	21·5	n_0p_2	18·4	n_0p_1	15·7
n_2p_0	21·9	n_2p_2	19·5	n_0p_2	14·4
n_2p_1	25·8	n_2p_1	21·5	n_1p_0	10·0
n_0p_1	21·1	n_1p_0	12·8	n_2p_1	16·2
n_1p_0	20·0	n_1p_1	19·8	n_0p_0	12·2
n_0p_0	15·7	n_1p_2	16·4	n_1p_2	15·8
Total 190·9		Total 162·9		Total 128·0	

The first step in the analysis is to calculate a two-way table for total yields. This is done in Table 4.1.3.

Table 4.1.3 Total yields of treatment combinations

	p_0	p_1	p_2	Total
n_0	43·2	59·5	56·1	158·8
n_1	42·8	58·8	49·6	151·2
n_2	52·1	63·5	56·2	171·8
Total	138·1	181·8	161·9	481·8

The block totals and the analysis of variance may then be calculated. This is done in exactly the same manner as for a randomized block experiment and is shown in Table 4.1.4.

Table 4.1.4 Analysis of variance

	d.f.	s.s.	m.s.
Blocks	2	220·69	110·34
Treatments	8	138·63	17·33
Residual	16	53·79	3·36
Total	26	413·11	

The residual mean square from this analysis may then be used to attach standard errors to the totals in Table 4.1.3. The standard error of the totals in the body of the table is $\sqrt{(3 \times 3\cdot36)} = \pm 3\cdot17$, and the standard error of the marginal totals is $\sqrt{(9 \times 3\cdot36)} = \pm 5\cdot50$.

We should now test the main effects and interaction by partitioning the total sum of squares for treatments. The sum of squares due to nitrate treatment is s.s. N, i.e.

$$\frac{(158\cdot8)^2 + (151\cdot2)^2 + (171\cdot8)^2}{9} - \frac{(481\cdot8)^2}{27} = 24\cdot12,$$

while the sum of squares due to phosphate treatment is s.s. P, i.e.

$$\frac{(138\cdot1)^2 + (181\cdot8)^2 + (161\cdot9)^2}{9} - \frac{(481\cdot8)^2}{27} = 106\cdot38,$$

and the interaction is thus

$$138\cdot63 - 24\cdot12 - 106\cdot38 = 8\cdot13.$$

The treatment sum of squares is thus partitioned as in Table 4.1.5.

Table 4.1.5 Partition of treatment sum of squares

	d.f.	s.s.	m.s.
N	2	24·12	12·06
P	2	106·38	53·19
NP	4	8·13	2·03
Treatments	8	138·63	

The components in this table may be tested using the residual mean square from Table 4.1.4. Here, the phosphate differences are highly significant ($P < 0\cdot01$), and the nitrate differences just fail to reach the 5 percent level of significance. Their interaction is insignificant.

The final step is to prepare tables of means and standard errors. Here the summary table would be as in Table 4.1.6.

Table 4.1.6 Summary table of means

	p_0	p_1	p_2	Mean
n_0	14·4	19·8	18·7	17·6
n_1	14·3	19·6	16·5	16·8
n_2	17·4	21·2	18·7	19·1
Mean	15·3	20·2	18·0	17·8

Standard error of means in body of table = $\pm 1\cdot06$
Standard error of marginal means = $\pm 0\cdot61$.

The experiment was designed to compare the relative effects of drilling and broadcasting the nitrate and phosphate. Examination of the final table of means shows advantages in drilling phosphate and broadcasting nitrate.

4.2 Factorial designs with several sets of factors

The analysis of factorial designs with several sets of factors follows lines almost identical with those described in the last section. The only additional point to be considered is the separation of the main effects and interactions in the analysis of variance. The steps in doing this are as follows—

(1) A series of tables of the type shown in Table 4.1.1 are constructed to give totals for each treatment combination. An illustration of what is needed is shown in Tables 6.3.2 and 6.3.3.

(2) The sums of squares for the main effects are then calculated directly from the totals for the levels of each factor.

(3) The sum of squares for any first-order interaction is calculated from the sum of squares of the totals of all combinations of the two factors involved *less* the corresponding sums of squares for main effects. This is done in the same manner as in the previous section.

(4) The sum of squares for any second-order interaction is calculated from the sum of squares of the totals of all combinations of the three factors involved *less* the corresponding sums of squares for main effects and first-order interactions.

(5) The process repeats itself to give the third-, fourth-, and higher-order interactions.

Usually, interactions higher than the second are of no interest, and a combined sum of squares for the higher-order interactions may be obtained by subtracting the sums of squares for the main effects and lower-order interactions from the total treatment sum of squares.

4.3 Experiments with factors at many levels

The factorial experiment may be applied when the factors are at many levels, but unless the levels are reasonably comparable, the usual general tests and methods of interpretation cannot be used. Although this difficulty is attendant upon all designs, it is usually more important when the levels of any factor give widely differing results. An example will serve to demonstrate the problem.

Table 4.3.1 gives the total weights in grams of the fresh matter of lettuces grown in an experiment carried out by Woodman and Johnson (1947). Here a factorial design was used to test three water treatments and twelve times of sowing, in 9 blocks of 36 plots.

An examination of the table shows obviously significant differences between times of sowing and also between water treatments. There is no point in making an overall test of these treatments. In addition, the interaction between time of sowing and water treatments, in its usually defined sense, is also obviously significant (compare, for example, the differences between water treatments for

Table 4.3.1 Total yields of lettuces

Time of sowing	Water treatment 1	2	3	Total
1	183	269	207	659
2	166	364	214	744
3	115	418	270	803
4	116	278	213	607
5	202	224	168	594
6	1037	1331	1158	3526
7	953	1145	932	3030
8	912	1375	735	3022
9	1079	1706	909	3694
10	735	1405	616	2756
11	847	1775	774	3396
12	642	1182	467	2291
Total	6987	11472	6663	25122

sowing times 1–5 with those for sowing times 8–12). Similarly, the wide differences between total yields indicate that the residual mean square in any analysis of variance is unlikely to be homogeneous. There is no point in carrying out an analysis of variance.

In order to make any individual comparisons between particular treatment combinations, it is necessary either to transform the observations so that the residual variance is homogeneous, or to carry out an analysis on a part of the data only, using, for example, a t-test. The use of a transformation may be preferable if a number of individual comparisons have to be made and if a suitable transformation may be derived without much trouble. Alternatively, a transformation may be used if a series of experiments requiring the same transformation are being made. However, for individual experiments in which very few comparisons are required it is easier to carry out separate analyses testing these comparisons.

In the analysis of this experiment, we might carry out approximate analyses for the periods 1–5 and 6–12, since the means in these periods are not strikingly different. Such analyses would act as indicators of the significance of the differences in these periods, but they would still be only approximate. In cases of doubtful significance, if the exact significance were required, it would be necessary to carry out t-tests.

Difficulties of this type are characteristic of factorial experiments involving factors at a large number of levels. Even where the mean yields do not take a wide range of values (such as in the figures for percentage moisture in this experiment, which varied between 84 and 90 percent), it is still advisable to make—even by inspection—a rapid check of the homogeneity of the error variance.

As a further example of the difficulties occurring in the interpretation of designs with factors at many levels, we shall consider an experiment carried out to determine the effects of different phosphate and liming levels on the yields of turnips. There were six levels of phosphate and three levels of liming, and three replications were arranged in three blocks of 18 plots. The yields from these plots are given in Table 4.3.2.

Table 4.3.2 Yields of turnips

Level of phosphate	Level of liming	Block I	Block II	Block III	Total
0	0	274	350	82	706
0	1	361	340	297	998
0	2	253	203	133	589
1	0	325	397	306	1028
1	1	317	356	352	1025
1	2	339	298	361	998
2	0	326	382	220	928
2	1	402	376	333	1111
2	2	336	355	270	961
4	0	379	418	388	1185
4	1	345	387	379	1111
4	2	361	379	274	1014
8	0	352	432	336	1120
8	1	334	339	307	980
8	2	318	293	266	877
16	0	339	322	389	1050
16	1	393	417	333	1143
16	2	358	342	353	1053
Total		6112	6386	5379	17877
Mean		339·6	354·8	298·8	331·1

An initial examination of the yields suggests that the variability at the lowest level of phosphate is greater than at the higher levels. The yields in the third block for the treatment combinations p_0l_0 and p_0l_2 are very low. Before carrying out a more extensive analysis, it is worthwhile investigating this possibility further. To do this, we might adjust the block means to be roughly equal, by adding -8, -24 and 32 to the yields. In this way, the yields from different replicates may be compared, and the variability in different treatment combinations estimated. Table 4.3.3 gives yields adjusted in this manner.

Table 4.3.3 Adjusted yields of turnips

Level of phosphate	Level of liming	Block I	II	III	Total	Range
0	0	266	326	114	706	212
0	1	353	316	329	998	37
0	2	245	179	165	589	80
1	0	317	373	338	1028	56
1	1	309	332	384	1025	75
1	2	331	274	393	998	119
2	0	318	358	252	928	106
2	1	394	352	365	1111	42
2	2	328	331	302	961	29
4	0	371	394	420	1185	49
4	1	337	363	411	1111	74
4	2	353	355	306	1014	49
8	0	344	408	368	1120	64
8	1	326	315	339	980	24
8	2	310	269	298	877	41
16	0	331	298	421	1050	123
16	1	385	393	365	1143	28
16	2	350	318	385	1053	67
Total		5968	5954	5955	17877	
Mean		331·6	330·8	330·8	331·1	

The differences between the highest and lowest yields in the three replicates are given in the last column. It can be seen that with the exception of the $p_0 l_0$ treatment, the variability between replicates is comparable for all treatments. The analysis of variance may thus be carried out as usual. The low yield of the $p_0 l_0$ treatment in block III requires further checking (see **14.8**), but since no good reason for its rejection could be found, it has been retained in the further analysis.

In general, where exceptional values are observed, the execution of experiments should be checked. If a good reason can be found, they might be rejected. For instance, if in this experiment it had been subsequently observed that plots near the gate of the field gave lower yields than elsewhere, the rejection of these plots might have been justified. However, the rejection of extreme observations requires very careful consideration and is not to be recommended as a general practice. Often, as for example with medical data, it is possible to find something exceptional about nearly every observation. In such cases, the rejection of extreme observations would give biased results.

The analysis of this experiment may now be completed as usual. A table of treatment totals is first constructed, and this is used to calculate the analysis of variance, shown in Table 4.3.4.

Table 4.3.4　Treatment totals and analysis of variance

Level of phosphate	Level of liming 0	1	2	Total
0	706	998	589	2293
1	1028	1025	998	3051
2	928	1111	961	3000
4	1185	1111	1014	3310
8	1120	980	877	2977
16	1050	1143	1053	3246
Total	6017	6368	5492	17877

	d.f.	s.s.	m.s.
P	5	73008	14602
L	2	21596	10798
PL	10	31192	3119
Treatments	17	125796	
Blocks	2	30119	
Residual	34	66628	1960
Total	53	222543	

The phosphate and lime effects are both highly significant and their interaction is significant at the 5 percent level. It is obvious that most of the phosphate effect is due to the difference between the zero level and the others, and we might therefore examine this component more closely. To do this, we first calculate, for each level of liming, the differences between the phosphate totals and five times the total for the zero level of phosphate, i.e. $p_{16} + p_8 + p_4 + p_2 + p_1 - 5p_0$. This gives the totals

Level of liming 0	1	2	Total
1781	380	1958	4119

By the rule of **2.3**, the appropriate divisor for these in calculating the sum of squares is $(1^2 + 1^2 + 1^2 + 1^2 + 1^2 + 5^2)n = 30n$, where n is the number of plots in each total. Thus the sum of squares for p_0 v. *the rest* is

$$\frac{(4119)^2}{30 \times 9} = 62\,838,$$

and the interaction, $(p_0 - \textit{the rest}) \times L$, is

$$\frac{(1781)^2 + (380)^2 + (1958)^2}{30 \times 3} - \frac{(4119)^2}{30 \times 9} = 16\,608,$$

with 2 degrees of freedom. A fuller discussion of this partition is given in the next section.

These two values account for the majority of the phosphate and interaction sums of squares, the remainder not being significant. Consequently, if we wished to demonstrate this effect, we might construct a table of means such as in Table 4.3.5.

Table 4.3.5 Table of means

Level of phosphate	Level of liming			Mean
	0	1	2	
0	235	333	196	255
Other levels	354	358	327	346

Standard error of means of 3 plots $= \pm\,25\cdot6$
Standard error of means of 9 plots $= \pm\,14\cdot8$
Standard error of means of 15 plots $= \pm\,11\cdot4$
Standard error of means of 45 plots $= \pm\,\;\;6\cdot6$

The difference between the lime treatments is significant when no phosphate is applied, but is insignificant on application of phosphate.

In testing the means at the zero level of phosphate in this experiment, it is particularly important to ensure that the variance is homogeneous, otherwise the test might be vitiated. Since there is here some indication that there might be a greater variability at the lowest level of phosphate, comparisons between the liming levels should either be made using a t-test (in which case only the difference between liming levels 1 and 2 is significant), or the differences should be treated as approximate until further experimentation has been carried out.

4.4 Components of interaction

The example of the previous section provides an illustration of how it is possible to partition both the main effects and the interactions in a factorial experiment. For the main effects, the procedure is the same as for any series of treatments. For the interaction, this procedure is only slightly modified.

Comparisons may be made at each level separately, and the changes or variations in these comparisons used to calculate components of interaction. The only extra point to be noted is how the overall divisor is to be obtained for any sum of squares. This is, quite simply, the product of the divisor that would be used for the comparisons at each level and of the divisor that would be required in using these comparisons as individual observations. Thus, for instance, in the example of the previous section, the overall divisor is $90 \times 1 = 90$, since the overall sum of squares between levels of liming is used in isolating the component $(p_0 - \text{the rest}) \times L$.

This component might have been further split into the two components $(p_0 - \text{the rest}) \times \text{linear } L$ and $(p_0 - \text{the rest}) \times \text{quadratic } L$. The divisors for these are $90 \times 2 = 180$ and $90 \times 6 = 540$, and their values are

$$(p_0 - \text{the rest}) \times \text{linear } L = \frac{(1781 - 1958)^2}{180} = 174$$

and

$$(p_0 - \text{the rest}) \times \text{quadratic } L = \frac{(1781 - 2 \times 380 + 1958)^2}{540} = 16\ 434,$$

totalling 16 608 as before.

To appreciate the full partitioning of the interaction in a factorial experiment where the comparisons were planned, consider the following example. Table 4.4.1 gives the total yields of oats and the analysis of variance obtained from

Table 4.4.1   Total grain yields

	k_0	k_1	k_2	Total
p_0	32·5	29·8	35·0	97·3
p_1	32·7	42·6	31·9	107·2
p_2	36·0	46·1	34·5	116·6
Total	101·2	118·5	101·4	321·1

Analysis of variance

	d.f.	s.s.	m.s.
Blocks	2	15·27	
Treatments	8	75·43	9·43
Residual	16	41·61	2·60
Total	26	132·31	

three replicates of a 3×3 factorial experiment. The lowest level represents no dressing, the middle level 33 kg per ha, and the highest level 66 kg per ha, for both the potash, k, and phosphate, p, treatments. The treatment sum of squares may be directly partitioned into components P, K and PK; P and K may be partitioned into linear and quadratic components. Thus, for instance,

$$\text{Linear } P = \frac{(-97\cdot3 + 116\cdot6)^2}{18} = 20\cdot69$$

$$\text{Quadratic } P = \frac{(97\cdot3 - 2 \times 107\cdot2 + 116\cdot6)^2}{54} = 0\cdot00.$$

The interaction may also be partitioned into components of the type linear $P \times$ linear K or linear $P \times$ quadratic K. This is done as shown in Table 4.4.2.

Table 4.4.2 Calculation of components of interaction

	Linear K	Quadratic K
p_0	2·5	7·9
p_1	−0·8	−20·6
p_2	−1·5	−21·7
Linear P	−4·0	−29·6
Quadratic P	2·6	27·4

The linear and quadratic differences between the K totals are calculated at each level of P. Thus, for instance, $32\cdot5 - 2 \times 29\cdot8 + 35\cdot0 = 7\cdot9$. The values are then used to calculate linear and quadratic totals in the p direction, e.g. $-1\cdot5 - 2\cdot5 = -4\cdot0$. Now the divisors for the linear and quadratic k effects at each level of p are 6 and 18 respectively, while those for the linear and quadratic effects of p are 2 and 6. In consequence, these final values have to be squared and divided by $6 \times 2 = 12, 18 \times 2 = 36, 6 \times 6 = 36$ and $18 \times 6 = 108$ to give rise to the linear $P \times$ linear K, linear $P \times$ quadratic K, quadratic

Table 4.4.3 Partition of treatment sum of squares

		d.f.	s.s.
P	Linear P	1	20·69
	Quadratic P	1	0·00
K	Linear K	1	0·00
	Quadratic K	1	21·91
PK	Linear $P \times$ linear K	1	1·33
	Linear $P \times$ quadratic K	1	24·34
	Quadratic $P \times$ linear K	1	0·19
	Quadratic $P \times$ quadratic K	1	6·95
Total		8	75·41

$P \times$ linear K, and quadratic $P \times$ quadratic K components, respectively, in the analysis of variance. The final partition of the treatment sum of squares is shown in Table 4.4.3.

Obviously, only the linear effect of p, the quadratic effect of k, and their interaction reach significance. This does not, of course, exclude consideration of other comparisons, but it serves to focus attention upon the salient features of this experiment, namely that the yield of grain increases steadily with the dressing of phosphate, but that the rate of increase is greater for the intermediate level of potash.

4.5 Interactions of quality and quantity

Sometimes the levels of one factor represent different qualities or availabilities of material, while the levels of the other represent different quantities of these qualities. In such experiments we might expect the differences between different qualities of treatment to increase with the quantity of the applied treatment. The averaging of such differences by the usual factorial techniques would then no longer be appropriate. The form of analysis should take into account the probable change in the quality differences with the quantities used. Usually this is done by an appropriate partitioning of the analysis of variance. The following example for a 3×3 design will illustrate the type of component that may be derived.

An experiment, carried out by K. M. Henry and H. W. Kosterlitz, tested three forms of milk, m_0, m_1, m_2, which were fed at three different protein levels, l_0, l_1, l_2, to rats. Since the lowest level was zero, and consequently l_0 was the same for all milk, seven treatment combinations were used: l_0, $l_1 m_0$, $l_1 m_1$, $l_1 m_2$, $l_2 m_0$, $l_2 m_1$, $l_2 m_2$. The basic design and analysis have already been considered in **2.6**. Table 4.5.1 gives the dietary totals and initial analysis of variance for the liver protein values taken in this experiment.

The dietary totals may be used in various comparisons. First, the response to different levels of protein may be estimated. The sum of squares for this is s.s. L, i.e.

$$\frac{(3967 \cdot 4)^2}{7} + \frac{(14228 \cdot 6)^2}{21} + \frac{(16636 \cdot 6)^2}{21} - \frac{(34832 \cdot 6)^2}{49} = 307633.$$

This may be split into linear and quadratic components, but since unequal numbers of observations enter into the totals, the usual formulae no longer apply. In this instance the appropriate sums of squares may be derived by regression methods or by using the rule for deriving independent comparisons given in **2.3**. They are, in fact,

$$\frac{(5 \times 16636 \cdot 6 - 2 \times 14228 \cdot 6 - 9 \times 3967 \cdot 4)^2}{1176} = 307594$$

and

$$\frac{(16636 \cdot 6 - 2 \times 14228 \cdot 6 + 3 \times 3967 \cdot 4)^2}{168} = 40$$

for the linear and quadratic components respectively.

Table 4.5.1 Treatment totals and analysis of variance

	m_0	m_1	m_2	Total
l_0	—	—	—	3967·4
l_1	4894·6	4569·9	4764·1	14228·6
l_2	5754·3	5327·0	5555·3	16636·6
Total	10648·9	9896·9	10319·4	34832·6

	d.f.	s.s.	m.s.
Litters	6	29525	4921
Weight grouping	6	20141	3357
Diets	6	328323	54720
Residual	30	74170	2472
Total	48	452159	

The remaining four degrees of freedom represent comparisons between the levels m_0, m_1 and m_2, and may be further partitioned into the linear and quadratic differences between these levels. First, if the differences increase steadily with level of protein, the differences at the level l_2 will be twice those at l_1. Therefore, twice the l_2 value should be added to the l_1 value to reflect the linear change in the differences. The values of $l_1m_0 + 2l_2m_0$, $l_1m_1 + 2l_2m_1$, and $l_1m_2 + 2l_2m_2$ are 16403·2, 15223·9 and 15874·7, respectively. The differences between these values divided by 35 will reflect the change in the differences between the diets m_0, m_1 and m_2 for an increase in the level of protein intake. These totals may be further used to calculate the sum of squares for the interaction (linear L) $\times$ M, which may be subdivided as required. In this instance the two components calculated were

$$(\text{linear } L) \times (m_2 - m_0) = \frac{(15874\cdot7 - 16403\cdot2)^2}{70} = 3990$$

and

$$(\text{linear } L) \times m_1 - \tfrac{1}{2}(m_0 + m_2)$$
$$= \frac{2(15223\cdot9 - \tfrac{1}{2}16403\cdot2 - \tfrac{1}{2}15874\cdot7)^2}{105} = 15949.$$

Lastly, the (quadratic L) $\times$ M components may be estimated. This is done by calculating the values $2l_1m_0 - l_2m_0$, $2l_1m_1 - l_2m_1$, $2l_1m_2 - l_2m_2$, i.e. 4034·9, 3812·8, 3972·9. The differences between these values divided by 14 will reflect the differences between the quadratic components of the various diets. The two sums of squares are

$$(\text{quadratic } L) \times (m_2 - m_0) = \frac{(3972 \cdot 9 - 4034 \cdot 9)^2}{70} = 55$$

and

$$(\text{quadratic } L) \times m_1 - \tfrac{1}{2}(m_0 + m_2) = \frac{2(3812 \cdot 8 - \tfrac{1}{2} 4034 \cdot 9 - \tfrac{1}{2} 3972 \cdot 9)^2}{105} = 696.$$

The final subdivision of the treatment sum of squares is given in Table 4.5.2.

Table 4.5.2   Subdivision of treatment sum of squares

	d.f.	s.s.
Linear L	1	307594
Quadratic L	1	40
Linear $L \times (m_2 - m_0)$	1	3990
Linear $L \times m_1 - \tfrac{1}{2}(m_0 + m_2)$	1	15949
Quadratic $L \times (m_2 - m_0)$	1	55
Quadratic $L \times m_1 - \tfrac{1}{2}(m_0 + m_2)$	1	696
Treatments	6	328324

In this instance this did not complete the experimental analysis as there was some slight variation in protein intake at the l_1 and l_2 levels. In order to account for this variation exactly, it would be necessary to carry out simultaneous regressions for the three diets, m_0, m_1, m_2, since the above analysis indicates that the dependence on level of intake is different for the different diets. However, since the uncontrolled variation in intake was not large, it is possible to adjust for this variation using an analysis of covariance. This adjustment gave rise to the revised analysis of variance shown in Table 4.5.3.

Table 4.5.3   Revised analysis of variance

	d.f.	s.s.	m.s.
Linear L	1	201	
Quadratic L	1	1902	
Linear $L \times (m_2 - m_0)$	1	1119	
Linear $L \times m_1 - \tfrac{1}{2}(m_0 + m_2)$	1	16551	
Quadratic $L \times (m_2 - m_0)$	1	94	
Quadratic $L \times m_1 - \tfrac{1}{2}(m_0 + m_2)$	1	579	
Residual	29	48963	1688

The covariance has reduced the error mean square by about 30 percent, and the linear $L \times m_1 - \frac{1}{2}(m_0 + m_2)$ interaction is now more striking. The large reduction in the linear L effect is due to the differences between levels being wiped out by the covariance. It shows in fact, that the effects of the slight variations in protein intake at each level are in general agreement with the differences observed at different levels.

From this experiment we thus derive the conclusions that the liver protein is linearly related to protein level of diet over the range tested; that diets m_2 and m_0 do not differ significantly from one another; but that diet m_1 gives a significantly lower increase in liver protein. As a final step, tables of adjusted means and standard errors should now be constructed to demonstrate these effects.

It is interesting to note that this experiment, by careful design, has yielded information on each of the points of importance. The accuracy has been increased by the initial removal of litter and weight effects and has been still further improved by the final use of covariance, while the appropriate partitioning of the treatment sum of squares has allowed the main points to be tested rapidly.

4.6 Dummy treatments

The problem dealt with in the last section exhibits a characteristic often found in other types of experiments, i.e. that the levels of one factor are identical for particular combinations of the other factors. For instance, where the levels of one factor represent methods of application of the other treatments, the methods are identical when no treatment is given. Thus, in an experiment testing different times of application of fertilizer, the time of application is irrelevant when no fertilizer is applied. Under such circumstances, the ordinary factorial analysis no longer applies, since the comparison of methods of application, averaged over all other treatment combinations, *including the zero level*, ceases to be meaningful. The zero level should obviously be excluded in such a comparison, and the analysis of variance will be correspondingly altered. An example will demonstrate the main modifications.

Davis, Cook and Baten (1942) reported the results of experiments on cannery peas using four fertilizer treatments, including the zero level, which were applied by three methods of placement. In this it was found that the method of placement did not, in itself, change the yields, so that the three methods of placement are equivalent for the zero level of fertilizer. However, it is by no means certain that the three methods are equivalent, and in this instance it seemed desirable to test this in the course of the analysis. The total numbers of plants per 12 metres of row for the five replicates of this experiment are given in Table 4.6.1.

The differences between methods of placement for the zero level of fertilizer, b_0, are assumed to be *dummy* comparisons. These values are therefore excluded in calculating the sums of squares for A and AB. The sum of squares for interaction should, in this experiment, be calculated from the 3×3 table formed by the combinations of a_0, a_1, a_2, with b_1, b_2, b_3. Lastly, the sum of squares for B

Table 4.6.1   Total numbers of plants (five replicates)

Method of placement	Fertilizer				Total (excluding b_0)
	b_0	b_1	b_2	b_3	
a_0	1092	1226	1155	1176	3557
a_1	1337	1271	1299	1237	3807
a_2	1300	1164	1162	919	3245
Total	3729	3661	3616	3332	10609
		14338			

may be calculated as usual from the totals for b_0, b_1, b_2 and b_3. This gives the subdivision of the treatment sum of squares shown in Table 4.6.2.

Table 4.6.2   Subdivision of treatment sum of squares

	d.f.	s.s.	m.s.
A (excluding b_0)	2	10571	5286
B	3	6099	2033
AB	4	4613	1153
Treatments	9	21283	

The number of degrees of freedom for treatment is nine, since there are ten distinct treatments. The total sum of squares for treatments may be directly calculated from

$$\frac{(3729)^2}{15} + \frac{(1226)^2 + (1271)^2 + \ldots + (919)^2}{5} - \frac{(10609)^2}{60} = 21283.$$

Alternatively, the two degrees of freedom comparing the dummy treatments, a_0b_0, a_1b_0, a_2b_0, may be calculated:

$$\frac{(1092)^2 + (1337)^2 + (1300)^2}{5} - \frac{(3729)^2}{15} = 6977.$$

These, together with the above nine degrees of freedom, provide the total eleven degrees of freedom for treatments, including the dummies.

Two courses may be adopted concerning these two degrees of freedom. If it is maintained that the differences between the dummy plots can only be chance differences, then these two degrees of freedom must be included in the error sum of squares. If, however, there is a possibility that there might be real differences between the dummy treatments, the two degrees of freedom should be tested and should not be included in the error sum of squares, even if they are not significant. Since in this example we have decided to adopt the latter course of action, the complete analysis of variance is as in Table 4.6.3.

Table 4.6.3   Complete analysis of variance

	d.f.	s.s.	m.s.
A (excluding b_0)	2	10571	5286
B	3	6099	2033
AB	4	4613	1153
Dummies	2	6977	3488
Treatments	11	28260	
Blocks	4	5228	
Residual	44	38672	879
Total	59	72160	

The differences between the dummies, a_0b_0, a_1b_0 and a_2b_0, give a variance ratio of 3·97, which is significant at the 5 percent level. It therefore appears that the method of placement has, in itself, affected the numbers of plants.

If significance had not been achieved, the analysis might now have been completed by the construction of a table of means and by the testing of particular comparisons. Here, since differences have been observed between the dummy treatments, it is relevant to ask whether these differences are comparable with the differences when fertilizer is applied, i.e. whether the differences observed between placement methods on the application of fertilizer can be ascribed to the damage caused by the method of placement. To answer this, the total derived by adding the sum of squares for A (excluding b_0) to that for dummies has to be subdivided into two components: A (including b_0) and $A \times (b_0 \text{ v. } b_1 + b_2 + b_3)$. The latter component tests whether the differences between methods of placement with fertilizer are the same as the differences when no fertilizer is used. This subdivision has been carried out in Table 4.6.4.

Table 4.6.4   Further subdivision of the analysis of variance

	d.f.	s.s.	m.s.
A (including b_0)	2	10244	5122
$A \times (b_0 \text{ v. } b_1 + b_2 + b_3)$	2	7304	3652
A (excluding b_0) + dummies	4	17548	

The significance of both of these components shows that the differences between the methods of placement are changed when fertilizer is used. The analysis may be completed by calculating a table of means and testing comparisons of particular interest. Table 4.6.5 gives means and standard errors of the different combinations.

Table 4.6.5   Table of means

Method of placement	Fertilizer				Mean (excluding b_0)
	b_0	b_1	b_2	b_3	
a_0	218	245	231	235	237
a_1	267	254	260	247	254
a_2	260	233	232	184	216
Mean	249	244	241	222	

Standard error of means in body of table $= \pm$ 13·3
Standard error of marginal means $\quad = \pm$ 7·7.

Further conclusions to be drawn are that the differences between b_1 and b_2 are not significant, but that b_3, a fertilizer containing nitrate, caused a much greater depression of plant number under method of placement a_2 (contact with seed). Method a_0 ($\frac{1}{2}$-inch out from the seed) gave a significantly lower plant number than method a_1 (2 inches out from the seed).

The above method of analysis may be carried out for all factorial experiments involving dummy comparisons. Where the dummy treatments are at only two levels, it is often easier to carry out an analysis using the differences between levels (as indicated in **3.6**) and to use the differences between dummy treatments as error.

Two other points should be noted. First, if the dummy treatments are identical, they are used in only a fraction of the comparisons. In the above example, if the b_0 values were identical, they would contribute only to the B effect; the A effect and AB interaction being calculated without reference to b_0. Thus, if the number of dummy plots had been reduced, the available information on A and AB would have remained unaltered, but less information would be available on the B effect. In general, the number of dummy treatments may be reduced only at the expense of a fraction of the comparisons. The decision whether or not to allow dummy treatments depends, in fact, upon the relative importance of the comparisons involved. Secondly, if the dummy treatments are identical, the error variance may be split into two components indicating (a) the differences between dummy treatments within each block, and (b) the change in the differences between treatments from block to block, i.e. the treatments × blocks interaction. If there are large differences between blocks, then the latter component may be larger than the former. When this is likely to be so, it is advisable to split the error sum of squares into these two portions and to test whether the two estimates of variance differ appreciably.

4.7 The general split-plot design

The split-plot design may be used with its plots split into any number of parts. Thus, for instance, several different fertilizers may be applied to plots containing different varieties. The fertilizer comparisons would then usually be more accurate than the comparisons of the varieties.

The procedure for the analysis of a split-plot experiment is similar to that for the halved-plot experiment as described in the last chapter. The treatment effects may be estimated directly from the treatment means. The analysis of variance falls into two parts as previously, and within-plot and between-plot errors need to be used.

If $a_1, a_2, \ldots$ represent a treatments applied to the main plots and $p_1, p_2, \ldots$ represent p treatments applied to the split-plots, the analysis of variance is of the type shown in Table 4.7.1.

Table 4.7.1 Typical analysis of variance for split-plot experiment

	d.f.	s.s.	m.s.
Blocks	$b-1$	s.s. B	
A	$a-1$	s.s. A	
Between-plot residual	$(b-1)(a-1)$	Obtained by differencing	s_1^2
Between plots	$N-1$	s.s. (plot totals)	
P	$p-1$	s.s. P	
AP	$(a-1)(p-1)$	s.s. T − s.s. A − s.s. P	
Within-plot residual	$(N-a)(p-1)$	Obtained by differencing	s^2
Total	$pN-1$	s.s. x	

The analysis here is for a randomized block experiment, so that the number of replications, n, of each main plot treatment equals the number of blocks b. A similar type of analysis would, however, be used for a Latin square or any other design.

4.8 Standard errors in split-plot experiments

The standard errors of various comparisons involved in a split-plot experiment might now be considered. The treatment means may first be placed in the form of a two-way table—

Table 4.8.1 Two-way table

Split-plot treatments	Main plot treatments			Mean
	a_1	a_2	. . .	
p_1				
p_2				
.				
.				
.				
.				
.				
Mean				

We then have the following standard errors of differences:

(1) Between overall means of main plot treatments

$$= \sqrt{\left(\frac{2s_1^2}{pn}\right)}$$

(2) Between overall means of split-plot treatments

$$= \sqrt{\left(\frac{2s^2}{N}\right)}$$

(3) Between means in same row of table, i.e. between plot treatments for a particular split-plot treatment

$$= \sqrt{\left[\frac{2(s_1^2 + (p-1)s^2)}{np}\right]}$$

(4) Between means in same column of table, i.e. between split-plot treatments for a particular plot treatment

$$= \sqrt{\left(\frac{2s^2}{n}\right)}$$

(5) Between means of two plot treatments for m particular split-plot treatments

$$= \sqrt{\left[\frac{2(ms_1^2 + (p-m)s^2)}{mnp}\right]}$$

(6) Between means of two split-plot treatments for m particular plot treatments

$$= \sqrt{\left(\frac{2s^2}{mn}\right)}.$$

The last two of these standard errors are provided to deal with instances where two main plot treatments need to be compared for some, but not all, of the split-plot treatments, or vice versa.

Some difficulty attaches to the use of standard errors derived from a combination of estimates such as in (3) and (5). The t-test for such errors is no longer valid, but it provides a good approximation to the true test. An approximate number of degrees of freedom for use in the t table is provided by weighting the reciprocals of the separate degrees of freedom of each estimate according to the square of the contribution made by that estimate. For instance, for formula

(5) above, the approximate number of degrees of freedom, F, is given by

$$\frac{[ms_1^2 + (p - m)s^2]^2}{F} = \frac{[ms_1^2]^2}{f_1} + \frac{[(p - m)s^2]^2}{f},$$

where f and f_1 are the degrees of freedom of s^2 and s_1^2 respectively.

4.9 Example of a split-plot experiment

The split-plot design is commonly used to test two sets of factors; one set being applied to the main plots of the experiment and the other to the split-plots within each plot. This results in the second set of comparisons and their interaction with the first set being estimated within plots, and in consequence these comparisons are usually more accurate.

The use of a split-plot design will usually be determined by such considerations of accuracy, but sometimes other matters will influence the design. For example, the experimental data of Table 4.9.1 give the weight increases of chicks

Table 4.9.1 Weight increases of chicks

		Diet							
		—				t			
		—		y		—		y	
Hen's food	Sex	Cage 1	Cage 2	Cage 3	Cage 4	Cage 5	Cage 6	Cage 7	Cage 8
	♂	199	146	197	208	144	77	85	165
		157	179	193	142	41	151	150	192
—		193	202	198	225	128	170	168	144
		262	214	207	200	170	181	148	161
	♀	145	161	153	150	127	86	82	135
		185	190	191	192	134	152	142	143
		185	210	221	186	146	172	176	134
		192	169	229	187	163	174	191	153
	♂	86	93	92	134	119	140	100	111
		106	130	115	124	134	123	118	111
d		157	169	122	55	143	135	123	114
		174	139	93	115	140	143	109	109
	♀	66	135	118	79	114	128	92	89
		105	131	107	114	116	124	71	111
		104	153	94	70	125	124	120	76
		110	144	93	90	135	138	81	114
Total		2426	2565	2423	2271	2079	2218	1956	2062

in the second two weeks after hatching, in an experiment carried out by K. Carpenter and J. Duckworth. This experiment involved eight cages of sixteen birds, each cage being fed one of four diets, with or without thyroxine, t, and with or without yeast, y. It was, in fact, impossible to feed different diets to birds within the same cage. Two other comparisons could, however, be made: sex differences and differences due to the diet received by the laying hens. Since these comparisons do not involve different treatment of the chicks, they were made within the cages. Eight birds within each cage were cocks and eight hens; of these, one half came from hens raised on a normal diet, and the other half from hens raised on a deficient diet, d.

An analysis of the differences between cages may be carried out as usual. The dietary means and the analysis of variance testing the differences between diets are given in Table 4.9.2. It should be noted that the residual mean square between groups is used in making the variance-ratio test.

Table 4.9.2   Table of means and analysis of variance

	—	t	Mean
—	156·0	134·3	145·1
y	146·7	125·5	136·1
Mean	151·3	129·9	140·6

Standard error of means in body of table $= \pm 4\cdot22$
$=$ Standard error of differences between marginal means.

	d.f.	s.s.	m.s.
T	1	14663·3	
Y	1	2592·0	
TY	1	2·5	
Residual between cages	4	2280·7	570·2
Between cages	7	19538·5	
Within cages	120	198701·5	
Total	127	218240·0	

Here the difference between thyroxine treatment is significant at the 1 percent level, while the effects of the yeast and of the interaction are not significant.

To carry out the within-cage analysis, the totals of groups of similarly-treated birds have first to be constructed. These are then analysed in the same manner as an ordinary factorial experiment, but the treatments applied to cages are isolated and treated as comparisons between cages. Thus, this experiment is

Table 4.9.3 Treatment totals and sums of squares

Treatment	Total	Plusing and minusing totals	Treatment effects	Sum of squares	
(1)	1437	18000	—	—	
t	1154	−1370	−21·4	14663·3	Between cages
y	1509	−576	−9·0	2592·0	Total = 17257·8
ty	1156	18	0·3	2·5	
d	948	−3306	−51·7***	85387·8	
td	1004	1596	24·9***	19900·1	
yd	765	−1062	−16·6* **	8811·3	
tyd	754	−108	−1·7	91·1	
$\male$	1552	546	8·5	2329·0	
$t\male$	1062	−188	−2·9	276·1	Within cages
$y\male$	1570	142	2·2	157·5	Total = 118710·8
$ty\male$	1213	292	4·6	666·1	
$d\male$	1054	264	4·1	544·5	
$td\male$	1077	234	3·7	427·8	
$yd\male$	850	−48	−0·8	18·0	
$tyd\male$	895	−114	−1·8	101·5	
			±4·81		

      * Value for 5 percent significance   = ± 9·53
    ** Value for 1 percent significance   = ± 12·61
  *** Value for 0·1 percent significance = ± 16·27

analysed as a 2^4 experiment. Table 4.9.3 gives the totals of treatment groups, the final column of the plusing and minusing, the treatment effects, and sums of squares. The symbol $\male$ has been used to denote the comparison of cocks and hens.

It should be noted that a check on the analysis is supplied by the sums of squares for T, Y and TY. Alternatively, the initial analysis between cages might be left until this stage.

The within-cage treatment sum of squares may now be subtracted from the total sum of squares within cages, as in Table 4.9.4. The residual mean square

Table 4.9.4 Within-cage analysis of variance

	d.f.	s.s.	m.s.
Treatment within-cages	12	118710·8	
Within-cage residual	108	79990·7	740·7
Within cages	120	198701·5	

within cages would normally now be used to attach standard errors to the effects in Table 4.9.3 and to test their significance as shown. Tables of means could then be constructed to demonstrate the significant effects.

In this instance, the residual mean square within cages is greater than that between cages. This rather unusual occurrence can be taken to indicate either of two things. First, it may mean that the variation between cages is no larger than that within cages. In this case a pooled mean square should be derived, and all comparisons may be taken as being of equal accuracy. This is the more common occurrence. Alternatively, it may indicate that the residual mean square within cages has been swollen by competition for the available food or by some other such agency. If it is admitted that this is a possibility, then the mean squares have to be kept separate, and the homogeneity of the within-group mean square has to be investigated more closely. In fact, a very good reason could be found for the difference between the residual mean squares in this experiment: the chicks had been stratified by weight before being fed the experimental diets. Thus the eight figures in the first row of Table 4.9.1 represent the eight largest male chicks in a random selection of 32 from hens receiving normal diets, etc. Obviously the effect of this stratification is to increase the within-cage residual mean square relative to the between-cage value.

If the figures of Table 4.9.1 are now considered as falling into sixteen strata (the comparisons between these in sets of four giving the effects D, $\male$, and $D\male$), the residual sum of squares within cages may be partitioned as in Table 4.9.5.

Table 4.9.5 Partition of residual sum of squares

	d.f.	s.s.	m.s.
Strata	12	26 106·5	2175·5
Residual	96	53 884·2	561·3
Within-cage residual	108	79 990·7	

The residual mean square when differences between strata are removed is very near the residual mean square between cages, and the two may be pooled to give the estimate 561·6 for the mean square, with 100[*] degrees of freedom.

This can now be used to test effects and interactions within strata, i.e. other than D, $\male$, and $D\male$. The mean square for testing D, $\male$, and $D\male$ is derived from the analysis by replacing each of the twelve degrees of freedom for the other

[*] This is not strictly true; in fact, the pooling of mean squares in a split-plot experiment gives rise to an estimate *whose degrees of freedom vary according to the use to which it is put.* Thus, for instance, if this estimate is to be used to test a between-cage comparison, say Y, the appropriate degrees of freedom will lie somewhere between 4 and 100, probably nearer the former. For a within-cage comparison, the degrees of freedom lie between 96 and 100, probably nearer the latter. In the extension of this example, 100 will be adopted as the appropriate number of degrees of freedom for within-cage comparisons.

treatments by the mean square, 561·6. The estimate so obtained thus combines the residual and strata mean squares in the ratio 112 : 12 to give

$$\frac{12 \times 2175 \cdot 5 + 112 \times 561 \cdot 6}{124} = 717 \cdot 8.$$

The appropriate number of degrees of freedom, F, of this estimate are given approximately by

$$\frac{(124 \times 717 \cdot 8)^2}{F} = \frac{(12 \times 2175 \cdot 5)^2}{12} + \frac{(112 \times 561 \cdot 6)^2}{100}, \text{i.e. } F = 82,$$

where the values 12 and 100 appearing in the denominators are the degrees of freedom of the two estimated mean squares. Here the D-effect is obviously significant and δ and $D\delta$ are insignificant.

The analysis may now be completed by constructing tables of means, a section of which is shown in Table 4.9.6.

Table 4.9.6 Table of means

	—	t	—	y	Mean
—	189·6	143·3	162·7	170·2	166·5 $\Big\} \pm 3\cdot35$
d	113·0	116·6	127·6	102·0	114·8
Mean	151·3	129·9	145·1	136·1	140·6
		$\pm 2\cdot96$			

Standard error of difference between two means in same row $= \pm 5\cdot92$
Standard error of difference between two means in same column $= \pm 6\cdot72$.

The variance of the difference between two means in the same column of this table is obtained by combining the residual and strata mean squares in the ratio 12 : 108, four degrees of freedom within strata being effectively lost owing to the introduction of the treatment t or y. This gives the estimated mean square

$$\frac{12 \times 2175 \cdot 5 + 108 \times 561 \cdot 6}{120} = 723 \cdot 0,$$

with approximately 80 degrees of freedom.

Similar comparisons may be made between other sub-groups of the experiment.

4.10 Covariance analysis in split-plot experiments

When concomitant observations are taken in a split-plot experiment, an analysis of covariance may be carried out in the normal manner. Since there are two residuals, there will also be two regression coefficients, for correcting within- and between-plot comparisons. This leads to some difficulty in compiling tables of means, and it is preferable to use the within-plot regression throughout if this does not differ from the between-plot regression. Usually this will be so, since the concomitant factor will work in the same manner within and between plots. Sometimes, however, there will be a difference between the within- and between-plot regressions. For example, if the plots are cages of animals, as in the previous section, the greatest weight-increases *within each cage* may be attained by the animals heaviest at the start of the experiment. However, if in this case the food supplied to each cage is limited, the heavier cages may not correspondingly have the larger total weight-increases. Often, then, it will be necessary to test whether the within-plot regression differs significantly from that between plots.

The method of testing the difference between the two regression coefficients is not the same as the method normally used in covariance analysis for testing the difference between treatment and error regression coefficients (see, e.g., Quenouille, *Introductory Statistics*, section 7.6), since there are two different error components in this instance. It is first necessary to calculate the two regression coefficients, say b and b_1, and their variances, say s^2 and s_1^2, with f and f_1 degrees of freedom. The difference between these is then tested using

$$\frac{b - b_1}{\sqrt{(s^2 + s_1^2)}},$$

which is approximately distributed as Student's t with F degrees of freedom where

$$\frac{(s^2 + s_1^2)^2}{F} = \frac{s^4}{f} + \frac{s_1^4}{f_1}.$$

If the regression coefficients do not differ significantly, the within-plot regression may be used to correct all terms, including the between-plot residual. The analysis proceeds as usual, and tables of adjusted means and standard errors may be easily derived. If there is a significant difference between the regressions, each has to be used separately to adjust the within- and between-plot comparisons. Different tables of adjusted means have then to be constructed to demonstrate within- and between-plot comparisons.

4.11 Missing split-plots

When there are missing observations in a split-plot experiment these might be estimated by minimizing either the within-plot or the between-plot error. Normally, the within-plot error should be used to estimate the missing observations, but it will sometimes be necessary to test whether this is the most suitable method of adjustment for the between-plot comparisons. For instance, if the death of an animal in one cage tends to make the other animals in that cage grow faster or more slowly, a different adjustment should be applied for within- and between-cage comparisons.

The appropriate technique in such cases is the use of a covariance analysis on dummy variables. With one missing value, a dummy variable, taking the value 1 for the missing split-plot and 0 for all other split-plots, should be used. A covariance may be then carried out in the manner described in the previous section to estimate and adjust for the missing observation and to test whether the same estimate can be used in between- and within-plot comparisons. With several missing values, a covariance using several dummy variables is required.

The covariance technique may also be used to adjust for other deficiencies in the measurements. One difficulty which sometimes occurs in agricultural experiments is that the yields from two adjacent plots or split-plots are accidentally mixed, so that the total of two plots is known, but the individual yields from each plot are unknown. In such cases, the correct procedure is to divide arbitrarily the total yield between the two plots for the initial analysis. A covariance on a dummy variable taking the value 1 and -1 for the two plots and 0 elsewhere will then redivide the total yield between the two plots so as to minimize the residual sum of squares.

5 Factorial Designs involving Factors at Two Levels

5.1 Confounding of a single comparison

One of the main disadvantages of the 2^m factorial experiment is that the number of treatment combinations increases rapidly with the number of factors. Thus, 32 treatment combinations are needed with five factors, 64 with six, and 128 with seven. This means that very large blocks would need to be used if a randomized block design were employed, and consequently the residual variation would be increased.

To overcome this difficulty, *confounding* is used. This enables the experiment to be carried out with blocks containing less than the full replication of the treatment combinations, thus increasing the accuracy of the experiment. This chapter is largely devoted to a consideration of the design and analysis of confounded 2^m factorial experiments.

In a 2^m factorial experiment, every main effect and interaction is measured by comparing one half of the treatment combinations with the other. Suppose, then, that the two groups of treatment combinations corresponding to a particular treatment comparison are placed in two blocks. Any difference between the two groups might then be ascribed either to an effect of blocks or to the particular treatment effect, and we cannot say which. In consequence, this treatment effect cannot be tested and is said to be *confounded*. However, all other effects are measured independently of this particular effect, and thus independently of any block differences. The sacrifice of one particular comparison therefore allows all other comparisons to be made within blocks, and in so far as the use of blocks reduces the residual mean square, these other comparisons will be made with improved precision.

As an example, suppose four factors, *A*, *B*, *C* and *D*, are tested in a 2^4 experiment. The interaction *ABCD* is derived by comparing the eight treatment combinations

(1), *ab, ac, ad, bc, bd, cd, abcd*

with the remainder

a, b, c, d, abc, abd, acd, bcd.

If these sets of eight treatments are placed in blocks, then the interaction *ABCD* is confounded, but all other effects are estimated from comparisons within blocks. For example, the main effect A is derived from the comparison of

I : (1), bc, bd, cd

with

II : $ab, ac, ad, abcd$

in the first block, and of

III : b, c, d, bcd

with

IV : a, abc, abd, acd

in the second block. Suppose that in the first block, each measurement is made up of an effect due to the particular treatment combination and an effect due to the block itself. This block effect is then present in each measurement in the block. Consequently, comparing the treatment combinations in I and II will eliminate this effect. Similarly, comparisons between III and IV would eliminate any block effects in the second block. Thus the main effect A is estimated independently of block effects. In the same way, we can see that all other effects, except the confounded $ABCD$ interaction, are free from block effects.

The choice of which particular comparison is to be sacrificed must depend upon practical considerations. In some experiments, the measurement of interactions is the prime concern and the measurement of main effects is of little interest. A main effect might then be sacrificed without prejudicing the experiment. Generally, however, interactions of the third order and above are of little interest. Experience has shown that such high-order interactions seldom reach significance in agricultural and biological experiments and may therefore be sacrificed.

In order to determine the two groups of treatment combinations appropriate to any treatment comparison, it is useful to remember that these combinations are divided according to whether they have an odd or even number of letters in common with the chosen comparison. For example, if in an experiment with four factors, A, B, C, D the comparison ABD is confounded, the appropriate blocks would be

(1), $c, ab, abc, ad, acd, bd, bcd,$

and

$a, ac, b, bc, d, cd, abd, abcd.$

To determine the signs with which these two groups of treatment would occur in the interaction ABD, it should be noted that the treatment combination with all factors at the higher level, here $abcd$, always occurs with a positive sign and that consequently all the members of the group containing this combination have positive signs.

5.2 Example of an experiment with confounding

Eight litters of four male and four female rats were used in an experiment to test the effects of feeding different levels of calcium c, fluorine f, and magnesium m, on organ and bone measurements. Each mineral was fed at two levels, and sex was taken as a further two-level factor, making four factors in all.

In order to make the majority of comparisons within litters, it was necessary to confound one comparison between litters. Since the third-order interaction of calcium, fluorine, magnesium and sex was of no interest, this was chosen. Thus, if the sign ♂ is used to denote the male animals, four litters, chosen at random, received the treatment combinations

$$(1), cf, cm, fm, c\male, f\male, m\male, cfm\male,$$

and the other four, the treatment combinations

$$c, f, m, cfm, \male, cf\male, cm\male, fm\male.$$

These treatments were randomized in each litter and the animals maintained on the diets for ten weeks.

The initial analysis of heart weights proceeds as usual, using the plusing and minusing technique to calculate treatment effects. This is done in Table 5.2.1. The larger effects are evidently F, ♂ and $F\male$.

To carry out the analysis of variance it is necessary to calculate the treatment sum of squares excluding $CFM\male$. This may be done either by subtracting the

Table 5.2.1 Calculation of treatment effects

Treatment	Total weight	(1)	(2)	(3)	(4)		Effect
(1)	2·99	5·90	11·78	23·37	56·14	Total	—
c	2·91	5·88	11·59	32·77	−0·32	C	−0·010
f	2·96	5·76	16·31	−0·17	1·78	F	0·056
cf	2·92	5·83	16·46	−0·15	−0·64	CF	−0·020
m	2·82	7·75	−0·12	0·05	−0·04	M	−0·001
cm	2·94	8·56	−0·05	1·73	0·22	CM	0·007
fm	3·00	7·77	−0·15	−0·25	0·20	FM	0·006
cfm	2·83	8·69	0·00	−0·39	0·18	CFM	0·006
♂	3·80	−0·08	−0·02	−0·19	9·40	♂	0·294
$c\male$	3·95	−0·04	0·07	0·15	0·02	$C\male$	0·001
$f\male$	4·43	0·12	0·81	0·07	1·68	$F\male$	0·052
$cf\male$	4·13	−0·17	0·92	0·15	−0·14	$CF\male$	−0·004
$m\male$	3·90	0·15	0·04	0·09	0·34	$M\male$	0·011
$cm\male$	3·87	−0·80	−0·29	0·11	0·08	$CM\male$	0·002
$fm\male$	4·33	−0·03	−0·45	−0·33	0·02	$FM\male$	0·001
$cfm\male$	4·36	0·03	0·06	0·51	(0·84)	$CFM\male$	(0·026)

sum of squares for $CFM\male$ from the treatment sum of squares or by summing the sums of squares for the other effects. If so desired, the sum of squares for $CFM\male$ may then be subtracted from the litter sum of squares and tested against the residual between litters. This has been done in Table 5.2.2.

Table 5.2.2 Analysis of variance

	d.f.	s.s.	m.s.
$CFM\male$	1	0·0110	0·0110
Residual between litters	6	0·2516	0·0419
Litters	7	0·2626	
Treatments (excluding $CFM\male$)	14	1·4864	0·1062
Residual within litters	42	0·3001	0·00715
Total	63	2·0491	

In this form, it may be seen that the analysis is very similar to that for the split-plot experiment. Here, the $CFM\male$ effect is estimated between plots and is consequently inaccurate compared with the other effects.

A standard error may now be attached to the effects estimated in Table 5.2.1. This is $\sqrt{(0·00715/16)} = \pm 0·021$, so that, as suspected, only F, $\male$ and $F\male$ are significant.

To demonstrate these effects a two-way table should be constructed as shown in Table 5.2.3. In this form, it can be seen easily that the effect of fluorine is marked only for the males, for whom the effect of fluorine is $0·108 \pm 0·030$.

Table 5.2.3 Table of means of fluorine treatments

	Low fluorine	High fluorine	Mean
Males	0·970	1·078	1·024
Females	0·729	0·732	0·730
Mean	0·849	0·905	0·877

Standard error of means in body of table $= \pm 0·021$
= Standard error of differences between marginal means.

It should be remembered in the analysis and interpretation of such experiments that the existence of a large main effect occasionally suggests the existence of interactions. Thus, for example, since there is a large difference in heart weight for the males and females, it might be expected that changes in the males would be larger than in the females. There is, however, no strong basis for any such assumption, and reasons might also be advanced for believing the reverse. However, if we desire, we can test the fluorine interaction on alternative assumptions. Thus, if we believe that owing to the difference in heart weights the effect for the females should be roughly two-thirds that for the males, we may calculate the interaction as

$$\tfrac{1}{3}(1 \cdot 078 - 0 \cdot 970) - \tfrac{1}{2}(0 \cdot 732 - 0 \cdot 728) = 0 \cdot 034,$$

with a standard error of

$$0 \cdot 021 \sqrt{\left(\frac{1}{9} + \frac{1}{9} + \frac{1}{4} + \frac{1}{4}\right)} = \pm\, 0 \cdot 018.$$

The observed value is therefore consistent with this hypothesis.

It is also well to remember, in making such tests, that directly any element of selection is introduced as a result of the examination of the data, the value of the tests of significance is reduced. If we examine 100 effects, then we should expect one of them to be significant at the 1 percent level. Correspondingly, the formation of hypotheses by inspection of data invalidates any test of these hypotheses on the same data.

5.3   Confounding of several comparisons

If the number of factors is large, then although the confounding of a single comparison will reduce the block size by one-half, this may still be larger than can be usefully applied. Thus, with six factors the total number of treatments is 64, and confounding of a single comparison gives blocks consisting of 32 treatment combinations, which is still large. This difficulty can be overcome by confounding more than one comparison. An example will demonstrate how this is done.

Suppose there are five factors A, B, C, D and E and that $ABCD$ is confounded. Using the "even and odd letter" rule given in **5.1**, the blocks are then

>(1), e, ab, abe, ac, ace, bc, bce, ad, ade, bd, bde, cd, cde, abcd, abcde

and

>a, ae, b, be, c, ce, abc, abce, d, de, abd, abde, acd, acde, bcd, bcde.

It has been pointed out that any other comparison is made within blocks. Thus the interaction CDE is derived from the comparison of

>I : (1), ab, ace, bce, ade, bde, cd, abcd

with

>II : e, abe, ac, bc, ad, bd, cde, abcde

in the first block, and of

>III : a, b, ce, abce, de, abde, acd, bcd

with

IV : *ae, be, c, abc, d, abd, acde, bcde*

in the second block. We see that the treatment combinations in I and III have an even number of letters in common with *CDE*, whilst those in II and IV have an odd number of letters in common with *CDE*.

If the four sets of treatment combinations I, II, III, and IV are then taken as blocks, three degrees of freedom, i.e. three independent comparisons, are confounded. One of these is *ABCD*, which would be derived by comparing blocks I and II with III and IV. A second is *CDE*, which would be derived by comparing blocks I and III with II and IV. The third, which is fixed once the other two have been chosen, is found by comparing blocks I and IV with II and III. It may be seen to be *ABE*.

Hence, taking a 2^5 experiment in four blocks of eight treatment combinations means that three degrees of freedom are confounded. Two confounded interactions suffice to determine the third. This is easily done by "multiplying" the two interactions and cancelling out the letters common to both. For example,

$$ABCD \times CDE = ABE,$$

since *C* and *D* are common to both. Similarly, we get

$$ABC \times CDE \quad = ABDE,$$

$$ABCDE \times ABC \quad = DE,$$

$$ABCE \times ABDE \quad = CD,$$

and each of these equations gives rise to a possible set of confounded interactions. The "multiplication" of any two members of such sets of interactions automatically leads to a third.

More generally, if the treatments are in 8, 16 or 32 blocks, three, four or five confounded interactions will suffice to determine the rest (provided any two do not "multiply" to give a third). For example, suppose an experiment to test six factors, *A–F*, is placed in eight blocks and the interactions *ABC*, *CDE*, *ADF* are confounded. The other confounded interactions can be written down using the standard order employed in **3.4**, i.e. each interaction is introduced in turn and is followed by all combinations of itself and the interactions previously introduced. Thus—

$$ABC$$
$$CDE$$
$$ABC \times CDE = ABDE$$
$$ADF$$
$$ABC \times ADF = BCDF$$
$$CDE \times ADF = ACEF$$
$$ABDE \times ADF = BEF.$$

These are the seven confounded interactions, and the "multiplication" of any two will lead to another member of this group. We may now examine the possible confounded designs.

Usually, the confounded interactions will be chosen to be of as high an order as possible. This does not imply that the highest-order interactions need be confounded, since the confounding of such interactions will usually require interactions of lower order also to be confounded. Thus, if $BCDE$ and $ABCDE$ are both confounded in a 2^5 experiment, so is A. In general, the most useful designs are those in which the confounded interactions are all of high order. Table 5.3.1 gives a list of some of the most frequently used designs of this type.

Table 5.3.1 List of confounded designs

Number of factors	Number of blocks	Size of blocks	Confounded interactions
4	4	4	AB, ACD, BCD
5	4	8	$ABC, ADE, BCDE$
	8	4	$AB, CD, ABCD, ACE, BCE, ADE, BDE$
6	4	16	$ABCD, ABEF, CDEF$
	8	8	$ABC, CDE, ABDE, ADF, BCDF, ACEF, BEF$
	16	4	$AB, CD, ABCD, EF, ABEF, CDEF, ABCDEF, ACE, BCE, ADE, BDE, ACF, BCF, ADF, BDF$

In certain situations there may be particular interactions which are of less importance than others. When this is so, alternative designs may be of some use. In particular, where the estimation of a main effect is of no importance or where it is impossible to apply a treatment to small plots, the main effect may be confounded. This occurs, for example, in some animal experiments where the sex difference is well-defined and of trivial importance. Table 5.3.2 thus gives a further list of confounded designs, in which the confounded interactions are not uniformly of the highest order possible.

5.4 Determination of a confounded design

The methods described in the last section may be formulated into a set of rules for writing down the design confounding any set of interactions. First, one block can be written down by taking treatment combinations with an even

Table 5.3.2 Further list of confounded designs

Number of factors	Number of blocks	Size of blocks	Confounded interactions
4	4	4	*AB, CD, ABCD* or *A, BCD, ABCD*
5	4	8	*AB, CDE, ABCDE* or *AB, ACDE, BCDE* or *A, BCDE, ABCDE*

	8	4	*AB, AC, BC, ADE, BDE, CDE,*
			    ABCDE or
			A, BC, ABC, BDE, ABDE, CDE,
			    ACDE

6	4	16	*ABC, DEF, ABCDEF* or *ABC, ADEF, BCDEF* or *A, BCDEF, ABCDEF*

	8	8	*AB, CD, ABCD, ACEF, BCEF,*
			    ADEF, BDEF or
			A, BCD, ABCD, BEF, ABEF,
			    CDEF, ACDEF

	16	4	*A, BC, ABC, DE, ADE, BCDE,*
			    ABCDE, BEF, ABEF, CEF,
			    ACEF, BDF, ABDF, CDF,
			    ACDF

number of letters in common with each of the confounded interactions. The writing down of this block will be helped if it is noted that any two treatment combinations "multiply" to give a third treatment combination of the same block. Thus, for example, if in a 2^5 design *ABC, ADE,* and *BCDE* are confounded, the treatment (1), *abe, ace,* and *acd* must all occur in the same block. The other treatments may be written down in the standard order as previously—

$$
\begin{array}{ll}
(1) & acd \\
abe & abe \times acd = bcde \\
ace & ace \times acd = de \\
abe \times ace = bc & bc \times acd = abd
\end{array}
$$

This gives the treatments in one block. The block containing the treatment combination (1) is called the *principal* block.

The other blocks may now be immediately written down by "multiplying" each treatment in the principal block by any treatment that has not already occurred. The design is thus—

Block

I	II(= I × a)	III(= I × b)	IV(= I × d)
(1)	a	b	d
abe	be	ae	abde
ace	ce	abce	acde
bc	abc	c	bcd
acd	cd	abcd	ac
bcde	abcde	cde	bce
de	ade	bde	e
abd	bd	ad	ab

This design has, of course, to be randomized both within and between blocks before application.

5.5 Estimation of error from high-order interactions

The large number of treatment combinations employed in a design testing several factors often presents difficulty, especially where the treatments are replicated several times. In this case, to reduce the size of the experiment only one replicate may be used, but then the error can no longer be estimated by comparing replications. However, the high-order interactions will provide an upper limit for the value of the error, and since, in general, these interactions will be small in comparison with the error, they may be used to provide an estimate of experimental error.

For example, in a 2^6 experiment in four blocks the subdivision of degrees of freedom would be as follows—

	Degrees of freedom	
Main effects	6	
First-order interactions	15	
Second-order interactions	20	
Third-order interactions	15	3 confounded
Fourth-order interactions	6	22
Fifth-order interactions	1	19 unconfounded
Total	63	

Nineteen degrees of freedom could thus be used to test the main effects and first- and second-order interactions. In consequence, the experimenter would be led to prefer such an arrangement to two replicates of a 2^5 experiment with one interaction confounded. This would have the following subdivision—

	Degrees of freedom	
Main effects	5	
First-order interactions	10	
Second-order interactions	10	
Third-order interactions	5	⎱ 6 ⎰ /1 confounded
Fourth-order interactions	1	\5 unconfounded
Residual	32	
	—	
Total	63	

This has 32 degrees of freedom in the residual as against 19 for the alternative arrangement, but an examination of the variance-ratio table shows that this is not an appreciable advantage (at the 5 percent level, $F_{(1,19)} = 4.38$, $F_{(1,32)} = 4.15$).[*] Since the former design tests more factors than the latter with little loss in accuracy, it may be seen that it is generally preferable to test a large number of factors without replication rather than a smaller number with replication.

It should be noted that if the assumption that the high-order interactions are negligible is justified, the experimenter has gained from the inclusion of as many factors as possible. If, however, some of the high-order interactions are not negligible, then it may be objected that the inclusion of extra factors is not justified since the inflation of the error causes the experiment to be less efficient. However, this criticism is offset by two facts. First, if any particular interaction in subsequent experiments proves to be of importance, this can be removed and examined. Secondly, and more important, if the additional factors that are introduced have non-negligible interactions, and if the levels of these factors are not always to be fixed at the same level in any experiment that may be carried out, the appropriate error should include the high-order interactions of these factors. To give an example, suppose we have the choice of carrying out two replications of experiments using male animals only or one replication using male and female animals. Any results from the former experiment could be applied only to male animals, while the results from the latter experiment could be applied generally. The latter experiment may therefore have a higher error than the former as a result of the greater generality that is achieved in its results.

The device of employing only a single replication is thus very useful. The experimenter, by including the maximum number of factors in his design, achieves in consequence more results of greater generality. This may cause the estimate of error to be larger than would be obtained using a small number of

---

[*] A full discussion of the effect of degrees of freedom cannot be undertaken here. The variance-ratio table provides, however, a guide to the effect of using different numbers. For further comments, see 12.6.

factors with replication, but the wider applicability of the conclusions will usually more than compensate for this increase.

5.6 Analysis of a 2^m experiment with confounding

The steps for the full analysis of a 2^m experiment with confounding can now be set out—

(1) The experimental results should be set out in a plan, and the block and treatment totals calculated.
(2) The main effects and interactions should be calculated by the plusing and minusing procedure of **3.4**.
(3) An analysis of variance should be carried out, the treatment sum of squares being derived from those effects that are neither confounded nor used as error.
(4) The treatment effects may be tested using the residual mean square from the analysis of variance, and tables of means constructed to demonstrate important effects and interactions.

The first two of these steps, i.e. the estimation of the treatment effects, are the most important, and sometimes it will be possible *simply from these steps* to pick out the important features of the experiment. Often, if necessary, it will be possible after these two steps to use the estimates of the higher-order interactions to obtain a rapid but sufficiently accurate estimate of the error of the other estimates. The procedure of the analysis of variance may then be avoided.

Thus, for example, if $\bar{h}$ is the mean magnitude of m higher-order interactions *irrespective of sign*, $5\bar{h}/4$ estimates the error of the main effects and interactions with roughly $0 \cdot 9m$ degrees of freedom. This may be a sufficiently accurate estimate of error for many purposes. In other cases a less accurate estimate, more rapidly obtained, may suffice.

5.7 Partial confounding

It has been assumed so far that, where more than one replication of a factorial experiment with confounding has been carried out, the same treatment effects were confounded in each replication. This procedure does not, however, have to be followed. It is possible to change the confounded effects in the different replications so that some information may be retained on each confounded effect. Thus, for a 2^3 experiment with two replicates the interaction ABC may be confounded in the first replicate, and a different interaction, AB say, in the second. The first replicate will provide an estimate of AB, the second of ABC, and both replicates will estimate the other effects. Such an experiment is *partially confounded*. Clearly the AB and ABC interactions will be estimated with a lower degree of precision than the other effects. This gives rise to a slight complexity in the analysis, but this is not serious. Table 5.7.1 gives a useful design for a 2^3 experiment in two blocks replicated four times. Each first- and second-order interaction is confounded once. It can be seen from the table that each inter-

Table 5.7.1 2^3 experiment with four replicates and two blocks per replicate

	Replicate							
	1		2		3		4	
Block	1	2	3	4	5	6	7	8
Treatments	(1)	a	(1)	a	(1)	a	(1)	a
	ab	b	ab	b	b	ab	a	ab
	ac	c	c	ac	ac	c	bc	c
	bc	abc	abc	bc	abc	bc	abc	ac
Confounded interaction	ABC		AB		AC		BC	

action can be estimated from three of the four replicates, whilst the main effects can be estimated from all four replicates.

The device of partial confounding allows some information to be retained on all effects, and block-to-block variation is eliminated at the same time. The usual calculation of the estimates of treatment effects and the analysis of variance has, however, to be modified accordingly. The estimates of each partially confounded effect must be made only from the blocks in which it is not confounded. The sum of squares are then calculated from these estimates, the reduction in the number of plots being acknowledged in the divisor.

As an example, we shall suppose that, in the experiment described in 5.2, the design had been carried out as in Table 5.7.2, the litters being allocated at

Table 5.7.2 Experimental design for partial confounding

Litter	I	II	III	IV	V	VI	VII	VIII
Treatments	(1)	c	(1)	c	(1)	c	(1)	f
	cf	f	m	cm	f	cf	c	cf
	cm	m	cf	f	cm	m	fm	m
	fm	cfm	cfm	fm	cfm	fm	cfm	cm
	♂	c♂	c♂	♂	c♂	♂	f♂	♂
	cf♂	f♂	cm♂	m♂	cf♂	f♂	cf♂	c♂
	cm♂	m♂	f♂	cf♂	m♂	cm♂	m♂	fm♂
	fm♂	cfm♂	fm♂	cfm♂	fm♂	cfm♂	cm♂	cfm♂
Total	7·39	7·42	6·59	6·51	7·51	7·19	6·70	6·83
Confounded interaction	CFM		CF♂		CM♂		FM♂	

random to the treatment groups. The same weights as employed in **5.2** have been used, but for the purposes of this example the litter-mates have been regrouped, so that the animals indicated as litter-mates in this example are not really so.

The treatment effects may be calculated by the usual plusing and minusing procedure, but the partially confounded effects have to be adjusted by omitting the blocks in which they are confounded. Thus the total, 0·18, for *CFM* contains the comparison of litter II with litter I, and this has to be subtracted to give a within-litter effect. The revised value for the total for *CFM* is therefore

$$0{\cdot}18 - 7{\cdot}42 + 7{\cdot}39 = 0{\cdot}15.$$

This is based on three-quarters of the observations, so that the appropriate divisor in estimating the effect *CFM* is $\frac{3}{4} \times 32 = 24$, and consequently,

$$CFM = \frac{0{\cdot}15}{24} = 0{\cdot}006.$$

The calculation of treatment effects thus proceeds as in Table 5.7.3.

Table 5.7.3   Calculation of treatment effects

Effect	(4)	Adjustment for confounding			Estimate of effect
Total	56·14				—
C	−0·32				−0·010
F	1·78				0·056
CF	−0·64				−0·020
M	−0·04				−0·001
CM	0·22				0·007
FM	0·20				0·006
CFM	0·18	− 7·42 + 7·39 =	0·15		0·006
$\male$	9·40				0·294
$C\male$	0·02				0·001
$F\male$	1·68				0·052
$CF\male$	−0·14	− 6·51 + 6·59 =	−0·06		−0·002
$M\male$	0·34				0·011
$CM\male$	0·08	− 7·19 + 7·51 =	0·40		0·017
$FM\male$	0·02	− 6·83 + 6·70 =	−0·11		−0·005
$CFM\male$	0·84				0·026

To find the treatment sum of squares, we note that the appropriate divisor for the sums of squares of partially confounded effects is $\frac{3}{4} \times 64 = 48$. Hence,

Treatment sum of squares

$$= \frac{1}{64} \left[\begin{array}{c} (-0{\cdot}32)^2 + 1{\cdot}78^2 + \ldots + 0{\cdot}84^2 \\ \text{omitting confounded effects} \end{array} \right]$$

$$+ \frac{1}{48} \left[0{\cdot}15^2 + (-0{\cdot}06)^2 + 0{\cdot}40^2 + (-0{\cdot}11)^2 \right] = 1{\cdot}5006.$$

The analysis of variance is thus constructed as in Table 5.7.4.

Table 5.7.4 Analysis of variance

	d.f.	s.s.	m.s.
Litters	7	0·1437	0·0205
Treatments	15	1·5006	0·1000
Residual	41	0·4048	0·0099
Total	63	2·0491	

The standard errors of the estimated effects may now be calculated. These are $\sqrt{(0{\cdot}0099/16)} = \pm 0{\cdot}025$ for the unconfounded effects and $\sqrt{(0{\cdot}0099/12)} = \pm 0{\cdot}029$ for the partially confounded effects. Tables of means to demonstrate these effects may be compiled in the usual way.

5.8 Designs involving factors at four levels

The design and analysis of experiments involving factors at four levels may be greatly simplified by considering the four levels as the combination of two factors each at two levels. Thus if a_0, a_1, a_2 and a_3 represent the four levels, these may be considered as replaced by treatment combinations (1), a, b and ab respectively. The comparison A is then equivalent to

$$\tfrac{1}{2}(ab - b + a - (1)) = \tfrac{1}{2}(a_3 - a_2 + a_1 - a_0).$$

Similar, B and AB are equivalent to

$$\tfrac{1}{2}(ab + b - a - (1)) = \tfrac{1}{2}(a_3 + a_2 - a_1 - a_0)$$

and

$$\tfrac{1}{2}(ab - b - a + (1)) = \tfrac{1}{2}(a_3 - a_2 - a_1 + a_0)$$

respectively. Thus the three degrees of freedom derived by comparing the four levels may be split into three separate components comparing the levels in pairs. Any one of these may be confounded or may form part of a confounded inter-action.

If the levels are equally spaced, then the second comparison is probably the most interesting since it largely reflects the linear trend between a_0 and a_3. For four levels, the linear, quadratic and cubic components are given by

$$A' = \tfrac{1}{10}(3a_3 + a_2 - a_1 - 3a_0)$$
$$A'' = \tfrac{1}{2}(a_3 - a_2 - a_1 + a_0)$$
$$A''' = \tfrac{1}{10}(a_3 - 3a_2 + 3a_1 - a_0).$$

The above comparisons may be seen to be $2A''' + A'$, $2A' - A'''$ and A''.

If the third of the above comparisons, i.e. AB, is thus confounded, we can estimate the linear component A', using the other two. If, however, we confound the first of the above comparisons, i.e. A, and assume that the cubic component A''' is negligible, we can estimate both A' and A''.

To demonstrate the use of this approach, suppose we wish to design an experiment to test three factors, C, D and E, each at two levels and a fourth at four levels a_0, a_1, a_2, a_3. If we wish to use blocks of eight treatment combinations, three degrees of freedom will be confounded.

First, we replace the factor at four levels by two factors each at two levels, as above. We then draw up a design confounding the resulting 2^5 experiment. If we confound ACD, BCE and $ABDE$, the blocks of this design would be—

I:	(1),	be,	ad,	abde,	ace,	abc,	cde,	bcd,
II:	a,	abe,	d,	bde,	ce,	bc,	acde,	abcd,
III:	b,	e,	abd,	ade,	abce,	ac,	bcde,	cd,
IV:	ab,	ae,	bd,	de,	bce,	c,	abcde,	acd.

We then "translate" the letters a and b back into the four levels a_0, a_1, a_2, a_3. The resulting design thus confounds

$$\tfrac{1}{2}(a_3 - a_2 + a_1 - a_0) \times CD, \quad \tfrac{1}{2}(a_3 + a_2 - a_1 - a_0) \times CE,$$

and

$$\tfrac{1}{2}(a_3 - a_2 - a_1 + a_0) \times DE.$$

It is—

I:	a_0,	a_2e,	a_1d,	a_3de,	a_1ce,	a_3c,	a_0cde,	a_2cd,
II:	a_1,	a_3e,	a_0d,	a_2de,	a_0ce,	a_2c,	a_1cde,	a_3cd,
III:	a_2,	a_0e,	a_3d,	a_1de,	a_3ce,	a_1c,	a_2cde,	a_0cd,
IV:	a_3,	a_1e,	a_2d,	a_0de,	a_2ce,	a_0c,	a_3cde,	$a_1cd.$

The procedure for constructing the analysis of variance is then exactly the same as for the 2^m experiment. The confounded components may be removed in the same manner, and the degrees of freedom tested individually or in groups as desired. For instance, the sum of the individual degrees of freedom AE, BE and ABE gives the three degrees of freedom of the interaction of E with the four levels of A.

This representation of a four-level factor by two two-level factors provides a useful approach to the confounding and analysis of factorial experiments. A similar representation of an eight-level factor can be made using three two-level factors, but this representation is less frequently needed.

6 Factorial Designs involving Factors at Three Levels

6.1 The I and J components of interaction

The interaction of two factors each at three levels may be formally divided into two components each with two degrees of freedom. Although no meaning can be attached to this division, it is worthy of note for two reasons. First, it provides a method of calculating the interaction directly and thus enables the analysis of variance to be self-checking. Complete recalculation of the treatment sum of squares is thus avoided. Secondly, it indicates a method by which confounding may be carried out in a 3^m experiment.

Let us consider an experiment with two factors, A and B, each at three levels. A slightly different notation from that of Chapter 4 will be used here. We shall let a treatment combination be represented by $l_1 l_2$, where l_1 is the level of factor A and l_2 the level of factor B. For the 3^2 experiment, the nine treatment combinations are set out in Table 6.1.1.

Table 6.1.1 Notation for treatment combinations in a 3^2 experiment

Level of factor A	Level of factor B		
	0	1	2
0	00	01	02
1	10	11	12
2	20	21	22

Now suppose that these nine treatment combinations are to be arranged in three blocks of three treatments per block. Four possible ways of doing this are give in Table 6.1.2. Here a design is obtained by superimposing one of the

Table 6.1.2 Four ways of arranging nine treatments into three blocks of three

Arrangement			
I	I	III	IV
α α α	α β γ	α γ β	α β γ
β β β	α β γ	β α γ	β γ α
γ γ γ	α β γ	γ β α	γ α β

arrangements on the 3×3 array of treatment combinations given in Table 6.1.1. Those treatments corresponding to α will constitute the first block, so that, for example, in arrangement I this block consists of the three treatment combinations with factor A at level 0. Similarly, the treatments in the second and third blocks are those corresponding to β and γ respectively. For example, arrangement IV gives the three blocks:

Block 1: 00 12 21
Block 2: 01 10 22
Block 3: 02 11 20

In arrangement I, the differences between the levels of factor A have been confounded with the differences between blocks. That is, the main effect of factor A has been confounded with blocks. Similarly, arrangement II confounds the main effect of factor B with blocks. In arrangement III the three blocks form a Latin square in relation to the factors A and B. Provided there is no interaction between factors and blocks, the factors A and B are orthogonal to blocks, that is, they are unaffected by differences between blocks. The same considerations hold for the Latin square given by arrangement IV. Further, arrangements III and IV constitute a set of orthogonal Latin squares. Hence the four arrangements given in Table 6.1.2 are all orthogonal and the comparisons between blocks represent the eight degrees of freedom for the 3^2 factorial design. The four degrees of freedom from arrangements III and IV represent the AB interaction. The two degrees of freedom given by arrangement III are called the "I component" of the AB interaction and will be denoted by $AB(I)$. The two degrees of freedom given by arrangement IV are called the J component of the AB interaction and will be denoted by $AB(J)$.

The main effects of A and B are given by the degrees of freedom corresponding to the variations between the row and column totals respectively. The $AB(I)$ interaction is given by the two degrees of freedom corresponding to the variations between the I-totals, namely

$$I_0 = 00 + 11 + 22$$
$$I_1 = 10 + 21 + 02$$
$$I_2 = 20 + 01 + 12.$$

The $AB(J)$ interaction is given by the two degrees of freedom corresponding to variations between the J-totals, namely

$$J_0 = 00 + 12 + 21$$
$$J_1 = 01 + 10 + 22$$
$$J_2 = 02 + 11 + 20.$$

We can see, therefore, that confounding in a 3^2 experiment is simply a case of using a Latin square with the blocks occupying the treatment positions and the two factors occupying the rows and columns respectively.

Before extending these ideas to the 3^3 and 3^m experiments in general, we shall demonstrate the use of the I and J totals in calculating interaction by considering again the experiment of **4.1**. Using the treatment totals given in Table 4.1.3, we may calculate the I and J totals:

I_0	158·2	J_0	156·3
I_1	162·4	J_1	158·5
I_2	161·2	J_2	167·0
Total	481·8	Total	481·8

From these, the I component of interaction, with two degrees of freedom, is

$$\frac{1}{9}\left[(158{\cdot}2)^2 + (162{\cdot}4)^2 + (161{\cdot}2)^2\right] - \frac{(481{\cdot}8)^2}{27} = 1{\cdot}04.$$

Similarly, the J component is

$$\frac{1}{9}\left[(156{\cdot}3)^2 + (158{\cdot}5)^2 + (167{\cdot}0)^2\right] - \frac{(481{\cdot}8)^2}{27} = 7{\cdot}09.$$

These total to give 8·13 as previously.

In point of fact, there is little to be gained by keeping these components separate, since the subdivision of interaction in this manner is primarily a computational device rather than a practical distinction. The total of the I and J components may thus be calculated directly by summing the squares of the six I and J totals, dividing by the appropriate divisor, and subtracting twice the correction for the mean.

The mean of any treatment combination can be reconstructed from the row, column, I and J totals in which that treatment combination falls. The totals for these should be added together and the overall total of all yields subtracted. This should then be divided by the number of observations in the row, column, I or J totals. Thus, here, the reconstructed yield for 01, i.e. nitrate at level 0 and phosphate at level 1, is

$$\frac{1}{9}(158{\cdot}8 + 181{\cdot}8 + 161{\cdot}2 + 158{\cdot}5 - 481{\cdot}8) = 19{\cdot}8.$$

However, a reconstruction of this type is seldom necessary.

More often, it will be necessary to adjust the treatment yields so that the three totals of one of the components, I or J, are all equal, without affecting the other component or the row and column totals. This is quite easily done by applying a correction to each mean. For instance, if the J totals are adjusted to be equal, it is necessary to add

$$\frac{156{\cdot}3}{9} - \frac{481{\cdot}8}{27} = -0{\cdot}5$$

to the means of the three treatment combinations making up total J_0. Similarly, the adjustments to treatment combinations in totals J_1 and J_2 are, respectively,

$$\frac{158{\cdot}5}{9} - \frac{481{\cdot}8}{27} = -0{\cdot}2 \quad \text{and} \quad \frac{167{\cdot}0}{9} - \frac{481{\cdot}8}{27} = 0{\cdot}7.$$

The revised table of means would than be as shown in Table 6.1.3.

Table 6.1.3   Means with adjusted J component of interaction

Level of nitrate	Level of phosphate			Total
	0	1	2	
0	13·9	19·6	19·4	17·6
1	14·1	20·3	16·0	16·8
2	18·1	20·7	18·5	19·1
Total	15·4	20·2	18·0	17·8

6.2   Experiments with three factors at three levels

If it is required to test three factors, A, B and C, each at three levels, there are 27 treatment combinations which can be set out as in Table 6.2.1. It is usually desirable to arrange these in three blocks of nine treatment combinations. One possible way of doing this would be to take the three levels of C in turn with the three treatments comprising I_0 of the last section to form the first block, with the treatments comprising I_1 to form the second block and with the treatments comprising I_2 to form the third block. The comparison between blocks would then be the same as the comparison between the I component of the AB interaction; that is, we would be confounding the $AB(I)$ interaction.

Table 6.2.1   Notation for treatment combinations in a 3^3 experiment

Level of A	Level of C								
	0			1			2		
	Level of B			Level of B			Level of B		
	0	1	2	0	1	2	0	1	2
0	000	010	020	001	011	021	002	012	022
1	100	110	120	101	111	121	102	112	122
2	200	210	220	201	211	221	202	212	222

The I and J components of any first-order interaction might similarly be confounded, but in general we shall prefer to confound two degrees of freedom from the second-order interaction rather than from a first-order interaction. To do this, it is necessary to split the second-order interaction into four components, each with two degrees of freedom. The first step in deriving these components is to calculate the I and J components of AB at each level of factor C. This gives rise to a series of totals such as in Table 6.2.2. The totals for the I and J components

Table 6.2.2 I and J totals in a 3^3 experiment

		Level of factor C			
0	1	2	0	1	2
I_{00}	I_{01}	I_{02}	J_{00}	J_{01}	J_{02}
I_{10}	I_{11}	I_{12}	J_{10}	J_{11}	J_{12}
I_{20}	I_{21}	I_{22}	J_{20}	J_{21}	J_{22}

may then be used to calculate the AB interaction. If, however, the I and J components of these 3×3 tables are calculated, we get a further set of totals defined by

$$W_0 = I_{00} + I_{11} + I_{22} \qquad X_0 = I_{00} + I_{12} + I_{21}$$
$$W_1 = I_{10} + I_{21} + I_{02} \qquad X_1 = I_{10} + I_{01} + I_{22}$$
$$W_2 = I_{20} + I_{01} + I_{12} \qquad X_2 = I_{20} + I_{11} + I_{02}$$

$$Y_0 = J_{00} + J_{11} + J_{22} \qquad Z_0 = J_{00} + J_{12} + J_{21}$$
$$Y_1 = J_{10} + J_{21} + J_{02} \qquad Z_1 = J_{10} + J_{01} + J_{22}$$
$$Y_2 = J_{20} + J_{01} + J_{12} \qquad Z_2 = J_{20} + J_{11} + J_{02}$$

The sum of squares of each of these sets of totals provides two degrees of freedom for the second-order interaction, which may therefore be calculated directly using these totals. These four components will be denoted by $ABC(W)$, $ABC(X)$, $ABC(Y)$ and $ABC(Z)$.

Any one of these components may now be confounded by arranging the nine treatment combinations contributing to each of its totals in different blocks. The main effects, first-order interactions and other components of the second-order interaction may then be estimated as usual. Table 6.2.3 gives the treat-

Table 6.2.3 $3 \times 3 \times 3$ designs confounding the second-order interaction

Level of A and B					Level of factor C							
	W_0	W_1	W_2	X_0	X_1	X_2	Y_0	Y_1	Y_2	Z_0	Z_1	Z_2
00	0	2	1	0	1	2	0	2	1	0	1	2
10	1	0	2	2	0	1	1	0	2	2	0	1
20	2	1	0	1	2	0	2	1	0	1	2	0
01	2	1	0	1	2	0	1	0	2	2	0	1
11	0	2	1	0	1	2	2	1	0	1	2	0
21	1	0	2	2	0	1	0	2	1	0	1	2
02	1	0	2	2	0	1	2	1	0	1	2	0
12	2	1	0	1	2	0	0	2	1	0	1	2
22	0	2	1	0	1	2	1	0	2	2	0	1

ment combinations occurring in each of the W, X, Y and Z totals. It thus provides a list of designs confounding each of these components.

The use of any one of these designs confounds two degrees of freedom of the second-order interaction; the remaining six are unconfounded.

If more than one replication is available, different components may be confounded in each replication. Such partial confounding allows some information to be obtained on all components of the second-order interaction. Unless, however, this interaction is of particular importance, it is computationally preferable to confound one particular component only.

Table 6.3.1   Plan and yield of turnips

	Factor levels	Yields	Factor levels	Yields	
	110	297·7	001	268·9	
	121	405·7	202	340·9	
	212	407·5	122	386·5	
	000	311·5	100	299·5	
$X_0 = 2988·9$	220	363·7	012	331·9	$X_1 = 3094·6$
	102	280·9	020	305·5	
	011	260·5	111	369·1	
	201	342·1	221	455·0	
	022	319·3	210	337·3	
	200	307·9	200	478·4	
	120	364·9	002	343·3	
	021	272·5	222	542·6	
	010	208·3	010	433·3	
$X_2 = 2655·3$	112	333·1	021	447·1	$X_2 = 4196·6$
	222	326·5	101	431·5	
	002	174·1	211	531·8	
	101	359·5	120	519·2	
	211	308·5	112	469·4	
	210	335·5	212	445·9	
	001	240·7	220	536·0	
	012	393·7	011	414·7	
	221	420·1	110	424·3	
$X_1 = 3335·8$	100	351·1	201	351·1	$X_0 = 3556·6$
	122	394·9	022	360·7	
	020	336·1	121	367·9	
	202	455·6	102	316·3	
	111	408·1	000	339·7	

6.3 Example of a 3^3 experiment with confounding

Table 6.3.1 gives the plan and yields of turnips of two replications of a 3^3 experiment to test nitrate, phosphate and potash dressings. Here the three levels of the first factor, nitrate, N, were 0, 33 and 66 kg N per ha, the three levels of the second factor, phosphate, P, were 0, 45 and 90 kg P_2O_5 per ha, and the three levels of the third factor, potash, K, were 0, 55 and 110 lb K_2O per ha. There are six blocks of nine plots, and inspection of Table 6.2.3 shows that the X component of NPK is confounded in each replicate. Each block total is indicated beside each block, together with the X component to which it corresponds.

As usual, the first step in the analysis is to form tables of totals for the various treatment combinations. This is done in Table 6.3.2. These may then be used to

Table 6.3.2 Total yields of treatment combinations

Level of nitrate	Level of potash								
	0			1			2		
	Level of phosphate			Level of phosphate			Level of phosphate		
	0	1	2	0	1	2	0	1	2
0	651·2	641·6	641·6	509·6	675·2	719·6	517·4	725·6	680·0
1	650·6	722·0	884·1	791·0	777·2	773·6	597·2	802·5	781·4
2	786·3	672·8	899·7	693·2	840·3	875·1	796·5	853·4	869·1

construct the various two-way tables, the I and J totals for NP, and, finally, the W, X, Y and Z totals. These tables of totals are given in Table 6.3.3.

As a check on this calculation, the X totals in this table may be compared with the totals of pairs of blocks in Table 6.3.1.

We may now proceed with the construction of an analysis of variance. The total and blocks sums of squares should be calculated from Table 6.3.1. The main effects and interactions may then be calculated from Table 6.3.3. The analysis of variance partitioning the total treatment sum of squares is given in Table 6.3.4.

The analysis of variance may now be completed by subtracting the blocks sum of squares and the unconfounded treatment sum of squares from the total. This gives the analysis of variance shown in Table 6.3.5.

This table shows that the nitrate and phosphate effects ate highly significant, but that no other effect or interaction achieves significance. The PK interaction is large, and it is possible that it conceals a component of some interest. We might, therefore, partition PK into four separate degrees of freedom. At the same time the linear and quadratic components of N and P might be extracted and tested. This has been done in Table 6.3.6. The smallness of the other sums of squares indicates that no other component could be significant.

Nearly all of the sums of squares for N and P may be accounted for by their

Table 6.3.3 Totals of treatment combinations

Level of nitrate	Level of phosphate			Total
	0	1	2	
0	1678·2	2042·4	2041·2	5761·8
1	2038·8	2301·7	2439·1	6779·6
2	2276·0	2366·5	2643·9	7286·4
Total	5993·0	6710·6	7124·2	19827·8

Level of nitrate	Level of potash			Total
	0	1	2	
0	1934·4	1904·4	1923·0	5761·8
1	2256·7	2341·8	2181·1	6779·6
2	2358·8	2408·6	2519·0	7286·4
Total	6549·9	6654·8	6623·1	19827·8

Level of phosphate	Level of potash			Total
	0	1	2	
0	2088·1	1993·8	1911·1	5993·0
1	2036·4	2292·7	2381·5	6710·6
2	2425·4	2368·3	2330·5	7124·2
Total	6549·9	6654·8	6623·1	19827·8

I totals for nitrate and phosphate	Level of potash			Total
	0	1	2	
I_0	2272·9	2161·9	2189·0	6623·8
I_1	1965·0	2350·9	2130·6	6446·5
I_2	2312·0	2142·0	2303·5	6757·5

J totals for nitrate and phosphate	Level of potash			Total
	0	1	2	
J_0	2208·1	2123·5	2152·2	6483·8
J_1	2191·9	2341·3	2191·9	6725·1
J_2	2149·9	2190·0	2279·0	6618·9

$W_0 = 6927\cdot3 \qquad X_0 = 6545\cdot5 \qquad Y_0 = 6828\cdot4 \qquad Z_0 = 6590\cdot0$

$W_1 = 6296\cdot0 \qquad X_1 = 6430\cdot4 \qquad Y_1 = 6534\cdot1 \qquad Z_1 = 6594\cdot4$

$W_2 = 6604\cdot5 \qquad X_2 = 6851\cdot9 \qquad Y_2 = 6465\cdot3 \qquad Z_2 = 6643\cdot4.$

Table 6.3.4 Subdivision of treatment sum of squares

	d.f	s.s.
N	2	66984·6
P	2	36400·5
K	2	321·6
NP	4	4329·4
NK	4	4150·1
PK	4	13757·6
NPK { Unconfounded W,Y,Z	6	15303·2
Confounded X	2	5273·9
Treatments	26	146520·9

Table 6.3.5 Analysis of variance

	d.f.	s.s.	m.s.	Variance ratio
N	2	66984·6	33492·3	20·84
P	2	36400·5	18200·3	11·33
K	2	321·6	160·8	0·10
NP	4	4329·4	1082·3	0·67
NK	4	4150·1	1037·5	0·65
PK	4	13757·6	3439·4	2·14
NPK	6	15303·2	2550·5	1·59
Blocks	5	158388·7		
Residual	24	38566·6	1606·9	
Total	53	338202·3		

Table 6.3.6 Linear and quadratic components of N, P and PK

	d.f.	s.s.	Variance ratio
Linear N	1	64566·8	40·18
Quadratic N	1	2417·8	1·50
Linear P	1	35544·8	22·12
Quadratic P	1	855·7	0·53
Linear $P \times$ Linear K	1	280·9	0·17
Linear $P \times$ Quadratic K	1	0·8	0·00
Quadratic $P \times$ Linear K	1	12856·1	8·00
Quadratic $P \times$ Quadratic K	1	619·8	0·39

linear components; neither of the quadratic components reaches significance. Likewise, most of the sum of squares for PK can be accounted for by the quadratic $P \times$ linear K component, which is significant at the 1 percent level. Summary tables should now be constructed as in Table 6.3.7.

Table 6.3.7   Summary tables of means

Level of nitrate	Level of phosphate			Level of potash			Mean
	0	1	2	0	1	2	
0	279·7	340·4	340·2	322·4	317·4	320·5	320·1
1	339·8	383·6	406·5	376·1	390·3	363·5	376·6
2	379·3	394·4	440·6	393·1	401·4	419·8	404·8
Mean	332·9	372·8	395·8	363·9	369·7	368·0	367·2

Level of phosphate	Level of potash			Mean
	0	1	2	
0	348·0	332·3	318·5	332·9
1	339·4	382·1	396·9	372·8
2	404·2	394·7	388·4	395·8
Mean	363·9	369·7	368·0	367·2

Standard error of mean in body of table = ± 16·4
Standard error of marginal means   = ± 9·4.

A further 2×2 table may, if necessary, be constructed to demonstrate the quadratic $P \times$ linear K effect. In this case, this results from a decreasing yield with increased application of K at the highest and lowest levels of P, and an increasing yield with increased application of K at the middle level of P.

It should be noted that, if it had been necessary to construct a three-way table to demonstrate the NPK interaction, it would have been necessary to adjust the means so that the confounded interaction $NPK(X)$ was zero. This would have been done by an extension of the method of **6.1**.

6.4   Experiments with more than three factors at three levels

To develop these ideas further and in particular to introduce a notation that will be useful when we consider fractional 3^m experiments in the next chapter, we shall now consider an alternative, though equivalent, representation of the components of the interactions.

We shall consider again the 3^2 experiment of **6.1**, where a treatment combination was represented by $l_1 l_2$, with l_1 being the level of factor A and l_2 the level of factor B. Now the three treatment combinations making up the I-total I_0 can be seen to satisfy the equation

$$l_1 + 2l_2 = 0,$$

where we use the rule that if the function $l_1 + 2l_2$ takes a value greater than or equal to 3 then we reduce the value by 3. The process is repeated again, if necessary, until the value is less than 3. The rule means that we are reducing the value *modulo* 3, or mod 3. The treatments making up I_1 satisfy the equation

$$l_1 + 2l_2 = 1 \text{ (mod 3)},$$

and those making up I_2 satisfy

$$l_1 + 2l_2 = 2 \text{ (mod 3)}.$$

Hence we can say that the treatment combinations giving the I-totals satisfy

$$l_1 + 2l_2 = 0,1,2 \text{ (mod 3)}.$$

We shall represent the $AB(I)$ interaction by the symbols AB^2, where the powers attached to the letters are the coefficients of the linear combination of l_1 and l_2. Similarly, the J-totals are obtained from the treatment combinations satisfying the three equations

$$l_1 + l_2 = 0,1,2 \text{ (mod 3)}.$$

The $AB(J)$ component can be represented by AB. The main effect of A is given by the comparison of the three totals for which

$$l_1 = 0,1,2 \text{ (mod 3)},$$

and the main effect of B by the three totals for which

$$l_2 = 0,1,2 \text{ (mod 3)}.$$

The eight degrees of freedom due to the treatments have, therefore, been split orthogonally into the four components A, B, AB^2 and AB, each with two degrees of freedom. It is clear that $AB = A^2B^2$ and $AB^2 = A^2B$. For convenience the power of the first digit is taken to be unity. The rule now for multiplying together two effects is that the power of each letter is reduced modulo 3 if necessary. For example,

$$A^2B = (A^2B)^2 = A^4B^2 = AB^2.$$

For the 3^3 experiment of **6.2** a treatment combination is given by $l_1l_2l_3$ and the main effects and components of interactions are given as follows, where all functions are reduced modulo 3 when necessary—

$$A : l_1 = 0, 1, 2$$
$$B : l_2 = 0, 1, 2$$
$$C : l_3 = 0, 1, 2$$
$$AB(I) = AB^2 : l_1 + 2l_2 = 0, 1, 2$$

$$AB(J) = AB : l_1 + l_2 = 0, 1, 2$$
$$AC(I) = AC^2 : l_1 + 2l_3 = 0, 1, 2$$
$$AC(J) = AC : l_1 + l_3 = 0, 1, 2$$
$$BC(I) = BC^2 : l_2 + 2l_3 = 0, 1, 2$$
$$BC(J) = BC : l_2 + l_3 = 0, 1, 2$$
$$ABC(W) = AB^2C^2 : l_1 + 2l_2 + 2l_3 = 0, 1, 2$$
$$ABC(X) = AB^2C : l_1 + 2l_2 + l_3 = 0, 1, 2$$
$$ABC(Y) = ABC^2 : l_1 + l_2 + 2l_3 = 0, 1, 2$$
$$ABC(Z) = ABC : l_1 + l_2 + l_3 = 0, 1, 2$$

This method can easily be extended to more than three factors. Suppose there are four factors, each at three levels, and we wish to place the 81 treatment combinations in three blocks of 27 treatment combinations. The third-order interaction could be split into eight components, each with two degrees of freedom, and one of these components confounded with blocks. For example, if the ABC^2D^2 component is confounded with blocks, one of the blocks will consist of the 27 treatment combinations satisfying

$$l_1 + l_2 + 2l_3 + 2l_4 = 0 \,(\text{mod } 3).$$

The treatment combinations in the other two blocks will satisfy, respectively,

$$l_1 + l_2 + 2l_3 + 2l_4 = 1, 2 \,(\text{mod } 3).$$

Alternatively, the 81 treatment combinations may be placed in nine blocks of nine treatment combinations. In this case eight degrees of freedom are confounded, that is four components of the interactions. The general rule is that if pairs of degrees of freedom corresponding to, say, F and G are confounded with blocks, then so are the pairs of degrees of freedom corresponding to FG and FG^2. Suppose that, in our example, we confound the components ABC^2D^2 and $ABCD$. Then, by the above rule, the following will also be confounded—

$$ABC^2D^2 \times ABCD = A^2B^2C^3D^3 = A^2B^2 = AB$$

and

$$ABC^2D^2 \times (ABCD)^2 = A^3B^3C^4D^4 = CD.$$

We have, therefore, confounded two components of the first-order interactions. A better design would probably confound four components of the second-order interactions. For example, if we confound AB^2C^2 and BC^2D then we also confound

$$AB^2C^2 \times BC^2D = ACD$$

and

$$AB^2C^2 \times (BC^2D)^2 = ABD^2.$$

The nine blocks are given by solutions to the equations

$$l_1 + 2l_2 + 2l_3 = i \,(\text{mod } 3)$$
$$l_2 + 2l_3 + l_4 = j \,(\text{mod } 3),$$

where i and j each take on the values 0, 1 and 2. There are then nine pairs of equations, each pair giving one block. The block containing the treatment combination 0000 is called the *principal block*. As in **5.4**, the other blocks can then be immediately written down by "adding" each treatment combination in the principal block to any treatment combination which has not already occurred. In adding, the levels of the treatment factors are reduced modulo 3 where necessary. For instance, $0122 + 1202 = 1021$. The full design is given in Table 6.4.1. As before, it is necessary to randomize within and between blocks before application of the design.

Table 6.4.1   A 3^4 experiment in nine blocks of nine treatment combinations confounding the AB^2C^2, BC^2D, ACD and ABD^2 components of interaction

Level of first and second factors	Level of third and fourth factors								
	Block								
	1	2	3	4	5	6	7	8	9
00	00	11	22	12	20	01	21	02	10
10	11	22	00	20	01	12	02	10	21
20	22	00	11	01	12	20	10	21	02
01	21	02	10	00	11	22	12	20	01
11	02	10	21	11	22	00	20	01	12
21	10	21	02	22	00	11	01	12	20
02	12	20	01	21	02	10	00	11	22
12	20	01	12	02	10	21	11	22	00
22	01	12	20	10	21	02	22	00	11

The analysis of the general 3^m experiment follows the same lines as that of the 3^3 experiment. Usually, however, unless the second- and higher-order interactions are of particular interest, they will be used as error. The sums of squares for blocks, main effects, and first-order interactions may then be eliminated from the total sum of squares, and the remainder used as error.

6.5   Confounding with factors at two and three levels

The previous sections have been primarily concerned with factorial designs of the 2^m, 3^m or $2^p \times 4^q$ types, but confounding is also possible in experiments where both two- and three-level factors are being tested. Such experiments can be constructed by combining the 2^p designs of Chapter 5 with the 3^q designs of this chapter.

For instance, a $2^2 \times 3$ experiment in two blocks of six plots each can be constructed by confounding the first-order interaction of the two-level factors.

Each level of the three-level factor is applied in turn to the treatment combinations (1) and ab to give the first block, and to the treatment combinations a and b to give the second block. Again, a $2^3 \times 3$ experiment in blocks of twelve plots can be obtained by applying each level of the three-level factor in turn to the blocks of treatment combinations (1), ab, ac, bc and a, b, c, abc. Here the ABC interaction is confounded with blocks. A 2×3^2 experiment in blocks of six plots will have the $BC(I)$ component of the BC interaction confounded if each level of the two-level factor is applied in turn to the blocks of treatment combinations 00, 11, 22; 01, 12, 20 and 02, 10, 21. As a final example, Table 6.5.1 gives a design for a $2^2 \times 3^2$ experiment in six blocks of six plots each. In each block,

Table 6.5.1 Design for a $2^2 \times 3^2$ experiment

Block	Levels of factors A and B		Levels of factors C and D		
1	(1)	ab	00	11	22
2	a	b	01	12	20
3	(1)	ab	02	10	21
4	a	b	00	11	22
5	(1)	ab	01	12	20
6	a	b	02	10	21

the two treatment combinations of the two-level factors A and B are combined with each of the three treatment combinations of the three-level factors C and D, giving six treatment combinations per block. The blocks of the 2^2 experiment confound the AB interaction, whilst the blocks of the 3^2 experiment confound the $CD(I)$ component of the CD interaction. In addition to these interactions, two degrees of freedom from the $ABCD$ interaction will be confounded. Other designs of type $2^p \times 3^q$ can similarly be constructed. The analysis of such designs is relatively straightforward.

A general method of constructing designs suitable for confounding in any factorial experiment has been given by Dean and John (1975); methods of obtaining partially confounded designs are given in John (1973).

7 Fractional Factorial Experiments

7.1 Fractional replication with factors at two levels

One of the difficulties of the factorial design is the manner in which the number of treatment combinations increases rapidly with the number of factors tested. Although this can be partially overcome by confounding and by using the high-order interactions of a single replicate as error, it does not completely remove the difficulty. Thus, for instance, for a single replicate testing eight factors each at two levels, the degrees of freedom in the analysis of variance would be as in Table 7.1.1.

Table 7.1.1   Degrees of freedom in 2^8 experiment

	d.f.	
Main effects	8	
First-order interactions	28	
Second-order interactions	56	
Third-order interactions	70	
Fourth-order interactions	56	
Fifth-order interactions	28	163
Sixth-order interactions	8	
Seventh-order interactions	1	
Total	255	

Here, 163 degrees of freedom are used in estimating third- and higher-order interactions. Even if the design is arranged in blocks of eight plots, more than 130 degrees of freedom are used in estimating such higher-order interactions, compared with 36 degrees of freedom used in estimating main effects and first-order interactions.

Usually, such high-order interactions are insignificant and are used as error, but even so it is evident that a large proportion of the possible comparisons contribute little to the analysis. It might therefore be asked whether a design could be used which involved fewer observations, but which still provided information on the important main effects and first-order interactions, or, alternatively, whether a design using the same number of observations could be used to provide information on more than eight factors. The general process by which this is accomplished is known as *fractional* replication.

There are two other important reasons for employing fractional factorial experiments. In the 2^8 experiment, a fully replicated design would involve "making-up" 256 treatment combinations. This may be impracticable or too costly. The use of a fractional design would mean that only a fraction of the 256 treatment combinations would have to be made up. The other reason is that, for practical motives, an investigator may prefer to carry out his experiment as a series of small experiments. He may be able to discover quickly which factors are important. Alternatively, he may wish to carry out his experiment in a sequential manner, planning his next experiment according to the results of the current one and building up a whole set of experimental results.

Against these advantages must be set the obvious reduction in the accuracy of the estimates of the effects. Further, as we shall see, the outcome of a fractional experiment is open to misinterpretation in a way that does not arise with fully replicated designs.

To illustrate the general ideas of a fractional experiment, we shall consider a 2^3 experiment in which only the four treatment combinations a, b, c and abc are used. This is a one-half replicate of the complete design. Now in the full experiment involving all eight treatment combinations the main effect A is defined by

$$A = \frac{1}{4}\Big[(a + ab + ac + abc) - ((1) + b + c + bc)\Big]$$

and the interaction BC is defined by

$$BC = \frac{1}{4}\Big[((1) + a + bc + abc) - (b + c + ab + ac)\Big],$$

so that

$$\tfrac{1}{2}(A + BC) = \frac{1}{4}\Big[(a + abc) - (b + c)\Big].$$

Hence we may say that with these four observations only, A is completely confounded with BC, because we cannot estimate A alone or BC alone, only their sum. We shall say that A and BC are *aliases*. Similarly, we can show that

$$\tfrac{1}{2}(B + AC) = \frac{1}{4}\Big[(b + abc) - (a + c)\Big],$$

$$\tfrac{1}{2}(C + AB) = \frac{1}{4}\Big[(c + abc) - (a + b)\Big],$$

so that B and AC and C and AB are aliases. We shall write $A = BC$, $B = AC$ and $C = AB$.

Another design exists for the three factors in four observations, namely using the remaining treatment combinations (1), ab, ac, and bc. We can show that

$$\tfrac{1}{2}(A - BC) = \frac{1}{4}\Big[(ab + ac) - ((1) + bc)\Big],$$

so that $A = -BC$, $B = -AC$ and $C = -AB$. The two designs are, therefore,

Design 1: a, b, c, abc
Design 2: (1), ab, ac, bc.

Either design represents a block in the system confounding the interaction ABC. Hence, using design 1 or design 2 means that we cannot estimate ABC at all. ABC is called the *defining contrast* of the design.

We have seen that the result of using a $\frac{1}{2}$-replicate of a 2^3 experiment is to lose one factorial effect, ABC, entirely and to leave each main effect mixed, or aliased, with one of the first-order interactions. In order to use fractional replication with the minimum risk of misinterpretation, it is important to know the aliasing system of the design. If we let the defining contrast be equal to the identity I then the aliasing system can be easily obtained by multiplying each effect in turn by the defining contrast. For example, the defining contrast for design 1 above is

$$I = + ABC.$$

Hence, the aliasing system is

$$A = + BC, \quad B = +AC, \quad C = +AB,$$

where we use the usual rule of multiplication. For design 2, the defining contrast is $I = -ABC$ with aliasing system $A = -BC$, $B = -AC$ and $C = -AB$.

In practice, we are unlikely to take a $\frac{1}{2}$-replicate of a 2^3 experiment, as the complete replicate only requires eight treatment combinations. To consider a more realistic situation, we shall now return to the 2^8 experiment. Suppose we take a $\frac{1}{2}$-replicate by choosing one of the blocks of 128 treatment combinations confounding the highest order interaction $ABCDEGFH$. If the $\frac{1}{2}$-replicate corresponding to $+ABCDEFGH$ is selected then since the treatment combination having all factors at the higher level has an even number of letters in common with $ABCDEFGH$, the design will consist of the 128 treatment combinations having an even number of letters in common with $ABCDEFGH$. The defining contrast is

$$I = ABCDEFGH,$$

and it can be seen that every main effect is aliased with a sixth-order interaction. For example,

$$A = BCDEFGH, \quad B = ACDEFGH.$$

Also every first-order interaction is aliased with a fifth-order interaction and all second-order with fourth-order interactions. The 70 third-order interactions divide themselves into 35 pairs of aliases, for example,

$$ABCD = EFGH, \quad ABCE = DFGH,$$

and so on. The degrees of freedom partition as in Table 7.1.2.

Table 7.1.2 Degrees of freedom in a $\frac{1}{2}$-replicate of a 2^8 experiment

	d.f.
Main effects (or sixth-order interactions)	8
First (or fifth) order interactions	28
Second (or fourth) order interactions	56
Third-order interactions	35
Total	127

If we can assume that fourth- and higher-order interactions are negligible, then this design will provide valid estimates of all main effects, first- and second-order interactions. Furthermore, if the third-order interaction can also be assumed to be negligible, the 35 degrees of freedom for these interactions could be used for an estimate of error.

If the number of factors involved is large, it is often possible to use a $\frac{1}{4}$-replicate. For instance, in the 2^8 design we could divide the 256 treatment combinations into four sets of 64, using one of the resulting sets as our design. This could be done by confounding say, $ABCDEF$, $DEFGH$ and $ABCGH$. The defining contrast for the design is, therefore,

$$I = ABCDEF = DEFGH = ABCGH,$$

and from this the aliasing system could be obtained. We can see that all main effects are aliased with third- or higher-order interactions. For example,

$$A = BCDEF = ADEFGH = BCGH,$$
$$B = ACDEF = BDEFGH = ACGH.$$

All first-order interactions are aliased with second- or higher-order interactions. If we can assume, therefore, that all second- and higher-order interactions are negligible, only 64 treatment combinations are needed to provide valid estimates of all main effects and first-order interactions. The degrees of freedom in the analysis of variance then partition as in Table 7.1.3. The second-order interactions provide 27 degrees of freedom for error.

Table 7.1.3 Degrees of freedom in a $\frac{1}{4}$-replicate of a 2^8 experiment

	d.f.
Main effects (and equivalent interactions)	8
First-order (and equivalent) interactions	28
Second-order (and equivalent) interactions	27
Total	63

The same methods can be used to obtain one-eighth, one-sixteenth, and so on, replicate designs. It may not always be possible to choose defining contrasts in such a way that the main effects and first-order interactions are not aliased with each other. For example, the most useful defining contrast for a $\frac{1}{8}$-replicate of a 2^8 experiment is of the form

$$I = ABCF = ACDG = BDFG = ABDEH = CDEFH = BCEGH = AEFGH.$$

All main effects are aliased with second- or third-order interactions, but only first-order interactions containing E or H are not aliased with other first-order interactions.

7.2 Confounding in fractional 2^m experiments

The $\frac{1}{2}$-replicate of the 2^8 experiment, of the previous section, gave a total of 128 treatment combinations. It is probable that there will be too many treatments for one block and, hence, we shall have to use confounding to keep down the block size. Suppose we arrange these treatments into two blocks of 64. Now the highest-order interaction $ABCDEFGH$ has already been confounded in the design. Confounding $ABCDEFG$ with blocks would mean that we are also confounding the main effect H, since these two effects are aliased. In this case, we would probably prefer to confound $ABCD$ with blocks as it is aliased with another third-order interaction $EFGH$. To arrange the 128 treatment combinations in eight blocks of sixteen we could confound

$$ABCD = EFGH, \quad ABEF = CDGH, \quad CDEF = ABGH, \quad ACEG = BDFH,$$
$$BDEG = ACFH, \quad BCFG = ADEH, \quad ADFG = BCEH.$$

We are only free to choose three of these effects; the remaining four will then be automatically determined. We can see from Table 7.1.2 that this now leaves 28 degrees of freedom for the third-order interactions, which may then be used for error.

Similarly, it is possible to arrange the $\frac{1}{4}$-replicate in blocks. For the 2^8 experiment of the previous section, the defining contrast is

$$I = ABCDEF = DEFGH = ABCGH.$$

If blocks of sixteen treatment combinations are used, we could confound

$$ADG = BCEFG = AEFH = BCDH,$$
$$BEH = ACDFH = BDFG = ACEG,$$
$$ABDEGH = CFGH \quad = ABF \quad = CDE.$$

In Table 7.1.3 the degrees of freedom for error are thus reduced to 24.

The construction of a fractional replication design confounding particular interactions is fairly easily carried out using the rules of Chapter 5, but, as already shown, the aliases of the confounded interactions should be carefully studied to ensure that no important effects have been unintentionally confounded.

The first step in the construction of the design is to form a block confounding the relevant interactions. In the above $\frac{1}{4}$-replicate, $ABCDEF$, $DEFGH$ and

ABCGH and *ADG, BEH, ABDEGH* and their aliases have to be confounded. One block confounding these interactions, using the rules of **5.4,** may be found to contain the treatment combinations: (1), *afg, cdg, acdf, bfh, abgh, bcdfgh, abcdh, ceh, acefgh, degh, adefh, bcef, abceg, bdefg, abde.*

We have next to decide which of the ¼-replicates formed by the blocks confounding *ABCDEF, DEFGH* and *ABCGH* we shall choose. This choice should be made at random. Suppose therefore we select the design which has an even number of letters in common with *ABCDEF,* but an odd number of letters in common with *DEFGH* and *ABCGH,* i.e. with defining contrast $I = + ABCDEF = + DEFGH = + ABCGH$. The four blocks of this design may now be constructed by multiplying the sixteen treatment combinations given above by *g, h, ad* and *adgh*. Here again it is necessary to ensure that the same block of the design is not repeated. The completed design in this instance is given in Table 7.2.1. This design has, of course, to be randomized before use.

Table 7.2.1   ¼-replicate of a 2^8 experiment in four blocks

Block							
1		2		3		4	
g	*cegh*	*h*	*ce*	*ad*	*acdeh*	*adgh*	*acdeg*
af	*acefh*	*afgh*	*acefg*	*dfg*	*cdefgh*	*dfh*	*cdef*
cd	*deh*	*cdgh*	*deg*	*acg*	*aegh*	*ach*	*ae*
acdfg	*adefgh*	*acdfg*	*adef*	*cf*	*efh*	*cfgh*	*efg*
bfgh	*bcefg*	*bf*	*bcefh*	*abdfh*	*abcdef*	*abdfg*	*abcdefgh*
abh	*abce*	*abg*	*abcegh*	*bdgh*	*bcdeg*	*bd*	*bcdeh*
bcdfh	*bdef*	*bcdfg*	*bdefgh*	*abcfgh*	*abefg*	*abcf*	*abefh*
abcdgh	*abdeg*	*abcd*	*abdeh*	*bch*	*be*	*bcg*	*begh*

Table 7.2.2   Standard order of treatments in a ½-replicate of a 2^4 experiment

Treatment combination	Effect
(*d*)	
a	$A = -BCD$
b	$B = -ACD$
ab(*d*)	$AB = -CD$
c	$C = -ABD$
ac(*d*)	$AC = -BD$
bc(*d*)	$BC = -AD$
abc	$ABC = -D$

The general approach to the analysis of fractional 2^m experiments is to select a subset of the factors for which the experiment is a complete replicate. The plusing and minusing may then proceed as usual. For example, consider a $\frac{1}{2}$-replicate of a 2^4 experiment with defining contrast $I = -ABCD$. If the factor D is temporarily removed, then the eight treatment combinations in standard order are given in Table 7.2.2. together with identification of the effects.

7.3   Example of a fractional factorial experiment

Table 7.3.1 gives the plan and yields of potatoes in lb per $\frac{1}{116}$ acre of an experiment, given in Finney (1945, 1946), to compare two sewage sludges, an

Table 7.3.1   Plan and yield of potatoes (in lb per $\frac{1}{116}$ acre)

			Bl	ock			
1		2		3		4	
(1)	177	np	180	nk	227	pk	191
rnpk	195	rk	147	rp	150	rn	223
ap	195	an	192	anpk	252	ak	197
arnk	198	arpk	225	ar	204	arnp	223
bnp	212	b	224	bpk	226	bnk	259
brk	259	brnpk	271	brn	267	brp	246
abn	168	abp	179	abk	195	abnpk	240
abrpk	199	abrnk	201	abrnp	165	abr	173

old primary raw sludge and a current primary raw sludge, with farmyard manure and with no organic manures. These were tested at two rates of application R, with the rates difference for plots without organic manures as a dummy comparison. The sludges were applied at 5 and 10 tons per acre and farmyard manure at 6 and 12 tons per acre. The double rate of application is represented by r and the single rate by the absence of the letter. In addition, there were three other factors, each at two levels, namely the presence and absence of nitrogen N, phosphate P and potash K. The organics factor at four levels can be regarded as two factors, A and B, each at two levels; with no manure denoted by (1), farmyard manure by b, new sludge by a and old sludge by ab.

Thirty-two plots were available for the experiment and these were set out in four blocks of eight plots. A $\frac{1}{2}$-replicate of a 2^6 experiment with defining contrast $I = -ARNPK$ was employed, i.e. the $\frac{1}{2}$-replicate consisted of those 32 treatment combinations having an even number of letters in common with $ARNPK$. In order to use blocks of eight plots, it is necessary to confound one first-order interaction. In this case, the potash response was considered to be unlikely to be much affected by the rate of application, so that the RK interaction was sacrificed. The three degrees of freedom confounded with blocks corresponded to

$$RK = -ANP$$
$$BNK = -ABRP$$
$$BRN = -ABPK.$$

Table 7.3.2 Calculation of treatment effects

Treatment	Yield	Plusing and minusing totals		Effect	Sum of squares	
(1)	177	6660	Total			
ar	204	−248	A	−15·50	1922	⎫
b	224	308	B	19·25	2965	Organics
abr	173	−640	AB	−40·00	12800	= 17867
rn	223	286	N	17·88	2556	⎭
an	192	−142	AN	−8·88	630	⎫
brn	267	−122	BN	−7·63	465	Organics
abn	168	90	ABN	5·63	253	× N = 1348
rp	150	38	P	2·38	45	⎫
ap	195	262	AP	16·38	2145	Organics
brp	246	−54	BP	−3·38	91	× P = 2356
abp	179	−62	ABP	−3·88	120	⎭
np	180	−32	NP	−2·00	32	
arnp	223	(216)	−RK	(13·50)	1458	(Block)
bnp	212	20	BNP	1·25	13	
abrnp	165	−100	−BRK	−6·25	313	
rk	147	304	K	19·00	2888	⎫
ak	197	112	AK	7·00	392	Organics
brk	259	128	BK	8·00	512	× K = 1002
abk	195	56	ABK	3·50	98	⎭
nk	227	122	NK	7·63	465	
arnk	198	34	−RP	2·13	36	
bnk	259	(82)	BNK	(5·13)	210	(Block)
abrnk	201	26	−BRP	1·63	21	
pk	191	194	PK	12·13	1176	
arpk	225	6	−RN	0·38	1	
bpk	226	−90	BPK	−5·63	253	
abrpk	199	(50)	−BRN	(3·13)	78	(Block)
rnpk	195	92	−AR	5·75	265	
anpk	252	−32	−R	−2·00	32	
brnpk	271	240	−ABR	15·00	1800	
abnpk	240	−124	−BR	−7·75	481	

Using the rules of **5.4**, one block of the design will be (1), $rnpk$, ap, $arnk$, bnp, brk, abn, and $abrpk$. The remaining blocks are obtained by multiplying these eight treatment combinations by np, nk and pk.

The first step in the analysis is to calculate the treatment effects. This is done in Table 7.3.2, using the plusing and minusing procedure, where the treatment combinations in the first column are in standard order when the factor R is removed. The effects are given in terms of the aliases of lowest order.

Since the rate of application in the absence of organic manure is a dummy treatment, the sums of squares for R and for the interactions AR, BR and ABR in Table 7.3.2 will have to be modified. The method for carrying out this adjustment has already been given in **4.6**. Table 7.3.3 gives the total yields for rate of application and organic manures.

Table 7.3.3 Total yields for rate of application and organic manures

Rate	No manure	Farmyard manure	Old sludge	New sludge	Total (excluding no manure)
Single	775	921	782	836	2539
Double	715	1043	738	850	2631
Total	1490	1964	1520	1686	5170
		6660			

The sum of squares for rates of application is

$$\frac{(2539)^2 + (2631)^2}{12} - \frac{(5170)^2}{24} = 353$$

and for organics (excluding no manure)

$$\frac{(1964)^2 + (1520)^2 + (1686)^2}{8} - \frac{(5170)^2}{24} = 12\ 582.$$

Hence the sum of squares for the organics $\times R$ interaction is

$$\frac{(921)^2 + (782)^2 + \ldots + (850)^2}{4} - \frac{(5170)^2}{24} - 353 - 12\ 582 = 1774.$$

The full analysis of variance table is given in Table 7.3.4. Tables of means can now be constructed directly from Table 7.3.1. Table 7.3.5 gives the means, converted to tons per acre, for organics and rate of application.

Table 7.3.4 Analysis of variance

	d.f.	s.s.	m.s.
Blocks	3	1747	
Organics	3	17687	5896
Rate (R)	1	353	353
Nitrogen (N)	1	2556	2556
Phosphate (P)	1	45	45
Potash (K)	1	2888	2888
Organics $\times$ R	2	1774	887
Organics $\times$ N	3	1348	449
Organics $\times$ P	3	2356	785
Organics $\times$ K	3	1002	334
RN	1	1	1
RP	1	36	36
NP	1	32	32
NK	1	465	465
PK	1	1176	1176
Residual	5	1050	210
Total	31	34516	

Table 7.3.5 Table of means (tons per acre)

Rate	No manure	Farmyard manure	Old sludge	New sludge	Mean
Single	—	11·92	10·12	10·82	10·96
Double	—	13·50	9·55	11·00	11·35
Mean	9·65	12·71	9·84	10·91	

10·78

Standard error of means in main body of table $= \pm 0.38$
Standard error of organics means $= \pm 0.27$
Standard error of rate means $= \pm 0.22$.

Farmyard manure was considerably better than other organics and it also gave an additional response to the double rate of application. In the presence of farmyard manure there was little response to the artificial manures. It should also be noted that, although the organics $\times$ P interaction is not significant as a whole, it contains one large component, AP, which represents the comparison between phosphate in the presence and absence of sludge.

7.4 Fractional replication with factors at three levels

By using the notation and rules of **6.4**, fractional replicates of experiments with several factors each at three levels can be constructed. Suppose we require a $\frac{1}{3}$-replicate of a 3^5 experiment. The 32 degrees of freedom for the fourth-order interaction can be split into 16 orthogonal components each with two degrees of freedom. One of the components, say $ABCDE$, could be confounded to give the $\frac{1}{3}$-replicate. The defining contrast for the design is $I = ABCDE$ and the aliases of the main effect A are given by $A \times ABCDE$ and $A \times (ABCDE)^2$, that is,

$$A = AB^2C^2D^2E^2 = BCDE.$$

Similarly, the aliases of any effect can be obtained. We see that all the main effects are aliased with components of third- or fourth-order interactions, whilst all first-order interactions are aliased with components of second- or third-order interactions. If second- and higher-order interactions can be assumed to be negligible then this design will provide valid estimates of main effects and first-order interactions. Further, these higher-order interactions will provide 30 degrees of freedom for error. The design is constructed of those treatment combinations satisfying the equation

$$l_1 + l_2 + l_3 + l_4 + l_5 = i \;(\text{mod } 3)$$

for $i = 0, 1, 2$. The 81 treatment combinations given in Table 7.4.1 satisfy this equation for $i = 0$.

In this $\frac{1}{3}$-replicate it may be necessary to use confounding to keep down the block size. For instance, the design may be arranged in nine blocks of nine treatment combinations. Eight degrees of freedom, or four components of interaction, are confounded with blocks. The best arrangement would involve confounding one component of a first-order interaction. If we confound ABC^2 and ADE^2 then, using the rule of **6.4**, we shall also be confounding AB^2CD^2E and BC^2D^2E. The aliases of these confounded components are

$$ABC^2 = ABD^2E^2 = CD^2E^2$$
$$ADE^2 = AB^2C^2D = BCE^2$$
$$AB^2CD^2E = ACE = BD$$
$$BC^2D^2E = AB^2E^2 = AC^2D^2.$$

Thus the BD, or $BD(J)$, component of a first-order interaction has been confounded with blocks. The 81 treatment combinations are placed in nine blocks so as to satisfy the nine pairs of equations

$$l_1 + l_2 + 2l_3 = i \;(\text{mod } 3)$$
$$l_1 + l_4 + 2l_5 = j \;(\text{mod } 3),$$

where i and j each take on the values 0, 1 and 2. The full design is given in Table 7.4.1. The analysis of variance would be partitioned as in Table 7.4.2, there being 24 degrees of freedom for error.

Table 7.4.1 $\frac{1}{3}$-replicate of a 3^5 experiment in nine blocks

Levels of first two factors	Block								
	1	2	3	4	5	6	7	8	9
	Levels of third, fourth and fifth factors								
00	000	021	012	222	210	201	111	102	120
10	101	122	110	020	011	002	212	200	221
20	202	220	211	121	112	100	010	001	022
01	122	110	101	011	002	020	200	221	212
11	220	211	202	112	100	121	001	022	010
21	021	012	000	210	201	222	102	120	111
02	211	202	220	100	121	112	022	010	001
12	012	000	021	201	222	210	120	111	102
22	110	101	122	002	020	011	221	212	200

Table 7.4.2 Degrees of freedom in a $\frac{1}{3}$-replicate of a 3^5 experiment

	d.f.
Blocks	8
Main effects	10
First-order interactions	38
Second-order interactions	24
Total	80

7.5 Other fractional factorial experiments

Fractional replicate designs may be used when factors are at levels other than two or three. The design of such experiments involving factors at four levels can be constructed by considering the four levels as the combination of two factors each at two levels. As in **5.8**, if a_0, a_1, a_2 and a_3 represent the four levels, these may be considered as replaced by treatment combinations (1), a, b and ab respectively. Suppose the three components A', A'' and A''' are defined as follows—

$$A' = \frac{1}{2}(a_3 - a_2 + a_1 - a_0)$$
$$A'' = \frac{1}{2}(a_3 + a_2 - a_1 - a_0)$$
$$A''' = \frac{1}{2}(a_3 - a_2 - a_1 + a_0).$$

The comparison A' corresponds to the main effect A of the two-factor experiment, the comparison A'' to the main effect B, and A''' to the interaction AB. The rules for "multiplying" comparisons together follow from those for the two-factor experiments. For instance, since $A \times AB = B$, we have $A' \times A''' = A''$.

Any pairs of factors in a 2^m experiment can be replaced by a factor at four levels. For example, consider the $\frac{1}{4}$-replicate of a 2^8 experiment obtained from the defining contrast

$$I = ABCDEFGH = BCFG = ADEH.$$

If we now replace AB by J, CD by K, EF by L and GH by M, we obtain a defining contrast for a $\frac{1}{4}$-replicate of a 4^4 experiment, namely

$$I = J'''K'''L'''M''' = J''K'L''M' = J'K''L'M''.$$

The aliases of any effect can easily be determined. For instance, for the main effect of factor J we have

$$J' = J''K'''L'''M''' = J'''K'L''M' = K''L'M''$$
$$J'' = J'K'''L'''M''' = K'L''M' = J''K'L'M''$$
$$J''' = K'''L'''M''' = J'K'L''M' = J''K''L'M''.$$

All the main effects are aliased with second- or third-order interactions. Some first-order interactions are aliased with other first-order interactions as well as with higher-order interactions.

Of course it will be possible to arrange these 64 treatment combinations into two blocks of 32, four blocks of 16, or eight blocks of eight treatment combinations. For the $\frac{1}{4}$-replicate of the 2^8 in four blocks of 16 we could, for example, confound the interactions (and their aliases)

$$BDEF\,(= ACGH = CDEG = ABFH)$$
$$ABCE\,(= DFGH = AEFG = BCDH)$$
$$ACDF\,(= BEGH = ABDG = CEFH).$$

Corresponding to these interactions, we may obtain a $\frac{1}{4}$-replicate of a 4^4 experiment in four blocks of 16 confounding the interactions (and their aliases)

$$J''K''L'''\,(= J'K'M''' = K'''L'M' = J'L''M'')$$
$$J'''K'L'\,(= K''L''M''' = J'L''M' = J''K'''M'')$$
$$J'K'''L''\,(= J''L'M'' = J'''K''M' = K'L'''M'').$$

This particular design is used in the serial factorial experiment of **11.8**.

The designs considered in **6.5** can be used to construct fractional replicate design for experiments in which factors at both two and three levels are being tested. Connor and Young (1961) and Webb (1971) have listed a number of such designs. A review of some of the methods available for constructing fractional replicate designs in other cases can be found in Addleman (1963).

7.6 Sequences of fractional factorial experiments

In using fractional replication, it must be remembered that if our assumption that the high-order interactions are negligible is correct, the fractional replicate will allow a larger number of effects to be estimated than could otherwise be obtained. If, however, the assumption is not justified, then not only will the error mean square be increased, but, more serious still, the estimates will be biased. In using fractional replication, it is therefore necessary that the assumption of negligible high-order interactions should be correct. Some initial information concerning these interactions is thus essential.

We have said that the outcome of a fractional experiment is open to misinterpretation in a way that does not arise with fully replicated designs. Consider, for example, a $\frac{1}{2}$-replicate of a 2^4 experiment with defining contrast $I = ABCD$. If the experiment shows an apparent effect in changing from the high to the low level of factor A, there is no way of knowing from these results whether the effect is really due to A, to the interaction BCD, or to a mixture of the two. Even if the second-order interactions can be assumed negligible, we are still faced with the problem of interpreting large first-order interactions. Sometimes the nature of the results makes one interpretation more plausible than another. Suppose, for example, that the effects $A\,(= BCD)$, $B\,(= ACD)$ and $AB = CD$ turn out to be large compared with other effects. It is reasonable to assume in this situation that the magnitude of the $AB = CD$ effect is due to the AB, and not the CD, interaction. However, if the $AC = BD$ and not the $AB = CD$ interaction was large, then it is not clear which interaction is important. Further observations will be needed if it is thought necessary to disentangle this aliasing relationship.

Suppose that, from a $\frac{1}{2}$-replicate of a 2^4 experiment with defining contrast $I = ABCD$, the only significant effects were A, B, $AC = BD$ and $AB = CD$. All other effects will be assumed to be negligible. It will also be reasonable to assume that the CD interaction is negligible and that it is now considered necessary to take further observations to disentangle the $AC = BD$ relationship. The coefficients of the significant factorial effects for the treatment combinations of the $\frac{1}{2}$-replicate are given in Table 7.6.1, together with the coefficients for two further treatment combinations a and acd. The I effect in this table corresponds to the block effect and is estimated by the overall mean of the observations.

Table 7.6.1   Coefficients of the significant effects in a 2^4 experiment

Effect	Treatment combinations									
	(1)	ab	ac	bc	ad	bd	cd	$abcd$	a	acd
I	$+1$	$+1$	$+1$	$+1$	$+1$	$+1$	$+1$	$+1$	$+1$	$+1$
A	-1	$+1$	$+1$	-1	$+1$	-1	-1	$+1$	$+1$	$+1$
B	-1	$+1$	-1	$+1$	-1	$+1$	-1	$+1$	-1	-1
AB	$+1$	$+1$	-1	-1	-1	-1	$+1$	$+1$	-1	-1
AC	$+1$	-1	$+1$	-1	-1	$+1$	-1	$+1$	-1	$+1$
BD	$+1$	-1	$+1$	-1	-1	$+1$	-1	$+1$	$+1$	-1

As was done in Table 3.2.1, the coefficients can be used to calculate the factorial effects. For instance, I is estimated by y_1, where

$$y_1 = \tfrac{1}{8}[(1) + ab + ac + bc + ad + cd + abcd].$$

We shall let y_2, y_3, y_4 and y_5 represent estimates of A, B, AB and $AC + BD$ respectively.

In addition, the table permits the effects estimated by the individual treatment combinations to be obtained. The treatment combination ab, for example, estimates

$$I + A + B + AB - AC - BD.$$

It is now seen that the $AC = BD$ alias can be disentangled by taking just one additional observation corresponding to any treatment combination in the omitted half of the 2^4 experiment. If a is taken, then from Table 7.6.1 it estimates

$$I + A - B - AB - AC + BD.$$

Since $y_1 + y_2 - y_3 - y_4 + y_5$ estimates $I + A - B - AB + (AC + BD)$, the mean difference between this quantity and a will provide an estimate of the interaction AC. This estimate subtracted from y_5 will estimate BD. These interactions are both estimated with standard error

$$\sqrt{\tfrac{1}{4}(\tfrac{5}{8} + 1)\sigma^2} = \pm 0\cdot 637\sigma.$$

If allowance must be made for blocking differences between the original half replicate and the additional observations, then at least two observations will be required to disentangle the $AC = BD$ relationship. From Table 7.6.1 we see that the difference between the two additional observations a and acd estimates $AC - BD$, free of block effects. The mean of this quantity and y_5, which estimates $AC + BD$, will estimate the AC interaction with standard error $\pm 0\cdot 395\sigma$. Similarly, the mean difference estimates BD. Other pairs of observations could equally well have been used, namely b and bcd, abc and abd or d and c. In this case, the original $\frac{1}{2}$-replicate has been augmented by a $\frac{1}{8}$-replicate of the 2^4 experiment.

Practical considerations permitting, a factorial experiment could therefore be carried out as a sequence of fractional experiments. The original design could be augmented by additional observations in order to disentangle any significant aliasing relationships. It should be realized, however, that the non-significance of an alias chain does not necessarily imply the non-significance of each effect in the chain. For instance, if the interactions AB and CD were of equal magnitude but of opposite sign, then the alias chain $AB + CD$ may not be significant. The experimenter still has a price to pay to offset against the advantages of fractional replication. Further designs for augmenting fractional replicates can be found in Daniel (1962), P. W. M. John (1966) and the book by P. W. M. John (1971).

8 Complex Factorial Designs

8.1 Modifications to the factorial design

The importance of the factorial approach in experimentation is that it allows several sets of factors and their interactions to the estimated simultaneously. In the previous three chapters, we have considered modifications which may be made to the factorial design that, in certain circumstances, improve its efficiency. In this chapter further modifications will be considered.

Modifications to the factorial design may, in the main, be grouped under three headings. First, there are designs in which certain comparisons are sacrificed, by confounding, to increase the accuracy of the other comparisons. So far, we have considered, in Chapters 5 and 6, confounding by arranging the treatment combinations in blocks. In the following sections, we shall consider confounding arrangements to eliminate row and column differences. Secondly, we may increase the accuracy of some comparisons at the expense of others without completely sacrificing them. This can be done using split-plot designs. Confounding may or may not be used in such designs. Lastly, if we can assume certain effects or interactions to be negligible or zero, the design may be modified to take these into account. In this manner, greater accuracy may be obtained on certain comparisons, yet only a fraction of all the treatment combinations may be required. These fractional factorial designs were discussed in the previous chapter. We shall now consider, in turn, designs falling into the first two of the above groups.

8.2 Quasi-Latin squares for 2^m experiments

Factorial designs may be laid out in Latin square formation. For instance, a 2^2 factorial design may be carried out in a 4×4 Latin square. However, if the number of treatment combinations is large, this requires a very large number of plots, unless some interactions are confounded between rows and columns. A design confounding any particular set of interactions may be easily constructed by applying the rules given in 3.5 to both rows and columns of the square. An example will demonstrate the method.

Suppose a factorial design to test a 2^6 experiment in an 8×8 square is required. Then seven degrees of freedom will be confounded with rows and seven with columns. We might choose *ABC, ADE, BCDE, BEF, ACEF, ABDF, CDF* to be confounded with rows, and *ACE, BDE, ABCD, BCF, ABEF, CDEF, ADF* to be confounded with columns. This choice confounds fourteen second- and third-order interactions.

By the rules of **3.5**, one row must be (1), *acd, def, acef, abe, bcde, abdf, bcf*, and one column must be (1), *ade, acf, cdef, bce, abcd, abef, bdf*. These may be taken as the first row and first column of the square. The other rows and columns are then calculated by "multiplying" this row and column together as in Table 8.2.1.

Table 8.2.1 Quasi-Latin square for a 2^6 factorial experiment

(1)	acd	def	acef	abe	bcde	abdf	bcf
ade	ce	af	cdf	bd	abc	bef	abcdef
acf	df	acde	e	bcef	abdef	bcd	ab
cdef	aef	c	ad	abcdf	bf	abce	bde
bce	abde	bcdf	abf	ac	d	acdef	ef
abcd	b	abcef	bdef	cde	ae	cf	adf
abef	bcdef	abd	bc	f	acdf	de	ace
bdf	abcf	be	abcde	adef	cef	a	cd

A similar principle may be applied if more than one replicate is used. For instance, if two replicates of a 2^5 experiment are to be used in an 8×8 square, three degrees of freedom will be confounded with rows and three degrees of freedom with columns. Suppose we decide to confound *ABC, ADE, BCDE* with rows and *ACE, BDE, ABCD* with columns. Then (1), *abe, de, abd, bc, ace, bcde, acd* may be taken as the first row, and (1), *ade, ac, cde, bce, abcd, abe, bd* as the first column. This gives the design shown in Table 8.2.2.

Table 8.2.2 Quasi-Latin square for a 2^5 factorial experiment

(1)	abe	de	abd	bc	ace	bcde	acd
ade	bd	a	be	abcde	cd	abc	ce
ac	bce	acde	bcd	ab	e	abde	d
cde	abcd	c	abce	bde	ad	b	ae
bce	ac	bcd	acde	e	ab	d	abde
abcd	cde	abce	c	ad	bde	ae	b
abe	(1)	abd	de	ace	bc	acd	bcde
bd	ade	be	a	cd	abcde	ce	abc

Alternatively, where replication occurs, partial confounding may be used. However, unless the second-order interactions are important, it is easier to use complete confounding.

It is also possible to set out a fractional factorial design in a Latin square. For instance, consider the $\frac{1}{2}$-replicate of a 2^7 experiment with defining contrast $I = ABCDEFG$. Suppose it is desired to set these 64 treatment combinations out in an 8×8 square. Then we might choose

$$ABC = DEFG, \quad ADE = BCFG, \quad BCDE = AFG, \quad BDF = ACEG,$$
$$ACDF = BEG, \quad ABEF = CDG, \quad CEF = ABDG$$

to be confounded with rows, and

$$ABD = CEFG, \quad ACF = BDEG, \quad BCDF = AEG, \quad BEF = ACDG,$$
$$ADEF = BCG, \quad ABCE = DFG, \quad CDE = ABFG$$

to be confounded with columns. This leads to the design given in Table 8.2.3.

Table 8.2.3   Quasi-Latin square for a $\frac{1}{2}$-replicate of a 2^7 experiment

(1)	abce	adef	bcdf	abfg	cefg	bdeg	acdg
abdg	cdeg	befg	acfg	df	abcdef	ae	bc
abef	cf	bd	acde	eg	abcg	adfg	bcdefg
defg	abcdfg	ag	bceg	abde	cd	bf	acef
acdf	bdef	ce	ab	bcdg	adeg	abcefg	fg
bcfg	aefg	abcdeg	dg	ac	be	cdef	abdf
bcde	ad	abcf	ef	acdefg	bdfg	cg	abeg
aceg	bg	cdfg	abdefg	bcef	af	abcd	de

The analysis can be carried out as usual. The sums of squares of the confounded interactions total to give the sums of squares for rows and columns, and thus provide a check on the plusing and minusing procedure.

Quasi-Latin squares have, of course, to be randomized before use, and two special problems are raised in this case. First, if replication is required, designs obtained in the above manner do not exhaust the possible designs. An alternative design confounding the same interactions could be obtained in Table 8.2.2. by, for instance, interchanging the treatments ac and bce, which fall in the same rows and columns. Sixteen such interchanges are possible (in the first four rows, the treatment combinations in columns 1, 3, 5 and 7 may be interchanged with those in the corresponding positions in columns 2, 4, 6 and 8). To choose a design, it is necessary to make these interchanges at random. The design so chosen is then randomly selected from the possible designs. It is, however, necessary to randomize the rows and columns of the square before use, and this raises a second problem.

In the design given in Table 8.2.1, the difference between the first four and second four rows confounds the comparison $ABDF$, while the difference between the first four and second four columns confounds the comparison ADF. In consequence, the comparison between the diagonally opposite pairs of quarters of the whole square represents the comparison $ABDF \times ADF = B$. This can also be seen directly by noting that in the upper right-hand and bottom left-hand quarters each treatment combination has factor B at the upper level, while the other quarters have factor B at the lower level. Hence, correlation between neighbouring plots will clearly result in the main effect of factor B being estimated less precisely than other effects. Now there is a strong tendency, even in a randomized design, for such blocks of comparisons to occur. To overcome this possible difficulty, it is necessary to restrict the randomization to those designs in which no such blocks occur.

This can be done, since the unconfounded 49 degrees of freedom representing main effects, first-order interactions, and error (i.e. higher-order interactions), are derived from the "products" of the confounded interactions for rows by those for columns. If, therefore, all designs incorporating 4×4 squares of treatment combinations which occur with the same sign in any particular interaction are rejected, the treatment and error components are similarly affected. This restriction of the randomization thus still gives an unbiased estimate of error.

To carry out this randomization, the first step is to randomize rows and columns as usual. A randomization of the first row and column of the quasi-Latin square of Table 8.2.1 is indicated in Table 8.2.4.

Table 8.2.4 First row and first column of randomized quasi-Latin square

						abef	
						acf	
						bdf	
						cdef	
						bce	
acef	bcde	acd	bcf	abe	abdf	(1)	def
						ade	
						abcd	

This has now to be examined to ensure that no 4×4 square of the above type would be included in the complete square.

To do this, we product consecutive sets of four treatment combinations together, using the rule of 5.5. If at least one set in the first column gives us a unit answer, the randomization is rejected. Here we have

$$abef \times acf \times bdf \times cdef = (1)$$
$$acef \times bcde \times acd \times bcf = (1).$$

We thus reject this randomization.

A second randomization is shown in Table 8.2.5.

Table 8.2.5 Randomized quasi-Latin square

df	**acf**	e	abdef	acde	bcd	ab	bcef
acd	**(1)**	acef	bcde	**def**	**abdf**	**bcf**	**abe**
abcf	**bdf**	abcde	cef	be	a	cd	adef
ce	**ade**	cdf	abc	af	bef	abcdef	bd
bcdef	**abef**	bc	acdf	abd	de	ace	f
abde	**bce**	abf	d	bcdf	acdef	ef	ac
aef	**cdef**	ad	bf	c	abce	bde	abcdf
b	**abcd**	bdef	ae	abcef	cf	adf	cde

In this instance, in the randomized first column, $(1) \times bdf \times ade \times abef = (1)$, but no such set of four can be found in the randomized first row. The randomization can therefore be accepted and the rest of the square filled in by producting.

This method of restricting the randomization is not so necessary if more than one replicate is used. The choice of a design at random then largely reduces the possibility of occurrence of squares of the same treatment. If, however, it is important to avoid this possibility a restricted randomization may be carried out.[*]

Sometimes there may be no obvious ordering in the rows or columns, as, for example, when rows represent litters of animals. Here there is no point in restricting the randomization since adjacent treatments in the quasi-Latin square are determined by our ordering of the litters and do not represent any specific association.

8.3   Quasi-Latin squares for 3^m experiments

A 3^m experiment may be placed in a quasi-Latin square. In particular, a 3^4 experiment may be carried out in a 9×9 square. Using the notation and rules of **6.4**, it is relatively easy to construct such squares.

Suppose we decide to confound AB^2C^2, ABD^2, ACD and BC^2D with rows, and AB^2C, ABD, AC^2D^2 and BCD^2 with columns. The first row may be taken as 0000, 1011, 2022, 0121, 1102, 2110, 0212, 1220, 2201, and the first column as 0000, 1022, 2011, 0112, 1101, 2120, 0221, 1210, 2202. The square may then be completed by "adding" the elements of each row and column together, as was done in constructing Table 6.4.1. The resulting quasi-Latin square is given in Table 8.3.1.

Table 8.3.1   Quasi-Latin square for a 3^4 experiment

0000	1011	2022	0121	1102	2110	0212	1220	2201
1022	2000	0011	1110	2121	0102	1201	2212	0220
2011	0022	1000	2102	0110	1121	2220	0201	1212
0112	1120	2101	0200	1211	2222	0021	1002	2010
1101	2112	0120	1222	2200	0211	1010	2021	0002
2120	0101	1112	2211	0222	1200	2002	0010	1021
0221	1202	2210	0012	1020	2001	0100	1111	2122
1210	2221	0202	1001	2012	0020	1122	2100	0111
2202	0210	1221	2020	0001	1012	2111	0122	1100

Squares of this type may be randomized as usual, since there is less chance of blocks of plots receiving the same treatment. However, restricted randomization may be employed by omitting all designs in which at least one sum of three consecutive treatment combinations in both the first row and the first column gives a value of unity. This restriction prevents 3×3 squares receiving treatment combinations which have at least one factor all at the same level.

Quasi-Latin squares may also be constructed in the same manner for 3^3 experiments in 9×9 squares. Table 8.3.2 gives one such design confounding AB^2C^2 with rows and AB^2C with columns.

---

[*]A discussion of restricted randomization has been given by Grundy and Healy (1950), who employ a slightly different procedure from that adopted here. The interested reader should refer to this paper for a fuller discussion of its uses.

Table 8.3.2 Quasi-Latin square for a 3^3 experiment

000	101	202	012	110	211	021	122	220
102	200	001	111	212	010	120	221	022
201	002	100	210	011	112	222	020	121
011	112	210	020	121	222	002	100	201
110	211	012	122	220	021	101	202	000
212	010	111	221	022	120	200	001	102
022	120	221	001	102	200	010	111	212
121	222	020	100	201	002	112	210	011
220	021	122	202	000	101	211	012	110

Alternative designs may be obtained by interchanging the treatments in sets of three. For instance, 202, 012 and 122 may be interchanged between any two rows or columns without altering the confounding.

Using the results of **6.5**, quasi-Latin squares may be constructed when some of the factors are at two levels and others are at three levels. Table 8.3.3 gives an example of a design for a 2×3^2 experiment in a 6×6 quasi-Latin square.

Table 8.3.3 Quasi-Latin square for a 2×3^2 experiment

000	011	022	100	111	122
012	020	001	112	120	101
021	002	010	121	102	110
100	111	122	000	011	022
112	120	101	012	020	001
121	102	110	021	002	010

The first digit in a treatment combination refers to the level of the two-level factor A and the second and third digits to the levels of the three-level factors B and C. The rows of the design constitute two replicates of the design, given in **6.5**, confounding the $BC(I)$ interaction, while the columns are two replicates of the design confounding the $BC(J)$ interaction. No information is therefore available on the BC interaction, but all other effects can be estimated independently of row and column differences.

Again, since replication occurs, partial confounding may be used. Table 8.3.4 gives another design for a 2×3^2 experiment in which $BC(I)$ is partially confounded between rows and $BC(J)$ is partially confounded between columns. Three-quarters information is available on each of these interactions. Only one-quarter information is available on the second-order interaction, but normally this will be used as error. For this design, and the design in Table 8.3.3, restricted randomization should be used in randomizing the rows and columns.

Table 8.3.4 Quasi-Latin square for a 2×3^2 experiment using partial confounding

000	011	022	110	121	102
021	002	010	101	112	120
012	020	001	122	100	111
110	121	102	020	001	012
101	112	120	011	022	000
122	100	111	002	010	021

8.4 Split-plot confounding

A split-plot design testing several sets of factors may be constructed by using all combinations of one group of factors in each plot, and by applying every combination of the remaining factors to each plot in turn. For example, with four varieties v_1, v_2, v_3, v_4 and three fertilizer treatments N, P, K, each at two levels, we may use each fertilizer combination on plots of the four varieties. The plots of each variety would then be split into eight parts. However, the more combinations that are tested within each plot, the larger the plot and, in general, the less accurate the comparisons both within and between plots. We thus concentrate on making a limited number of important comparisons within each plot, and the comparisons of lesser importance are made between plots. To do this, we may resort to confounding some comparisons between plots.

For instance, if the fertilizer combinations (1), np, nk, pk are tested with each variety in half the plots and n, p, k, npk with each variety in the other half, the main effects and first-order interactions of these fertilizers can be estimated from within-plot comparisons. The second-order interaction, NPK, is now confounded between plots and is estimated with the same accuracy as the varietal comparisons. The number of treatments per plot has been reduced to four by this confounding, and apart from NPK, the accuracy of each comparison has been increased in consequence.

Designs with split-plot confounding may be constructed by first deciding which sets of treatment combinations are to be used within the plots. These sets of the treatment combinations should then be treated as the levels of a further factor in the main-plot design. For instance, a design testing two fertilizers N and P, each at three levels within plots, three varieties, v_1, v_2, v_3, and three depths of ploughing, d_1, d_2, d_3, might be constructed using the I components of the fertilizers within plots. A confounded design might then be constructed as in Table 8.4.1.

In this table, I_1 represents plots in which n_0p_0, n_1p_1, n_2p_2, are applied, I_2 represents plots in which n_1p_0, n_2p_1, n_0p_2, are applied, etc. Two degrees of freedom from $NPVD$ are confounded between blocks in this design. The analysis of variance would normally proceed as in Table 8.4.2.

Although the construction of this analysis of variance presents nothing new, and the computation may be carried out as usual, two new problems are raised: the construction of a table of means to demonstrate, e.g. in the above example, the NP interaction, and the method of making an overall test of this interaction. The same types of problems are raised whenever estimates are derived in part from between-plot comparisons and in part from within-plot comparisons, and, in particular, whenever split-plot partial confounding is used.

Table 8.4.1 Example of 3^4 split-plot design

Block		
1	2	3
$I_1v_1d_1$ $I_3v_2d_2$	$I_1v_1d_3$ $I_3v_2d_1$	$I_1v_1d_2$ $I_3v_2d_3$
$I_2v_1d_2$ $I_1v_3d_2$	$I_2v_1d_1$ $I_1v_3d_1$	$I_2v_1d_3$ $I_1v_3d_3$
$I_3v_1d_3$ $I_2v_3d_3$	$I_3v_1d_2$ $I_2v_3d_2$	$I_3v_1d_1$ $I_2v_3d_1$
$I_1v_2d_3$ $I_3v_3d_1$	$I_1v_2d_2$ $I_3v_3d_3$	$I_1v_2d_1$ $I_3v_3d_2$
$I_2v_2d_1$	$I_2v_2d_3$	$I_2v_2d_2$

Table 8.4.2 Subdivision of degrees of freedom in analysis of variance

	d.f.	
Blocks	2	
V	2	
D	2	
VD	4	
$NP(I)$	2	
$NPV(W$ and $X)$	4	
$NPD(W$ and $X)$	4	Between-plot error, 14
$NP(I) \times VD$	6	
Between plots	26	
N	2	
P	2	
$NP(\mathcal{J})$	2	
NV	4	
PV	4	
ND	4	
PD	4	
$NPV(Y$ and $Z)$	4	
$NPD(Y$ and $Z)$	4	
NVD	8	Within-plot error, 32
PVD	8	
$NP(J) \times VD$	8	
Total	80	

If the between-plot error is large and $NP(I)$ is insignificant, then in constructing a table of means we should, in effect, equate the I components to zero, as if they had been completely confounded. On the other hand, if $NP(I)$ is very highly significant, then the size of the between-plot error is irrelevant and a table of means may be directly constructed, the I and J components being equally represented. The decision as to which of these two courses to follow depends upon the relative sizes of the within- and between-plot error mean squares and upon the significance of the component tested between plots. If here the within- and between-plot errors are of comparable magnitude, then the table of means demonstrating the NP interaction should be directly constructed. If, however, the between-plot error is substantially larger than the within-plot error, the I components should be equated to zero unless $NP(I)$ is significant.

To derive an overall test for the NP interaction, it is necessary to use Fisher's method of combining probabilities. The probabilities of each variance ratio have to be calculated and minus twice their natural logarithms added. The sum of these two quantities is distributed as a $\chi^2(4)$.

When some comparisons are partially confounded and thus can be estimated both within- and between-plots, these give rise to two sets of components in the analysis of variance. The within- and between-plot estimates may be combined by weighting them according to their inverse variances, i.e. their *invariances*. If x and x' are two estimates with variances s^2 and s'^2 based upon f and f' degrees of freedom, then the joint estimate is

$$\frac{x/s^2 + x'/s'^2}{1/s^2 + 1/s'^2},\text{(*)}$$

with variance $1/[1/s^2 + 1/s'^2]$. The quantity

$$\frac{(x/s^2 + x'/s'^2)^2}{1/s^2 + 1/s'^2}$$

is then distributed approximately as a variance ratio with 1 and F degrees of freedom, where

$$\frac{1}{F}\left(\frac{1}{s^2} + \frac{1}{s'^2}\right) = \frac{1}{s^2 + s'^2}\left(\frac{1}{f} + \frac{1}{f'}\right).$$

For an overall test of any set of p within- and between-plot comparisons, the mean of the set of such variance ratios should be tested as a variance ratio with p and F degrees of freedom.

The example of the next section will provide a demonstration of the analysis of an experiment in which estimates are derived both from within and between plots.

(*) A slightly more accurate estimate is obtained using weights $(f-2)/fs^2$ instead of $1/s^2$. This method is used in 13.2 in combining independent estimates.

8.5 A complex split-plot experiment

An experiment carried out by J. Duckworth and J. W. Howie tested mice raised on three diets d_1, d_2, d_3. The mice were caged by two different methods, not having and having access to their faeces F, and both sexes were tested. For this, 48 litters of four mice, two males and two females, were used, and each of these was treated according to one of the arrangements shown in Table 8.5.1.

Table 8.5.1 $3 \times 2 \times 2$ design in six litters of four animals

(1) $d_1\male$, $d_2\male f$, $d_2\female$, $d_1\female f$ (4) $d_3\male$, $d_1\male f$, $d_1\female$, $d_3\female f$

(2) $d_2\male$, $d_1\male f$, $d_1\female$, $d_2\female f$ (5) $d_2\male$, $d_3\male f$, $d_3\female$, $d_2\female f$

(3) $d_1\male$, $d_3\male f$, $d_3\female$, $d_1\female f$ (6) $d_3\male$, $d_2\male f$, $d_2\female$, $d_3\female f$

Eight replicates of this design were used, and two replicates were randomized on each of four shelves in an animal house.

Examination of Table 8.5.1 shows that $D\male F$ is totally confounded between litters, and D is partially confounded between litters; other comparisons are made within the litters.

Table 8.5.2 gives a section of the data from this experiment: the weight increases, w, of the mice during the four weeks after weaning. The litter number of each animal is indicated in this table.

The initial analysis proceeds as usual: treatment and litter totals are constructed and used to form an analysis of variance. The reader might check for himself that if the main effect D is not removed the analysis of variance is as in Table 8.5.3.

The determination of the components of D within and between litters is more difficult. We shall consider general methods for such designs in Chapter 10, but meantime we may use a method which is often useful in deriving components of this type.

If x is used to denote a dummy variable taking the value -1 for animals receiving the diet d_1, 0 for those receiving d_2, and 1 for those receiving d_3, an analysis of covariance may be carried out on x. This will adjust the residual for the linear component of D, i.e. it will give the sum of squares appropriate to this component. The regression coefficients will give the difference $\frac{1}{2}(d_3 - d_1)$ estimated both within and between litters.

Similarly, if a covariance is carried out on a dummy variable y taking the value -1 for diets d_1 and d_3 and 2 for diet d_2, this adjusts for the quadratic component of D. The regression coefficients in this instance give the within- and between-litter components of the difference $\frac{1}{6}(2d_2 - d_1 - d_3)$.

Since the variables x and y are orthogonal to one another and to the other effects and interactions, these analyses of covariance proceed as in Table 8.5.4.

Table 8.5.2   Weight increases of mice

Sex	Shelf	d_1 Litter	d_1 Weight increase	d_1 f Litter	d_1 f Weight increase	d_2 Litter	d_2 Weight increase	d_2 f Litter	d_2 f Weight increase	d_3 Litter	d_3 Weight increase	d_3 f Litter	d_3 f Weight increase
♂	1	2	10·0	3	14·9	1	10·9	5	10·7	3	14·2	1	10·3
		6	12·4	4	2·4	4	10·9	6	13·0	5	14·2	2	16·9
		8	10·5	10	14·0	10	9·7	7	8·2	7	8·5	9	11·1
		9	16·9	11	15·0	12	12·1	8	5·8	11	9·0	12	13·9
	2	16	15·2	13	13·9	15	10·9	14	12·4	13	11·3	16	15·8
		17	14·7	15	18·6	18	10·4	17	12·0	14	11·4	18	11·5
		21	11·5	20	19·6	19	10·8	22	11·0	20	16·3	19	15·3
		24	11·0	23	15·9	23	11·1	24	11·8	22	16·0	21	13·3
	3	28	15·9	26	13·6	27	8·8	25	13·8	25	12·3	28	14·1
		30	12·0	27	13·4	29	10·4	30	17·4	26	14·5	29	7·1
		31	16·6	32	17·3	32	10·6	31	13·1	35	13·6	33	18·7
		33	11·1	35	16·3	34	9·7	36	8·4	36	14·0	34	10·9
	4	39	19·7	38	13·0	38	10·0	37	5·7	37	8·4	41	9·2
		42	13·0	40	11·6	41	8·4	39	12·0	40	14·9	42	16·9
		44	19·5	43	12·7	43	12·6	44	18·5	47	9·6	45	14·2
		45	14·0	48	16·5	46	10·4	47	9·9	48	16·1	46	16·6
Total			224·0		228·7		167·7		183·7		204·3		215·8

Table 8.5.2 (*continued*)

Sex	Shelf	d_1 — Litter	d_1 — Weight increase	d_1 f Litter	d_1 f Weight increase	d_2 — Litter	d_2 — Weight increase	d_2 f Litter	d_2 f Weight increase	d_3 — Litter	d_3 — Weight increase	d_3 f Litter	d_3 f Weight increase
	1	3	8·8	2	8·7	5	7·0	1	6·9	1	8·3	3	9·6
		4	5·5	6	6·2	6	10·2	4	6·4	2	9·2	5	7·6
		10	7·9	8	6·9	7	7·6	10	4·7	9	8·3	7	7·8
		11	8·3	9	9·6	8	5·4	12	7·8	12	9·9	11	9·9
	2	13	9·9	16	10·8	14	9·6	15	8·8	16	8·8	13	7·0
		15	10·8	17	8·2	17	6·8	18	9·5	18	8·9	14	11·3
		20	11·3	21	11·6	22	5·3	19	9·1	19	8·8	20	12·8
		23	8·7	24	10·2	24	6·5	23	9·2	21	8·8	22	11·1
♀	3	26	7·2	28	7·4	25	8·1	27	8·4	28	7·0	25	6·6
		27	11·9	30	11·0	30	7·7	29	10·2	29	6·1	26	6·6
		32	10·0	31	10·9	31	5·4	32	4·9	33	10·0	35	9·1
		35	13·6	33	7·4	36	6·3	34	6·3	34	7·9	36	11·6
	4	38	10·4	39	11·8	37	5·8	38	7·4	41	7·3	37	11·3
		40	9·9	42	11·0	39	1·2	41	8·8	42	11·7	40	8·0
		43	7·0	44	13·1	44	10·0	43	10·8	45	8·1	47	10·8
		48	4·6	45	10·1	47	11·3	46	10·2	46	9·8	48	15·0
Total			145·8		154·9		114·2		129·4		138·9		156·1
Total (both sexes)			369·8		383·6		281·9		313·1		343·2		371·9

Table 8.5.3   Initial analysis of variance

	d.f.	s.s.
Shelves	3	85·31
$D\male F$	2	0·37
Residual between litters	42	483·90
Between litters	47	569·58
$\male$	1	771·61
F	1	28·29
$D\male$	2	15·49
$\male F$	1	0·45
DF	2	2·77
Residual within litters	137	879·53
Total	191	2267·72
D	2	213·45

Table 8.5.4   Analyses of covariance

	d.f.	s.p. (wx)	s.s.(x)	s.p.(wy)	s.s.(y)
Shelves	3	0·00	0·00	0·00	0·00
$D\male F$	2	0·00	0·00	0·00	0·00
Residual between litters	42	−24·45	32·00	−108·25	96·00
Between litters	47	−24·45	32·00	−108·25	96·00
$\male$	1	0·00	0·00	0·00	0·00
F	1	0·00	0·00	0·00	0·00
$D\male$	2	0·00	0·00	0·00	0·00
$\male F$	1	0·00	0·00	0·00	0·00
DF	2	0·00	0·00	0·00	0·00
Residual within litters	137	−13·85	96·00	−170·25	288·00
Total	191	−38·30	128·00	−278·50	384·00

As a check, we have

$$\frac{(-38\cdot30)^2}{128\cdot00} + \frac{(-278\cdot50)^2}{384\cdot00} = 213\cdot45 = \text{sum of squares for } D \text{ ignoring litters.}$$

The sums of squares for the linear components of D between and within litters are thus $(-24\cdot45)^2/32\cdot00 = 18\cdot68$ and $(-13\cdot85)^2/96\cdot00 = 2\cdot00$, while the corresponding sums of squares for the quadratic components are $(-108\cdot25)^2/96\cdot00 = 122\cdot06$ and $(-170\cdot25)^2/288\cdot00 = 100\cdot64$. The analysis of variance may be completed as in Table 8.5.5.

Table 8.5.5 Completed analysis of variance

	d.f.	s.s.	m.s.	Variance ratio
Shelves	3	85·31	28·44	3·31
Linear D	1	18·68	18·68	2·18 ⎫ 8·20
Quadratic D	1	122·06	122·06	14·23 ⎭
$D\male F$	2	0·37	0·18	0·02
Residual between litters	40	343·16	8·58	
Between litters	47	569·58		
Linear D	1	2·00	2·00	0·35 ⎫ 8·93
Quadratic D	1	100·64	100·64	17·50 ⎭
$\male$	1	771·61	771·61	134·19
F	1	28·29	28·29	4·92
$D\male$	2	15·49	7·74	1·35
$\male F$	1	0·45	0·45	0·08
DF	2	2·77	1·38	0·24
Residual within litters	135	776·89	5·75	
Total	191	2267·72		

In this instance, the quadratic effect of D is highly significant, but the linear effect is negligible. No overall test of D is required, since the variance ratios, both within and between litters, are highly significant. The F and $\male$ effects are also significant.

To estimate the dietary effects, we note that the estimated difference, $\frac{1}{2}(d_3 - d_1)$, between litters is $-24\cdot45/32\cdot00 = -0\cdot764$ with variance $8\cdot58/32\cdot00 = 0\cdot2681$. Within litters, this difference is $-13\cdot85/96\cdot00 = -0\cdot144$, with variance $5\cdot75/96\cdot00 = 0\cdot0599$. If these are combined, the overall estimate of $\frac{1}{2}(d_3 - d_1)$ is

$$\frac{(-0\cdot764)/0\cdot2681 + (-0\cdot144)/0\cdot0599}{1/0\cdot2681 + 1/0\cdot0599} = -0\cdot257,$$

with variance

$$\frac{1}{1/0\cdot2681 + 1/0\cdot0599} = 0\cdot048\ 96.$$

The appropriate number of degrees of freedom, F^*, for this estimate is given by

$$\frac{1}{F^* \times [0\cdot04896} = \frac{1}{0\cdot2681 + 0\cdot0599}\left(\frac{1}{40} + \frac{1}{135}\right),$$

i.e.

$$F^* = 207.$$

Similarly we may show that the overall estimate of $\frac{1}{6}(2d_2 - d_1 - d_3)$ is $-0\cdot689$ with variance $0\cdot016\ 34$. From these two estimates, we get

$$d_1 - \bar{d} = 0\cdot257 + 0\cdot689 = 0\cdot946$$
$$d_2 - \bar{d} = 2 \times (-0\cdot689) = -1\cdot378$$
$$d_3 - \bar{d} = -0\cdot257 + 0\cdot689 = 0\cdot432.$$

If these had been directly estimated from the overall means, the values $1\cdot025$, $-1\cdot450$ and $0\cdot425$ would be obtained. Thus, in constructing tables of means, $-0\cdot079$, $0\cdot072$, and $0\cdot007$ must be added to means of d_1, d_2, and d_3 respectively. Table 8.5.6 gives the means and standard errors for this experiment.

Table 8.5.6 Table of means and standard errors

	d_1	d_2	d_3	Mean	
—	11·48	8·88	10·73	10·36	
f	11·91	9·86	11·63	11·13	Standard error of difference = ± 0·346
♂	14·07	11·05	13·14	12·75	
♀	9·32	7·68	9·23	8·74	
Mean	11·69	9·37	11·18	10·75	

Standard error of difference = ± 0·443

Standard error of differences between means in same column = ± 0·599.
Standard error of differences between means in same row = ± 0·613.

In this table, the standard errors of the differences between means in the same column may be derived directly from the within-litter mean square. The variance of the difference between the overall diet means is obtained by multiplying the above estimate by 4, i.e. $4 \times 0\cdot048\ 96 = 0\cdot195\ 84$. The square root of this gives the value shown.

To obtain the variance of differences between means in the same row, we note that these might be obtained from the marginal means by adding a within-litter interaction. For instance,

$$d_1\mathcal{3} - d_2\mathcal{3} = (d_1 - d_2) + \tfrac{1}{2}(d_1\mathcal{3} - d_2\mathcal{3} - d_1\female + d_2\female).$$

Thus the variance of such comparisons is given by the sum of the variances of the two components, i.e. $0.19584 + \dfrac{1}{32} \times 5.75 = 0.37553$, and its square root provides the standard error. It should be noted that the appropriate number of degrees of freedom for comparisons of this type can be directly calculated, even though one of the components is itself heterogeneous. Thus, in this instance, the appropriate number of degrees of freedom, F^*, is given by

$$\frac{(0.37553)^2}{F^*} = \frac{(0.19584)^2}{207} + \frac{(0.17969)^2}{135}$$
$$F^* = 332.$$

In this instance, the degrees of freedom of all components are so large that we should not normally bother to estimate them unless a very high degree of accuracy was required.

In this experiment, the increase in efficiency achieved by making many of the comparisons within litters is not great. The relative efficiency of within- and between-litter comparisons is $8.58 : 5.75$, i.e. $1.49 : 1.00$. If, however, the animals had been completely randomized the expected value of the mean square would be

$$\frac{47 \times 8.58 + 144 \times 5.75}{191} = 6.45.$$

The relative increase in accuracy due to the use of litter-mates is thus $6.45 : 5.75 = 1.12 : 1.00$ on all comparisons other than D. On D, the relative increase in accuracy is $6.45/32 : 0.19584 = 1.03 : 1.00$.

Neither of these improvements in accuracy is very large, and it would seem that the complexity of the design has not benefited the comparisons greatly. It must, however, be remembered that sometimes much greater increases in accuracy will be achieved (cf. the examples of 4.5). At the same time, it may often happen that, owing to limitations of space, experimental material and so on, it is necessary to achieve the maximum accuracy with a given amount of material. In such cases a complex design will give results of an accuracy unobtainable in any other way.

9 *Response Surface Methods*

9.1 Introduction

In the analysis of factorial experiments, both complete and fractional, we have been concerned only with the measurements or responses at the given levels of the factors. With quantitive factors, the estimation of responses at factor levels other than those included in the experiment may be of interest. This would be the case, for instance, if the purpose of the experiment was to try to determine the factor levels that gave the maximum response. To do this it is necessary to postulate that the expected response at a particular combination of the factors can be expressed as some function of the factor levels. It may be that the response will vary linearly as the levels are changed. For an m-factor experiment we may, therefore, postulate that the expected response η is given by

$$\eta = \beta_0 + \beta_1 x_1 + \beta_2 x_2 + \ldots + \beta_m x_m,$$

where x_1 is the level of factor A, x_2 is the level of factor B, and so on. Alternatively, the expected response may be better described by a quadratic model. Or for part of the experimental region the expected response may be adequately described by a linear model, but for other parts a quadratic or higher polynomial model may be necessary. For the case of two factors, a quadratic response model is given by

$$\eta = \beta_0 + \beta_1 x_1 + \beta_2 x_2 + \beta_{11} x_1{}^2 + \beta_{22} x_2{}^2 + \beta_{12} x_1 x_2.$$

We may wish to examine the experimental region to see what form the relationship takes, i.e. what the response surface looks like. One procedure is to postulate a response model, conduct an experiment to estimate the parameters in the model, and then examine the model to see whether it adequately fits the data. This could lead to a new response model and the need to estimate and test the parameters of this model. With experimental conditions which are reasonably stable and where responses can be quickly obtained, this can often be achieved by adding further experimental points to the design carried out at the previous stage.

9.2 First-order designs

We shall first of all consider designs which enable us to estimate linear response models of the form

$$\eta = \beta_0 + \beta_1 x_1 + \beta_2 x_2 + \ldots + \beta_m x_m.$$

The 2^m designs discussed in earlier chapters are suitable[*] for fitting models of this type. Since the factors are quantitative it will be convenient to code the levels of the factors such that the lower level of the factor is -1 and the upper level $+1$. The layout of the 2^2 experiment is given in Table 9.2.1.

Table 9.2.1   Layout for a 2^2 experiment

Yields	x_1	x_2	Treatment combination
y_1	-1	-1	(1)
y_2	1	-1	a
y_3	-1	1	b
y_4	1	1	ab

The intercept β_0 is estimated by

$$b_0 = \tfrac{1}{4}(y_1 + y_2 + y_3 + y_4) = \bar{y}.$$

Since $\Sigma x_1 = \Sigma x_2 = 0$, the average amount by which y changes for a unit change is x is estimated by

$$b = \frac{\text{sum of products of } x \text{ and } y}{\text{sum of squares of } x}$$

and its corresponding sum of squares in the analysis of variance will be

$$\frac{[\text{sum of products of } x \text{ and } y]^2}{\text{sum of squares of } x}.$$

We therefore estimate β_1 and β_2 by

$$b_1 = \tfrac{1}{4}(-y_1 + y_2 - y_3 + y_4) = \tfrac{1}{4}[(a + ab) - ((1) + b)] = \tfrac{1}{2}A,$$

and

$$b_2 = \tfrac{1}{4}(-y_1 - y_2 + y_3 + y_4) = \tfrac{1}{2}B, \text{ respectively.}$$

If we were to add a cross-product term $\beta_{12}x_1x_2$ to our model then β_{12} would be estimated by

$$b_{12} = \tfrac{1}{4}(y_1 - y_2 - y_3 + y_4) = \tfrac{1}{4}[((1) + ab) - (a + b)] = \tfrac{1}{2}AB.$$

However, there is little point in adding this term without adding the other quadratic terms $\beta_{11}x_1^2$ and $\beta_{22}x_2^2$. For a single replicate of the 2^2 experiment, the sums of squares due to each of the components in the linear model are $4b_0^2$, $4b_1^2$ and $4b_2^2$ respectively. The sum of squares due to the AB interaction, $4b_{12}^2$, can be regarded as a measure of the fit of the model. If this component is large relative

---

[*] They are also optimal in the sense of minimizing the volume of the confidence region associated with the estimates of the regression parameters.

to the experimental error, it suggests that the linear model is not an adequate fit and that a quadratic model may be more appropriate.

Generally, the main effects of a 2^m experiment provide estimates of the regression parameters in the m-factor linear response model. The interaction terms provide a measure of goodness of, or lack of, fit.

If the number of treatment combinations is too many for the purpose of the experiment, then fractional 2^m designs may be employed. For example, suppose we postulate a linear response model for five factors each at two levels. A $\frac{1}{2}$-replicate of a 2^5 experiment would involve 16 treatment combinations; six degrees of freedom would be used for estimating the parameters in the model, leaving 10 degrees of freedom for lack of fit. If we use the design with defining contrast $I = ABCDE$ then the main effects, or regression coefficients, can be estimated independently of each other.

Using a $1/2^s$ replicate of a 2^m experiment that permits the independent estimation of all main effects leads to the partition of the degrees of freedom given in Table 9.2.2. In this table, $n_1 (= 2^{m-s})$ denotes the number of points included in the experiment.

Table 9.2.2   Partition of degrees of freedom

	d.f.
Linear terms	m
Lack of fit	$n_1 - m - 1$
Total	$n_1 - 1$

An estimate of experimental error can be obtained by replicating the design or by adding a number of points at the centre of the design, i.e. at the point where each x_i is zero. Of course, there would be little point in adopting the former procedure if it has already been decided that there are too many treatment combinations for a complete replicate of the factorial experiment. Adding centre points has the advantage that it does not alter the estimates of the regression parameters, except that b_0 is now the mean of all the responses, including those at the centre. The interaction terms will be unaffected and, as before, will provide a measure of lack of fit. In addition, if there are n_2 points at the centre, the sum of squares of the responses at these points, corrected for their mean, will provide $n_2 - 1$ degrees of freedom for measuring the experimental error. A further degree of freedom for lack of fit will also be available. The sum of squares of this component is given by

$$\frac{n_1 n_2}{n_1 + n_2} (\bar{y}_1 - \bar{y}_2)^2,$$

where $\bar{y}_1$ is the mean response for the n_1 exterior points and $\bar{y}_2$ is the mean response for the n_2 centre points.

9.3 Second-order designs

The second-order or quadratic response model is, for two factors,

$$\eta = \beta_0 + \beta_1 x_1 + \beta_2 x_2 + \beta_{11} x_1^2 + \beta_{22} x_2^2 + \beta_{12} x_1 x_2.$$

As we have already seen, a 2^2 experiment only permits the estimation of four parameters and is therefore unsuitable for fitting second-order response models. A 3^2 experiment would permit the estimation of all six parameters, but the 3^m experiments suffer from a number of disadvantages in fitting these response models. First, it has been shown that the coefficients of the squared terms, β_{11} and β_{22}, are estimated with relatively low precision. Furthermore, as the number of factors increases, the experiment becomes very large. This disadvantage can to a certain extent be overcome by using fractional factorial designs. Finally, as we have already indicated, the second-order response model is often fitted after a linear response model has been found to be inadequate. It is advantageous, therefore, to be able to augment the first-order designs to estimate the second-order model. The designs we shall now consider are called *composite* designs.

To the basic 2^m factorial design are added a number of axial points and centre points. For example, to the basic 2^2 design of Table 9.1.1 we can add the following points—

x_1	x_2
$-\alpha$	0
α	0
0	$-\alpha$
0	α
0	0

These points refer to the levels of the two factors in coded units. For instance, suppose that the lower and upper levels of a factor are 10 and 20, corresponding to coded values of -1 and $+1$ respectively. Then a coded value of 0 corresponds to the value 15, a coded value of $+\alpha$ to $15 + 5\alpha$, and a coded value of $-\alpha$ to $15 - 5\alpha$.

In order to obtain an estimate of experimental error in this composite design, the centre point could be replicated a number of times or, alternatively, the whole design could be replicated. The value of α is chosen to satisfy some requirement of the experiment.

We shall initially consider choosing α so as to make the regression coefficients in our second-order response model orthogonal to each other. We shall modify the model so that each x-variable is measured about its mean. For a design with one centre point, the means of x_1, x_2 and the cross-product term $x_1 x_2$ are all zero, whilst the means of x_1^2 and x_2^2 are both given by

$$c = \frac{(4 + 2\alpha^2)}{9}.$$

The full set of variables in the model are given in Table 9.3.1. The first two columns give the design for the experiment.

Table 9.3.1 Second-order composite design

x_1	x_2	$x_1{}^2 - c$	$x_2{}^2 - c$	$x_1 x_2$
-1	-1	$1 - c$	$1 - c$	1
1	-1	$1 - c$	$1 - c$	-1
-1	1	$1 - c$	$1 - c$	-1
1	1	$1 - c$	$1 - c$	1
$-\alpha$	0	$\alpha^2 - c$	$- c$	0
α	0	$\alpha^2 - c$	$- c$	0
0	$-\alpha$	$- c$	$\alpha^2 - c$	0
0	α	$- c$	$\alpha^2 - c$	0
0	0	$- c$	$- c$	0

It can be seen that x_1, x_2 and $x_1 x_2$ are orthogonal to each other and to $x_1{}^2 - c$ and $x_2{}^2 - c$. We choose α, therefore, to make the squared terms orthogonal to each other, that is, to satisfy

$$\Sigma(x_1{}^2 - c)(x_2{}^2 - c) = 0,$$

i.e.

$$4(1 - c)^2 - 4c(\alpha^2 - c) + c^2 = 0.$$

This gives a value of $\alpha = 1 \cdot 0$, which means in fact that the above composite design is a 3^2 experiment where the levels of each factor are, in coded units, -1, 0 and $+1$. In general, however, these composite designs are not 3^m experiments. For instance, for a 2^3 experiment with six axial points and one centre point the value of α is $1 \cdot 215$. In general, α is given by the square root of

$$\alpha^2 = \frac{\sqrt{[2^m q(2^m q + 2mp + n)]} - 2^m q}{2p},$$

where

$m =$ number of variables or factors,
$q =$ fraction of the 2^m experiment,
$n =$ number of centre points,
$p =$ replications of the α-point sets, where an α-point set consists of $2m$ axial points in a 2^m experiment.

In these composite designs, therefore, all the terms in the response model are orthogonal to one another, so that the regression coefficients are estimated by the ratio of the sum of products of x and y to the sum of squares of x. The variance of an estimated coefficient is given by

$$\text{var } (b) = \frac{\sigma^2}{\text{sum of squares of } x}.$$

From the fitted regression model the response can be predicted for a given set of factor levels. In the design of Table 9.3.1, with $c = \frac{2}{3}$, for a given combination of the two factors, say $x_1 = X_1$ and $x_2 = X_2$, the predicted response is given by

$$\hat{y} = b_0 + b_1 X_1 + b_2 X_2 + b_{11}(X_1^2 - \tfrac{2}{3}) + b_{22}(X_2^2 - \tfrac{2}{3}) + b_{12} X_1 X_2,$$

with variance

$$\text{var } (\hat{y}) = \text{var } (b_0) + X_1^2 \text{ var } (b_1) + X_2^2 \text{ var } (b_2) + (X_1^2 - \tfrac{2}{3})^2 \text{ var } (b_{11})$$
$$+ (X_2^2 - \tfrac{2}{3})^2 \text{ var } (b_{22}) + X_1^2 X_2^2 \text{ var } (b_{12}),$$

i.e.

$$\text{var } (\hat{y}) = \sigma^2 [\tfrac{1}{9} + \tfrac{1}{6} X_1^2 + \tfrac{1}{6} X_2^2 + \tfrac{1}{2}(X_1^2 - \tfrac{2}{3})^2 + \tfrac{1}{2}(X_2^2 - \tfrac{2}{3})^2 + \tfrac{1}{4} X_1^2 X_2^2].$$

This variance depends, not only upon the design used, but also on the particular combination of the two factors for which the response is predicted. It is possible to determine all those combinations for which this variance is the same. That is, contours could be drawn, in the experimental region, along which this variance is constant.

The contours for the orthogonal design of Table 9.3.1 would show that, for a fixed distance ρ from the design centre, the variance of the predicted response would be larger in some directions than in others. For instance, for a value of $\rho^2 = x_1^2 + x_2^2 = 2$, we get

$$\text{var } (\hat{y}) = \frac{29}{36} \sigma^2 \quad \text{for } x_1 = 1 \text{ and } x_2 = 1,$$

$$\text{var } (\hat{y}) = \frac{48}{36} \sigma^2 \quad \text{for } x_1 = \sqrt{2} \text{ and } x_2 = 0.$$

Such a design may therefore be considered unsatisfactory unless there are *a priori* reasons why greater precision should be required in certain directions rather than in others.

Such contour lines can in fact be obtained for any second-order design, although the expression for the variance of the predicted response $\hat{y}$ would, if the terms were not all orthogonal to each other, be made more complicated by the covariances or correlations between the estimates of the regression coefficients. Designs have been proposed for which these contours are at a constant distance from the centre of the design. These designs then have the intuitively appealing property that the precision of the predicted response for any combination of the factors depends only upon the distance of that combination from the centre of the design, and does not depend upon its direction. Designs possessing this property are called *rotatable* second-order designs.

The composite designs given earlier can still be used to construct rotatable second-order designs. Suppose now that in the design of Table 9.3.1 we put

$\alpha = \sqrt{2}$ and, consequently, $c = \frac{8}{9}$. The squared terms in the response model will no longer be orthogonal to each other, so that, in calculating the variance of the predicted response, the covariance between these terms must also be included. Using regression methods, we can show that for $x_1 = X_1$ and $x_2 = X_2$

$$\text{var}\,(\hat{y}) = \sigma^2[\tfrac{1}{9} + \tfrac{1}{8}X_1{}^2 + \tfrac{1}{8}X_2{}^2 + \tfrac{11}{32}(X_1{}^2 - \tfrac{8}{9})^2 + \tfrac{11}{32}(X_2{}^2 - \tfrac{8}{9})^2$$
$$+ \tfrac{14}{32}(X_1{}^2 - \tfrac{8}{9})(X_2{}^2 - \tfrac{8}{9}) + \tfrac{1}{4}X_1{}^2X_2{}^2].$$

This simplifies to a function involving only the distance $\rho = \sqrt{(X_1{}^2 + X_2{}^2)}$, namely

$$\text{var}\,(\hat{y}) = (11\rho^4 - 28\rho^2 + 32)\sigma^2/32.$$

Hence the design of Table 9.3.1 with $\alpha = \sqrt{2}$ is rotatable.

Generally, if to a $1/2^s$ replicate of a 2^m experiment are added a number of α-points and centre points, a rotatable design is obtained when $\alpha = 2^{(m-s)/4}$. Of course, with these values of α the squared terms in the response model are no longer orthogonal to each other. Fitting and examining the response model is consequently more complicated, although not unduly so.

It should also be noted that the first-order designs with n_1 exterior points and n_2 centre points, given in 9.2, are rotatable, since for these designs

$$\text{var}\,(\hat{y}) = \sigma^2\left[\frac{1}{n_1 + n_2} + \frac{1}{n_1}(X_1{}^2 + X_2{}^2 + \ldots + X_m{}^2)\right].$$

As before, the sum of squares $\Sigma X_i{}^2$ measures the square of the distance from the given treatment combination to the centre of the design.

Whenever a symmetrical arrangement of the factor points around the centre of the design is considered desirable, composite designs given in this section will be appropriate. Asymmetrical or *non-central* composite designs may be appropriate in other situations; see, for example, the book by Cochran and Cox (1957). References to these and other response-surface designs can be found in the review paper by Hill and Hunter (1966).

9.4 Blocking

As we have already seen in other experimental situations, greater precision may be achieved by arranging the experimental units into blocks. In particular, response surface experiments are frequently conducted in two stages, fitting and testing a first-order response model and then including additional points in order to fit a second-order response model. If experimental conditions are different at the two stages it will be necessary to arrange these stages in two blocks.

Box and Hunter (1957) have shown that for the blocks effects to be orthogonal to the regression coefficients each block must be a rotatable first-order design, and that the fraction of the total sum of squares for each variable contributed by each block must be proportional to the number of observations in each block.

Consider, for instance, the first-order 2^2 design with points $(+1, +1)$, $(-1, +1)$, $(+1, -1)$, $(-1, -1)$ and n_1 centre points $(0, 0)$ comprising one block, and the axial points $(-\alpha, 0)$, $(\alpha, 0)$, $(0, -\alpha)$, $(0, \alpha)$ and n_2 centre points $(0, 0)$ comprising the second block. Hence we have a total of $n = n_1 + n_2 + 8$ experimental points.

Clearly each block gives rise to a rotatable first-order design since within each block $\Sigma x_1 = \Sigma x_2 = 0$ and $\Sigma x_1 x_2 = 0$. For the other condition to be satisfied, α must be chosen so that

$$\frac{4}{4 + 2\alpha^2} = \frac{4 + n_1}{n},$$

i.e.

$$\alpha^2 = \frac{2(n_2 + 4)}{n_1 + 4}.$$

If $n_1 = n_2$ then $\alpha^2 = 2$, which is the value required for a rotatable second-order design. In some of the other 2^m designs it will not be possible to achieve both rotatability and orthogonality of block effects simultaneously. From the ease of analysis viewpoint it would be best to choose orthogonality over rotatability, although this would slightly affect the spherical nature of the contours of the variances of the predicted responses.

9.5 Computer construction of response surface designs

In certain circumstances the designs of the previous sections may not be entirely suitable for the experiment under consideration. It may be known in advance that certain combinations of the factors are of no interest, and these would not be considered, therefore, as belonging to the experimental region. For instance, a second-order composite design will be unsuitable if it is decided, on practical grounds, that treatment combinations with all factors at the higher levels should not be examined. In a chemical reaction experiment, potentially dangerous high-pressure and high-temperature combinations might be rejected on safety grounds.

Suppose that the relevant experimental region is defined by a discrete repertoire of N possible experimental points, and it is required to choose a design of $n \, (< N)$ points which will be used to fit and test a polynomial response model of a given order. The properties of any such design may be examined. Variances and covariances of the estimates of the regression coefficients and the standard errors of the predicted responses at each of the N repertoire points can be calculated. A number of alternative designs, each with n points, can be constructed and their properties calculated and compared. It is clear that some criteria must be decided upon if a choice is to be made between these designs. One reasonable criterion is to choose the design which minimizes the volume of the confidence region associated with the estimated regression coefficients, that is, which minimizes the *determinant* of the matrix of the variances and covariances of these estimated coefficients. Another criterion is to choose the n points so that the maximum standard error of the predicted responses over the experimental region of N points is as small as possible.

7—EDA * *

The number of alternative designs which must be examined in order to find the optimum design may be very large. To overcome this problem an electronic computer can be used to search systematically through the designs, to calculate their properties, and to choose the best design according to the selected criterion. Even with a computer, however, the task of looking at all possible designs may be too time-consuming. Methods have been devised—and further methods are required—which will enable such a search to be carried out quickly and which will at the same time produce optimum, or near optimum, designs. Some of these methods build the design sequentially, that is, by adding in experimental points one at a time. These have an advantage that a few points which have already been run can be incorporated into an extended design. For example, it may be desirable to add points to a design already used to fit and test a lower-order polynomial model, as when a 2^m first-order design is augmented to give a composite second-order design. Further details on the use of the computer to construct response-surface designs can be found in Box and Draper (1971), Mitchell (1974) and Goldsmith (1974).

So far, we have assumed that we are able to postulate an underlying response model. However, it may be that no assumptions can be made about the form of the model at the outset of the experiment. In designing such an experiment the main aim might therefore be to achieve a wide coverage of the experimental region so that a number of alternative models could be fitted. Kennard and Stone (1969) describe a method of constructing designs whereby the next point to be included in the design is as far away as possible, in the experimental region, from the previously selected points. Again, such a sequential method of design construction would normally necessitate the use of an electronic computer.

9.6   Example of a response surface analysis

Smith and Rose (1963) report an investigation carried out for the specific purpose of creating an excellent pie-crust recipe. Three process variables were considered, namely, amounts of water (x_1), of flour (x_2) and of shortening (x_3). Three responses were measured, namely flakiness (y_1), gumminess (y_2) and specific volume (y_3). Both flakiness and gumminess were subjective measures, in the range 1 to 10, based on an evaluation of a panel of trained judges. A high score on flakiness (above 7) and a low score on gumminess (below 3.75) was considered good. The centre of the experimental region was chosen to correspond to the combination of the process variables used prior to the experiment. The actual amounts of x_1, x_2 and x_3 were coded.

The responses were not expected to be linear in the experimental region and a second-order response model was postulated. The experimental design chosen was a composite design consisting of 16 points, namely the eight points of the 2^3 factorial design, six α-points and two centre points. The design was replicated twice. The value of α was chosen so as to make the design orthogonal. In this case $\alpha = 1.287\,18$. The 16 points of each replication are given in Table 9.6.1.

Table 9.6.1   Design matrix

x_1	x_2	x_3
-1	-1	-1
-1	-1	1
-1	1	-1
-1	1	1
1	-1	-1
1	-1	1
1	1	-1
1	1	1
$-1\cdot287\,18$	0	0
$1\cdot287\,18$	0	0
0	$-1\cdot287\,18$	0
0	$1\cdot287\,18$	0
0	0	$-1\cdot287\,18$
0	0	$1\cdot287\,18$
0	0	0
0	0	0

The fitted response model for flakiness was

$$y_1 = 6\cdot895 + 0\cdot063x_1 - 0\cdot123x_2 + 0\cdot152x_3 - 0\cdot115x_1^2 - 0\cdot040x_2^2$$
$$- 0\cdot115x_3^2 + 0\cdot094x_1x_2 - 0\cdot344x_1x_3 - 0\cdot031x_2x_3.$$

This can be used as a predictive equation for flakiness using the coded values of x_1, x_2 and x_3. Table 9.6.2 provides a test of the significance and adequacy of this model.

Table 9.6.2   Analysis of variance for flakiness

	d.f.	s.s.	m.s.	Variance ratio
Due to fitted model	9	3·3110	0·36789	2·60
Lack of fit	5	1·3267	0·26534	2·52
Residual	17	1·7920	0·10541	
Total	31	6·4297		

The lack-of-fit component is not significant at the 5 percent level, indicating that within the experimental region a second-order response model is adequate. Similar analyses were obtained for gumminess and specific volume. In each case the prediction equations were good ones, and the model was adequate for predictive purposes. Details of testing the significance and lack of fit of such models can be found in, for example, the book by Draper and Smith (1966).

9.7 Examining the fitted surface

Usually the purpose of fitting a response model is to be able to locate the optimum operating levels of the factors. The model will either yield these optimum values or at least indicate which part of the experimental region should be examined in more detail. It will be necessary, therefore, to examine the response model over the experimental region in order to get some indication of the nature of the response surface.

Initially the experiment may have been conducted some distance from the optimum. A series of small experiments may then be necessary in order to move towards the optimum region. As such experiments are normally conducted over a small part of the experimental region, a linear response model will usually provide an adequate fit to the surface. Nearer the optimum region it becomes necessary to fit a non-linear model in order to locate the optimum response.

Suppose that an experiment in m variables resulted in the linear model

$$y = b_0 + b_1 x_1 + b_2 x_2 + \ldots + b_m x_m$$

being fitted, and that the centre of this experiment is at the point where each factor is at the zero level. To achieve this, the original variables would have to be coded. In order to locate the maximum response, we would require this experiment to indicate the direction in which we should now move in order to approach the optimum region; that is, we require the direction of *steepest ascent*. Suppose we move to a point P which has the ith factor at level a_i ($i = 1, 2, \ldots, m$). The expected response at this point is

$$\hat{y}_p = b_0 + b_1 a_1 + b_2 a_2 + \ldots + b_m a_m,$$

and the distance from P to the centre of the experiment is given by

$$r = \sqrt{(a_1^2 + a_2^2 + \ldots + a_m^2)}.$$

The point P is chosen so as to maximize $\hat{y}_p$ for a fixed value of r. The appropriate values of a_i are given by

$$a_i = \frac{r b_i}{\sqrt{(\Sigma b_i^2)}} \quad (i = 1, 2, \ldots, m)$$

that is, they are proportional to the slope b_i. The factor levels at P can then be determined either by fixing r or alternatively by fixing one of the factor levels. For example, suppose a linear model involving three factors was fitted, giving $b_1 = 1\cdot3$, $b_2 = -0\cdot5$ and $b_3 = 2\cdot7$. Taking $a_1 = 3$ gives $r = 7\cdot011$, and hence the point P is given by

$$a_1 = 3\cdot00, \quad a_2 = 1\cdot15, \quad a_3 = 6\cdot23.$$

The appropriate distance to move will depend upon experimental considerations. The greatest gain in expected response is achieved by moving in large steps. However, it must be realized that the fitted model is only likely to be valid over a small part of the experimental region, so that moving too far from the centre may result in the response at P being considerably different from the predicted response $\hat{y}_p$.

Nearer the optimum region a second-order response model might be fitted. We shall now discuss methods of examining the surface of such a model. Consider the fitted second-order model

$$y = b_0 + b_1 x_1 + b_2 x_2 + b_{11} x_1^2 + b_{22} x_2^2 + b_{12} x_1 x_2$$

for two factors at levels x_1 and x_2 respectively. A better understanding of this equation will be obtained if all the values of x_1 and x_2 are found such that the predicted response from the fitted model will be, say, Y. Plotting these values on a graph for different values of Y would then yield a contour surface of the responses over the experimental region. Two examples of such surfaces, using arbitrary yields, are given in Fig. 9.7.1. In (a) the maximum response is clearly

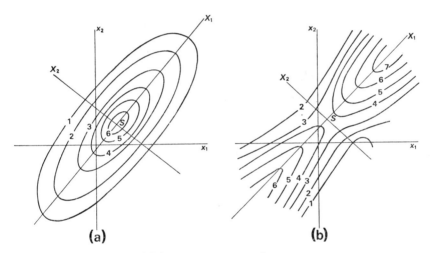

Fig. 9.7.1   Two response surface contours

near the point marked S. In (b) the maximum response lies on the line represented by X_1. In both figures the point S is called the "stationary point" of the surface.

Drawing these contour surfaces is extremely tedious for two and three factors and virtually impossible for more than three factors. An alternative method of examining a second-order response surface is, however, available and will be illustrated by considering the example given in the previous section. In this example the fitted response model was

$$y = 6\cdot895 + b_1 x_1 + b_2 x_2 + b_3 x_3 + b_{11} x_1^2 + b_{22} x_2^2 + b_{33} x_3^2 + b_{12} x_1 x_2$$
$$+ b_{13} x_1 x_3 + b_{23} x_2 x_3,$$

where

$$b_1 = 0 \cdot 063, \quad b_2 = -0 \cdot 123, \quad b_3 = 0 \cdot 152,$$
$$b_{11} = -0 \cdot 115, \quad b_{22} = -0 \cdot 040, \quad b_{33} = -0 \cdot 115,$$
$$b_{12} = 0 \cdot 094, \quad b_{13} = -0 \cdot 344, \quad b_{23} = -0 \cdot 031.$$

By a suitable change of origin, it will now be possible to eliminate the linear terms from this model. It can be rewritten in terms of

$$x_1' = x_1 - \hat{x}_1, \quad x_2' = x_2 - \hat{x}_2 \quad \text{and} \quad x_3' = x_3 - \hat{x}_3,$$

where $\hat{x}_1$, $\hat{x}_2$ and $\hat{x}_3$ are obtained as the solution to the equations

$$2b_{11}\hat{x}_1 + b_{12}\hat{x}_2 + b_{13}\hat{x}_3 = -b_1$$
$$b_{12}\hat{x}_1 + 2b_{22}\hat{x}_2 + b_{23}\hat{x}_3 = -b_2$$
$$b_{13}\hat{x}_1 + b_{23}\hat{x}_2 + 2b_{33}\hat{x}_3 = -b_3. ^{(*)}$$

The point $(\hat{x}_1, \hat{x}_2, \hat{x}_3)$ is the stationary point of the fitted surface. In this example'

$$\hat{x}_1 = 0 \cdot 790, \quad \hat{x}_2 = -0 \cdot 435, \quad \hat{x}_3 = -0 \cdot 464.$$

The predicted response at this stationary point is given by $y = 6 \cdot 911$. Replacing x_1, x_2 and x_3 in the response model by x_1', x_2' and x_3' gives

$$y = 6 \cdot 911 - 0 \cdot 115 x_1'^2 - 0 \cdot 040 x_2'^2 - 0 \cdot 115 x_3'^2 + 0 \cdot 094 x_1' x_2' - 0 \cdot 344 x_1' x_3'$$
$$- 0 \cdot 031 x_2' x_3'.$$

This model can be simplified even further by eliminating the cross-product terms. This is done by rotating the axes of the response surface about its new origin. In Fig. 9.7.1 the new axes are given by X_1 and X_2 with origin at S. In the example, x_1', x_2' and x_3' are replaced by X_1, X_2 and X_3, where

$$X_1 = 0 \cdot 675 x_1' + 0 \cdot 363 x_2' - 0 \cdot 643 x_3'$$

$$X_2 = -0 \cdot 193 x_1' + 0 \cdot 927 x_2' + 0 \cdot 321 x_3'$$

$$X_3 = 0 \cdot 712 x_1' - 0 \cdot 093 x_2' + 0 \cdot 696 x_3'.$$

The fitted response model then becomes

$$y = 6 \cdot 911 + 0 \cdot 074 X_1^2 - 0 \cdot 055 X_2^2 - 0 \cdot 289 X_3^2.$$

The model has now been reduced to its *canonical* form. The coefficients of X_1^2, X_2^2 and X_3^2 in the model are given by the eigenvalues of the matrix

$$\begin{pmatrix} b_{11} & \frac{1}{2}b_{12} & \frac{1}{2}b_{13} \\ \frac{1}{2}b_{12} & b_{22} & \frac{1}{2}b_{23} \\ \frac{1}{2}b_{13} & \frac{1}{2}b_{23} & b_{33} \end{pmatrix}$$

and the coefficients of x_1', x_2' and x_3' in X_1, X_2 and X_3 by their corresponding eigenvectors. The definition of and method of calculating eigenvalues and

---

(*) Obtained by equating to zero the partial derivatives of y with respect to x_1, x_2 and x_3.

eigenvectors are given in most books on matrix algebra; see, for example, Graybill (1969).

Using the canonical form of the model, we see immediately that the maximum response is achieved when $X_2 = 0$ and $X_3 = 0$. Non-zero values of X_2 and X_3 will decrease the expected response. For X_1 the expected response will increase as we move away from zero in either direction. For two factors, this type of response surface is illustrated in Fig. 9.7.1(b). Putting $X_2 = 0$ and $X_3 = 0$ in the equations for X_2 and X_3 gives

$$0 = -0.193x_1' + 0.927x_2' + 0.321x_3'$$

$$0 = 0.712x_1' - 0.093x_2' + 0.696x_3',$$

from which we get $x_1' = 1.86x_2'$. Substituting this into the first of the two equations above and into the equation for X_1 gives

$$0 = 0.5680x_2' + 0.321x_3'$$

$$X_1 = 1.6185x_2' - 0.643x_3'.$$

These equations give $x_2' = 0.3628X_1$ and $x_3' = -0.6420X_1$. Alternatively, in terms of the original variables,

$$x_1 = 0.6748X_1 + 0.790$$

$$x_2 = 0.3628X_1 - 0.435$$

$$x_3 = -0.6420X_1 - 0.464.$$

The expected response at a particular value of X_1 and at $X_2 = X_3 = 0$ can be easily obtained from the response model in canonical form. The actual values of x_1, x_2 and x_3 corresponding to the value of X_1 can be obtained from the above expressions. Some values are given in Table 9.7.1.

Table 9.7.1 Some expected response values

X_1	x_1	x_2	x_3	y
−3	−1·418	−1·622	1·462	7·577
−2	−0·559	−1·161	0·820	7·207
−1	0·116	−0·798	0·178	6·985
0	0·790	−0·435	−0·464	6·911
1	1·466	−0·072	−1·106	6·985
2	2·141	0·291	−1·748	7·207
3	2·815	0·653	−2·390	7·577

In examining this surface, it must be realized that the fitted model may only be adequate over the experimental points used. In other parts of the experimental region, a different model may be necessary. For this reason, greater importance may be attached, when examining the surface and Table 9.7.1, to the expected response at say $X_1 = -3$ than at $X_1 = 3$. This suggests further experimentation at the higher levels of x_3 and the lower levels of x_1 and x_2. This suggestion was supported from an examination of the response surfaces for gumminess and specific volume.

Reducing the second-order response model to its canonical form has, therefore, simplified considerably the examination of the response surface.

9.8   Experiments on mixtures

Sometimes two treatments would not be applied simultaneously, except as a mixture whose strength equals that of the individual treatments. For example, in most feeding experiments, animals receiving dietary combinations cannot be expected to eat twice or three times as much as others, and even if they could, the results from such experiments would be of dubious application. In consequence the treatment combinations are mixtures of the main treatments or *components*, and the usual factorial analysis no longer applies.

Using response surface exploration, the aim of a mixture experiment will be to permit the estimation of the properties of the response surface so that it will be possible to find the mixture, i.e. combination of the components, which maximizes the expected response.

Suppose that we have m components in the experiment and that we are concerned with the proportions, and not the total amount, of each component in the mixture. If x_i represents the proportion of the ith component in the mixture, then $x_i \geqslant 0$ for all components and

$$\sum_{i=1}^{m} x_i = 1.$$

The first problem will be to decide upon an appropriate model to describe the response surface. Then, given a model, it will be necessary to choose an experimental design which will provide estimates of the parameters of the model, together with standard errors, and which will provide a test of the adequacy of the fit of the model. Numerous models have been proposed, and we shall first consider fitting polynomial models.

Suppose that the response surface over the entire factor space, or over some part of the factor space, can be represented by a first-order polynomial, i.e. the expected response can be written as

$$\eta = \beta_0 + \beta_1 x_1 + \beta_2 x_2 + \ldots + \beta_m x_m.$$

The regression methods used in the previous sections of this chapter cannot now be used to estimate the $m + 1$ parameters of this model. This is because the restriction $x_1 + x_2 + \ldots + x_m = 1$ means that the model can be rewritten as

$$\eta = \gamma_1 x_1 + \gamma_2 x_2 + \ldots + \gamma_m x_m,$$

where $\gamma_i = \beta_0 + \beta_i$. Thus there are m, and not $m + 1$, parameters to be determined. Usual regression methods can be employed with this *reparametrized* model. It should be noted that other reparametrizations of this model are possible, so that the estimates of the coefficients are not unique, although the predicted response obtained from a fitted model will be unique.

For a second-order polynomial with $m = 3$, the expected response is written as

$$\eta = \beta_0 + \beta_1 x_1 + \beta_2 x_2 + \beta_3 x_3 + \beta_{11} x_1^2 + \beta_{22} x_2^2 + \beta_{33} x_3^2 + \beta_{12} x_1 x_2 + \beta_{13} x_1 x_3$$
$$+ \beta_{23} x_2 x_3.$$

One possible reparametrization is given by noting that there are m constraints of the form

$$x_1 = x_1(x_1 + x_2 + x_3) = x_1^2 + x_1 x_2 + x_1 x_3,$$

so that

$$\beta_{11} x_1^2 = \beta_{11} x_1 - \beta_{11} x_1 x_2 - \beta_{11} x_1 x_3.$$

With similar expressions for $\beta_{22} x_2^2$ and $\beta_{33} x_3^2$ the model can be written as

$$\eta = \gamma_1 x_1 + \gamma_2 x_2 + \gamma_3 x_3 + \gamma_{12} x_1 x_2 + \gamma_{13} x_1 x_3 + \gamma_{23} x_2 x_3,$$

where $\gamma_i = \beta_0 + \beta_i + \beta_{ii}$ and $\gamma_{ij} = \beta_{ij} - \beta_{ii} - \beta_{jj}$. For the second-order model in general we have

$$\eta = \sum_{i=1}^{m} \gamma_i x_i + \sum\sum_{i<j} \gamma_{ij} x_i x_j,$$

and $\frac{1}{2} m(m + 1)$ coefficients have to be determined.

In a kth-order polynomial, the model can be reparametrized so that a total of

$$\frac{m(m + 1)(m + 2) \ldots (m + k - 1)}{1 \cdot 2 \cdot 3 \cdot \quad \ldots \quad k}$$

parameters have to be determined.

In order to estimate these parameters, Scheffé (1958) introduced simplex-lattice designs. To fit a kth-order polynomial the proportions of any component are taken as

$$0, \frac{1}{k}, \frac{2}{k}, \ldots, 1,$$

and all possible mixtures with these proportions are used. The number of experimental points in this design will then be the same as the number of parameters that have to be determined in the model. For example, the simplex-lattice design to fit a second-order model with three components is given in Table 9.8.1.

The parameters in the response model can easily be estimated. With $x_1 = 1$, $x_2 = 0$ and $x_3 = 0$ we get γ_1 estimated by $\hat{\gamma}_1 = y_1$. Similarly, $\hat{\gamma}_2 = y_2$ and $\hat{\gamma}_3 = y_3$. With $x_1 = \frac{1}{2}$, $x_2 = \frac{1}{2}$ and $x_3 = 0$ we get

$$\hat{\gamma}_{12} = 4y_4 - 2(y_1 + y_2).$$

Similarly,

$$\hat{\gamma}_{13} = 4y_5 - 2(y_1 + y_3)$$
$$\hat{\gamma}_{23} = 4y_6 - 2(y_2 + y_3).$$

The predicted response at a given set of proportions, say $x_1 = X_1$, $x_2 = X_2$ and $x_3 = X_3$ (subject to $X_1 + X_2 + X_3 = 1$) is given by

$$\hat{y} = \hat{\gamma}_1 X_1 + \hat{\gamma}_2 X_2 + \hat{\gamma}_3 X_3 + \hat{\gamma}_{12} X_1 X_2 + \hat{\gamma}_{13} X_1 X_3 + \hat{\gamma}_{23} X_2 X_3.$$

Table 9.8.1 Simplex-lattice design for a second-order model and three components

x_1	x_2	x_3	Response
1	0	0	y_1
0	1	0	y_2
0	0	1	y_3
$\frac{1}{2}$	$\frac{1}{2}$	0	y_4
$\frac{1}{2}$	0	$\frac{1}{2}$	y_5
0	$\frac{1}{2}$	$\frac{1}{2}$	y_6

If the variance of each response is assumed to be σ^2 it is possible to derive an expression for the variance of the predicted response $\hat{y}$, although in general this is not straightforward since the estimates of the parameters are correlated. Of course, unless the design of Table 9.8.1 is replicated, no degrees of freedom will be available to estimate the experimental error σ^2. If the goodness of fit of this model is to be tested then it will be necessary to augment the design by including a number of additional points: for instance, points at $x_1 = \frac{1}{3}$, $x_2 = \frac{1}{3}$ and $x_3 = \frac{1}{3}$, or in some regions of the factor space where the adequacy of the model is suspect. Although the analysis has now lost its simplicity, the addition of such points will, in addition to providing a test of goodness of fit, improve the estimate of the variance of the predicted response in those regions of interest.

The main disadvantage of simplex-lattice designs is that the mixtures contain at most k components. For instance, in a second-order model the responses are observed on mixtures consisting of either a single component or two components; see Table 9.8.1. In order to obtain an adequate representation of the response surface it would be desirable to use mixtures involving many more of the components.

To overcome this difficulty, Scheffé (1963) proposed the simplex–centroid design. The design points correspond to the m permutations of $(1, 0, 0, \ldots, 0)$, the $\frac{1}{2}m(m-1)$ permutations of $(\frac{1}{2}, \frac{1}{2}, 0, \ldots, 0)$, the $\frac{1}{6}m(m-1)(m-2)$ permutations of $(\frac{1}{3}, \frac{1}{3}, \frac{1}{3}, 0, \ldots, 0)$, $\ldots$ and the point $\left(\frac{1}{m}, \frac{1}{m}, \frac{1}{m}, \ldots, \frac{1}{m}\right)$. These designs, therefore, only contain mixtures in which the components present appear in equal proportions. Again there is no great difficulty in fitting the reparametrized kth ($k \leqslant m$) order polynomial response model and in estimating the expected response and its precision.

Lambrakis (1968a, b, 1969) has considered alternatives to the simplex-lattice designs, whilst Draper and Lawrence (1965) have considered designs for $m = 3$ and $m = 4$ which exclude the pure components, i.e. mixtures having $x_i = 1$. All of these designs are concerned with the problem of fitting a polynomial response model over the entire factor space.

Often, however, for both economic and physical reasons, it may not be feasible to consider mixtures over the entire factor space; instead they will have to be restricted to a sub-region of the space. In other words, the proportions of some or all of the components are restricted to certain narrow limits. McLean and Anderson (1966), Kurotori (1966), Thompson and Myers (1968) and Gorman (1970) have developed designs and procedures for conducting mixture experiments for these situations.

9.9 Mixture experiments when some components are inert or additive

The polynomial models considered in the previous section suffer from a number of disadvantages in mixture experiments. The use of these polynomials for prediction purposes should be treated with caution, especially when the observations cover only a small part of the factor space. Extrapolation outside the sub-region of the observations can often lead to unusual results; see Gorman and Hinman (1962). With mixture experiments they also suffer from the additional disadvantage of being unable to account satisfactorily for components which are inert, i.e. cause no response at all, or which are additive in the sense that they do not have any joint effects with other components.

Consider, for example, the expected response in the second-order polynomial model with three components given by

$$\eta = \gamma_1 x_1 + \gamma_2 x_2 + \gamma_3 x_3 + \gamma_{12} x_1 x_2 + \gamma_{13} x_1 x_3 + \gamma_{23} x_2 x_3.$$

With the simplex-lattice design for $k = 2$ and $m = 3$ given in Table 9.8.1, we get six independent equations relating the response to the mixture, from which the coefficients can be evaluated. If η_i is the response to the pure component and η_{ij} is the response to the 50 : 50 mixture, then for $x_i = 1$ we get

$$\eta_i = \gamma_i,$$

and for $x_i = x_j = \frac{1}{2}$ we get

$$\eta_{ij} = \tfrac{1}{2}\gamma_i + \tfrac{1}{2}\gamma_j + \tfrac{1}{4}\gamma_{ij}.$$

The joint effect of the ith and jth components is then measured by

$$\gamma_{ij} = 4\eta_{ij} - 2\eta_i - 2\eta_j.$$

Suppose, however, that the third component does not have a joint effect with any combination of the other two components. Then it would be reasonable to assume that the response to any mixture of the three components is additive.

This means that in the example we would expect the response for the mixture $(\frac{1}{2}p, \frac{1}{2}p, q)$, where $p + q = 1$, to be the sum of p times the response of the mixture $(\frac{1}{2}, \frac{1}{2}, 0)$ and q times the response of the pure component $(0, 0, 1)$, i.e.

$$p\eta_{12} + q\eta_3 = \tfrac{1}{2}p\gamma_1 + \tfrac{1}{2}p\gamma_2 + q\gamma_3 + \tfrac{1}{4}p\gamma_{12}.$$

However, in the absence of any joint effect between the third component and the other two components, the polynomial model with $x_1 = \frac{1}{2}p$, $x_2 = \frac{1}{2}p$ and $x_3 = q$ gives

$$\tfrac{1}{2}p\gamma_1 + \tfrac{1}{2}p\gamma_2 + q\gamma_3 + \tfrac{1}{4}p^2\gamma_{12},$$

which differs from what we would expect from an additive model in the coefficient associated with γ_{12}. Thus the polynomial model is seen to be ineffective in dealing with a component having an additive effect.

Of course, given that the third component has an additive effect, it is easy to formulate a more appropriate, non-polynomial model. For example, consider the model

$$\eta = \gamma_1 x_1 + \gamma_2 x_2 + \gamma_3 x_3 + \gamma_{12} x_1 x_2/(x_1 + x_2),$$

where the last term is defined as zero when $x_1 = x_2 = 0$. This model has the desired additive property, as can be seen by putting $x_1 = x_2 = \frac{1}{2}p$ and $x_3 = q$ into the model. Another property of the model is that it reduces to the second-order polynomial model for two components when $x_3 = 0$.

Becker (1968) introduced alternatives to the polynomial models which overcome these difficulties and which are therefore more appropriate for mixture experiments that possibly have one or more components, inert or additive. A second-order model which is completely additive is

$$\eta = \gamma_1^* x_1 + \gamma_2^* x_2 + \gamma_3^* x_3 + \gamma_{12}^* \min(x_1, x_2) + \gamma_{13}^* \min(x_1, x_3) \\ + \gamma_{23}^* \min(x_2, x_3).$$

For instance, the response for the mixture $(\frac{1}{2}, \frac{1}{2}, 0)$ is

$$\eta_{12} = \tfrac{1}{2}\gamma_1^* + \tfrac{1}{2}\gamma_2^* + \tfrac{1}{2}\gamma_{12}^*,$$

and for the pure component $(0, 0, 1)$ it is $\eta_3 = \gamma_3^*$. In the absence of any joint effect between the third component and the other two components, the response for the mixture $(\frac{1}{2}p, \frac{1}{2}p, q)$ will, from the model, be

$$\tfrac{1}{2}p\gamma_1^* + \tfrac{1}{2}p\gamma_2^* + q\gamma_3^* + \tfrac{1}{2}p\gamma_{12}^*,$$

which is equal to $p\eta_{12} + q\eta_3$, the response expected from an additive model, with $\gamma_{12}^* = \frac{1}{2}\gamma_{12}$.

Similarly, for an inert third component the response, using this additive model, for the mixture $(\frac{1}{3}, \frac{1}{3}, \frac{1}{3})$, say, is

$$\tfrac{1}{3}\gamma_1^* + \tfrac{1}{3}\gamma_2^* + \tfrac{1}{3}\gamma_{12}^*,$$

which is two-thirds that obtained for the mixture $(\frac{1}{2}, \frac{1}{2}, 0)$, as we would expect. The response from the polynomial model, on the other hand, is

$$\tfrac{1}{3}\gamma_1^* + \tfrac{1}{3}\gamma_2^* + \tfrac{2}{9}\gamma_{12}^*.$$

This additive model is suitable, therefore, if one or more of the components are inert or additive. It is most appropriate for testing the significance of the joint effects of the components. Two other additive (second-order) models given by Becker are

$$\eta = \gamma_1 x_1 + \gamma_2 x_2 + \gamma_3 x_3 + \gamma_{12} x_1 x_2/(x_1 + x_2) + \gamma_{13} x_1 x_3/(x_1 + x_3) \\ + \gamma_{23} x_2 x_3/(x_2 + x_3),$$

where $x_i x_j/(x_i + x_j) = 0$ when both $x_i = x_j = 0$, and

$$\eta = \gamma_1 x_1 + \gamma_2 x_2 + \gamma_3 x_3 + \gamma_{12} \sqrt{(x_1 x_2)} + \gamma_{13} \sqrt{(x_1 x_3)} + \gamma_{23} \sqrt{(x_2 x_3)}.$$

These models are more appropriate for fitting the response surface and for prediction purposes; see Becker (1968).

Becker (1968) gives one example where both the polynomial model and his models have been fitted to the same set of data. Another example has been provided by Snee (1973), who uses data given in McLean and Anderson (1966). The best fit to the data in both of these examples is given by Becker's models.

The experimental designs of the previous sections can still be employed with these models. Using regression analysis procedures, the estimated coefficients in any of the models will not be too difficult to obtain. Predicted responses at various mixtures of the components can then be obtained, together with their standard errors, thereby providing a basis for exploring the response surface.

10 Incomplete Block Designs for a Single Set of Treatments

10.1 Types of design

When a large number of treatments have to be tested simultaneously, a complete replication may extend over a wide area or use a large quantity of material. For instance, in biological work on animals, it would be desirable to compare treatments within litters, but the size of litter will often be less than the number of treatments to be applied. Alternatively, in an experiment on plant virus diseases, comparisons would be made within plants, but the number of leaves per plant may be too small. In such cases it is usually preferable to adopt a design in which blocks involving less than a complete replication are used, and to eliminate differences between blocks in the treatment comparisons. The number of possible designs is very large and cannot be considered in full here. We shall, however, consider some of the more useful designs.

Designs testing a large number of treatments may be classified into three types. First, there are designs in which the treatments are randomized with control treatments scattered throughout, so that each of the treatments may be compared with the controls and hence with one another. Usually, this is an inefficient method of experimentation. Secondly, there are designs in which comparisons between pairs of treatments are all made equally accurate. These *balanced* designs may be used to eliminate block differences, as in balanced incomplete blocks and balanced lattices, or to eliminate row and column differences, as in Youden squares and lattice squares. Thirdly, there are designs in which certain treatment comparisons are partially sacrificed in order to increase the accuracy of the others. Designs of this type give rise to comparisons of differing accuracy. Such designs are usually employed either because certain comparisons are regarded as more important than others and hence need to be more accurately determined, or because balanced designs of the required size are not available.

We shall not consider the first type here. In it the accuracy of comparisons with the control treatments is increased at the expense of other comparisons. While it may be argued that this is sometimes desirable, in general, where we have compared each treatment with the controls, the relative merits of exceptional treatments have then to be considered. For this purpose, the use of control treatments is inefficient. Sometimes, however, when the number of treatments is very large, the use of control treatments will permit a rapid and inexpensive weeding-out of ineffective treatments prior to a more exhaustive investigation involving efficient designs. For the purpose of such pilot investigations, the method of controls might therefore be employed. For intensive investigation and comparison of treatments, designs of the type to be described in this chapter will be found more useful.

10.2 Balanced incomplete blocks

In balanced incomplete block designs every pair of treatments occur together in the same number of blocks, and hence all treatment comparisons are of equal accuracy. A possible design in balanced incomplete blocks is that in which all possible sets of v treatments or varieties, taken k at a time, are used. Such designs are called *unreduced* balanced incomplete blocks. For instance, five treatments may be arranged in ten blocks of three treatments: *ABC, ABD, ABE, ACD, ACE, ADE, BCD, BCE, BDE, CDE.* In this design, each treatment is repeated six times, and each pair of treatments occur together in three blocks. However, the use of every possible set of k treatments, out of a total of v, requires a large number of replications, and it is preferable to use balanced designs in which every possible combination is not employed. Designs sometimes exist which require fewer blocks and replicates than the unreduced designs. In general, if there are v treatments, each replicated r times, in b blocks with k treatments per block, then the total number of experimental units is given by $bk = vr$. Further, if each pair of treatments occur together in λ blocks then $\lambda(v - 1) = r(k - 1)$, since a particular treatment occurs with each of the other $v - 1$ treatments in λ blocks and also in r blocks with $k - 1$ treatments. Since all these parameters must be integers, the two relationships given above can be used to show that a design does *not* exist, but it is not necessarily true that even if they are satisfied a design exists. For instance, no design exists for $v = 21, b = 28, r = 8, k = 6$ and $\lambda = 2$, although the two relationships hold.

Two series of arrangements can be obtained using a complete set of $p - 1$ orthogonal $p \times p$ Latin squares (tabulated in *Statistical Tables*). Such sets exist when p is a prime or a power of a prime. The first arrangement has p^2 treatments, each replicated $p + 1$ times with p treatments per block. The p^2 treatments are taken to fill the cells of a $p \times p$ square. The first p blocks correspond to the rows of this square, and the next p blocks to the columns. Each of the $p - 1$ Latin squares is then superimposed in turn onto this square and, for each square, all treatments paired with the same letter make up a block. Table 10.2.1 gives the design, before randomization, arising from the 5×5 set of orthogonal squares.

The second arrangement has $p^2 + p + 1$ treatments, each replicated $p + 1$ times, with $p + 1$ treatments per block. To each set of blocks obtained by the first arrangement is added one of the $p + 1$ new treatments. The last block of the design consists entirely of these additional treatments. For instance, we can derive a further balanced design from that of Table 10.2.1 by adding treatment 26 to each of the first five blocks, treatment 27 to each of the next five blocks, and so on, and finally adding the block of treatments 26–31.

This does not exhaust the possible balanced incomplete block designs, and other designs may be found. Such designs have been listed in *Statistical Tables*. Table 10.2.2 gives a list of designs, for any size of block, testing up to twelve treatments. Since it is always possible to form designs by taking all possible combinations of treatments these designs have been omitted from this table.

It should be noted that every set of balanced incomplete blocks gives rise to a second set, obtained by replacing each block by another containing the remaining treatments. For instance, from Table 10.2.2, the design for seven treatments in blocks of four would be *CDFG, ABFG,* . . ., *ABCD.*

Table 10.2.1 Balanced incomplete block design derived from the complete set of 5 × 5 orthogonal squares

Block	Treatment					Block	Treatment				
1	1	2	3	4	5	16	1	9	12	20	23
2	6	7	8	9	10	17	2	10	13	16	24
3	11	12	13	14	15	18	3	6	14	17	25
4	16	17	18	19	20	19	4	7	15	18	21
5	21	22	23	24	25	20	5	8	11	19	22
6	1	6	11	16	21	21	1	8	15	17	24
7	2	7	12	17	22	22	2	9	11	18	25
8	3	8	13	18	23	23	3	10	12	19	21
9	4	9	14	19	24	24	4	6	13	20	22
10	5	10	15	20	25	25	5	7	14	16	23
11	1	10	14	18	22	26	1	7	13	19	25
12	2	6	15	19	23	27	2	8	14	20	21
13	3	7	11	20	24	28	3	9	15	16	22
14	4	8	12	16	25	29	4	10	11	17	23
15	5	9	13	17	21	30	5	6	12	18	24

The analysis of an incomplete block design is complicated by the fact that blocks and treatments are no longer orthogonal to one another. Treatment comparisons may, in fact, be made both within and between blocks. First, we shall give the within-block or *intra-block* analysis, in which comparisons are made within blocks and adjusted for differences between block effects.

Suppose that T_i is the total yield of plots receiving the ith treatment, that B_i is the total yield of all blocks containing the ith treatment, and that $Q_i = kT_i - B_i$. The estimated total treatment yields, adjusted for block effects, are then given by

$$P_i = \frac{rQ_i}{v\lambda} + \frac{G}{v},$$

where G = overall total.

Table 10.2.2 List of balanced incomplete block designs

Number of treatments, v	Size of block, k	Blocks of treatments
6	3	ABC, ABD, ACE, ADF, AEF, BCF, BDE, BEF, CDE, CDF
7	3 or 4	ABE, CDE, ACF, BDF, ADG, BCG, EFG
8	4	ABCD, ABEF, ABGH, ACEG, ACFH, ADEH, ADFG, BCEH, BCFG, BDEG, BDFH, CDEF, CDGH, EFGH
9	3 or 6	ABC, ADG, AEI, AFH, BDI, BEH, BFG, CDH, CEG, CFI, DEF, GHI
	4 or 5	ABDE, ABFI, ABGH, ACDF, ACEH, ACGI, ADHI, AEFG, BCDG, BCEF, BCHI, BDFH, BEGI, CDEI, CFGH, DEGH, DFGI, EFHI
10	3 or 7	ABC, ABD, ACE, ADF, AEG, AFH, AGI, AHJ, AIJ, BCF, BDJ, BEH, BEI, BFG, BGI, BHJ, CDG, CDH, CEF, CGJ, CHI, CIJ, DEI, DEJ, DFI, DGH, EFJ, EGH, FGJ, FHI
	4 or 6	ABCD, ABFI, ACHJ, ADEG, AEHI, AFGJ, BCEG, BDHJ, BEFH, BGIJ, CDFI, CEIJ, CFGH, DEFJ, DGHI
	5	ABCDE, ABDEJ, ABFGH, ABGHI, ACDGI, ACEFG, ACFIJ, ADFHJ, AEHIJ, BCDHI, BCEFH, BCFIJ, BDFGJ, BEGIJ, CDGHJ, CEGHJ, DEFGI, DEFHI
11	5 or 6	ABCEH, ABDGK, ACFJK, ADHIJ, AEFGI, BCDFI, BEIJK, BFGHJ, CDEGJ, CGHIK, DEFHK

The adjusted sum of squares due to treatments is given by

$$\frac{1}{kv\lambda} \Sigma Q_i^2,$$

and the full intra-block analysis of variance table is given in Table 10.2.3. The residual mean square, s^2, provides an estimate of the within-block variance σ^2.

Table 10.2.3 Intra-block analysis of variance for a balanced incomplete block design

	d.f.	s.s.	m.s.
Treatments (adjusted)	$v - 1$	$\dfrac{\Sigma Q_i^2}{kv\lambda}$	
Blocks (unadjusted)	$b - 1$	s.s. B	
Residual	$rv - v - b + 1$	By subtraction	s^2
Total	$rv - 1$	s.s. y	

The standard error of the difference between two adjusted means is

$$s\sqrt{\left(\frac{2k}{\lambda v}\right)}.$$

Information contained on treatment comparisons in the block comparisons may also be considered. Whether it is actually worth incorporating with the intra-block information depends on the extent to which the grouping of the experimental units into blocks achieves a marked reduction in the error mean square. If this grouping is successful, that is, if the block effects are large, then the amount of information contributed by the between-block comparisons will be small. In order to use this *inter-block* information, we assume that the block effects are random components with between-block variance σ'^2. The combined intra- and inter-block estimates of the adjusted total treatment yields are given by

$$Y_i = T_i + \mu W_i,$$

where

$$W_i = (v - k)T_i - (v - 1)B_i + (k - 1)G$$
$$\mu = \frac{\omega - \omega'}{\omega v(k - 1) + \omega'(v - k)}$$
$$\omega = \text{reciprocal of within-block variance} = 1/\sigma^2$$
$$\omega' = \text{reciprocal of between-block variance} = 1/\sigma'^2.$$

The quantities ω and ω' which enter into Y_i are not known and have to be estimated from the observations themselves. In order to do this, the mean square for blocks, corrected for treatment differences, has to be calculated. The analysis of variance table required to obtain this value is as in Table 10.2.4.

Table 10.2.4 Inter-block analysis of variance for a balanced incomplete block design

	d.f.	s.s.	m.s.
Treatments (unadjusted)	$v-1$	s.s. T	
Blocks (adjusted)	$b-1$	By subtraction	s'^2
Residual	$rv-v-b+1$	From Table 10.2.3	s^2
Total	$rv-1$	s.s. y	

The appropriate weighting factors are now given by

$$\omega = \frac{1}{s^2}, \quad \omega' = \frac{v(r-1)}{k(b-1)s'^2 - (v-k)s^2}.$$

If $s'^2 < s^2$, then μ should be taken as zero.

The standard error of the difference between two adjusted treatment is then

$$\sqrt{\left[\frac{2k(v-1)}{r\{\omega v(k-1) + \omega'(v-k)\}}\right]}.$$

10.3 Example of a balanced incomplete block analysis

To provide an example of the analysis for balanced incomplete blocks, we shall use data reported by Welch, Putnam and Gamboa (1945). Table 10.3.1

Table 10.3.1 Results of a balanced incomplete block design

Group	a 936	b 502	c 175	d 333	e 1127	f 711	Total
1	1	5	4				10
2	5	10		6			21
3	2		9		3		14
4	4			8		6	18
5	2				4	7	13
6		6	7			5	18
7		5		7	2		14
8		7			2	4	13
9			8	4	2		14
10			10	8		7	25
Total	14	33	38	33	13	29	160

Potency of penicillin (units per mg)

gives the degrees of pain experienced by groups of three patients when injected with penicillin of different potency. Each result shown in this table represents a total from the three patients, the degree of pain experienced by each patient being measured on a five-point scale 0–4. The experiment was, in fact, planned to allow the comparison of different sites of injection to be made as well, but this section need not concern us here.

It will be seen that three potencies are used on each group and that the design is arranged in 10 blocks (see the first design in Table 10.2.2). Thus, $v = 6$, $b = 10$, $k = 3$, $\lambda = 2$, $r = 5$ in this instance.

We shall first consider intra-block comparisons only. The totals T_i, B_i and Q_i are given in Table 10.3.2.

Table 10.3.2   Intra-block totals in balanced incomplete blocks

| | Potency | | | | | | |
	a	b	c	d	e	f	Total
T_i	14	33	38	33	13	29	$160 = G$
B_i	76	76	81	92	68	87	$480 = 3G$
$Q_i = 3T_i - B_i$	−34	23	33	7	−29	0	0

The sum of squares due to treatments, adjusted for blocks, is given by

$$\frac{1}{kv\lambda} \Sigma Q_i^2 = 101\cdot78.$$

The unadjusted block sum of squares is

$$\text{s.s. } B = \tfrac{1}{3}\left[10^2 + 21^2 + \ldots + 25^2\right] - \frac{160^2}{30} = 60\cdot00,$$

and the total sum of squares is

$$\text{s.s. } y = 1^2 + 5^2 + \ldots + 7^2 - \frac{160^2}{30} = 182\cdot67.$$

The full intra-block analysis of variance is given in Table 10.3.3.

Table 10.3.3   Intra-block analysis of variance

	d.f.	s.s.	m.s.
Potencies (adj.)	5	101·78	20·356
Between groups (unadj.)	9	60·00	
Residual	15	20·89	1·393
Total	29	182·67	

The differences between potencies are tested by the variance ratio, $20·356/1·393 = 14·61$, which is significant at the 5 percent level. The adjusted treatment totals, P_i, and means are now given in Table 10.3.4.

Table 10.3.4   Intra-block treatment totals and means

| | Potency of penicillin (units per mg) | | | | | |
| | 175 | 333 | 502 | 711 | 936 | 1127 |
	c	d	b	f	a	e
Total: P_i	40·42	29·58	36·25	26·67	12·50	14·58
Mean	8·08	5·92	7·25	5·33	2·50	2·92

The standard error of the difference between two of these adjusted means is then

$$\sqrt{\left(\frac{6 \times 1·393}{12}\right)} = \pm\, 0·834.$$

To recover the information on the comparisons between blocks or groups of patients, we first calculate the adjusted sum of squares due to blocks. This is given in Table 10.3.5, where the unadjusted treatment sum of squares is given by

$$\text{s.s. } T = \tfrac{1}{5}\left[14^2 + 33^2 + \ldots + 29^2\right] - \frac{160^2}{30} = 112·27,$$

and the residual and total sum of squares are the same as in Table 10.3.3. The block sum of squares is then obtained by subtraction.

Table 10.3.5   Inter-block analysis of variance

	d.f.	s.s.	m.s.
Potencies (unadj.)	5	112·27	
Between groups (adj.)	9	49·51	5.501
Residual	15	20·89	1·393
Total	29	182·67	

The differences between groups are tested by the variance ratio, $5·501/1·393 = 3·95$, which is significant at the 5 percent level. Since the block effects are large, little will be gained by recovering inter-block information. However, for illustrative purposes, this analysis will be completed. The weighting factors are now given by

$$\omega = \frac{1}{1 \cdot 393} = 0 \cdot 718,$$

$$\omega' = \frac{24}{27 \times 5 \cdot 501 - 3 \times 1 \cdot 393} = 0 \cdot 166,$$

and

$$\mu = \frac{0 \cdot 718 - 0 \cdot 166}{12 \times 0 \cdot 718 + 3 \times 0 \cdot 166} = \frac{0 \cdot 552}{9 \cdot 114} = 0 \cdot 0606.$$

The totals $W_i = 3T_i - 5B_i + 2G$, adjusted treatment totals, $T_i + \mu W_i$, and means are now given in Table 10.3.6.

Table 10.3.6 Combined treatment totals and means

| | Potency of penicillin (units per mg) | | | | | |
| | 175 | 333 | 502 | 711 | 936 | 1127 |
	c	d	b	f	a	e
W_i	29	−41	39	−28	−18	19
$T_i + \mu W_i$	39·76	30·52	35·36	27·30	12·91	14·15
Mean	7·95	6·10	7·07	5·46	2·58	2·83

The standard error of the difference between two of these adjusted means is

$$\sqrt{\left(\frac{30}{5 \times 9 \cdot 114}\right)} = \pm 0 \cdot 811.$$

The gain in information from the recovery of inter-block information is $(0 \cdot 834/0 \cdot 811)^2 = 1 \cdot 06$, or 5·75 percent, excluding losses due to inaccurate weighting. As indicated earlier, it is evident, in this instance, that little is gained in utilizing the information on treatment comparisons contained in the comparison of groups of patients.

10.4 Youden squares

In a balanced incomplete block design, when the number of treatments is equal to the number of blocks, the design may be so arranged that each treatment occurs once in each position within the block. Consequently, the position effect will be orthogonal to both the block and treatment effects. For example, according to Table 10.2.2, eleven treatments may be tested in eleven blocks of five treatments. These blocks can be arranged as in Table 10.4.1.

Each treatment in this design occurs in each position in the blocks. Designs of this type are called *Youden squares*.

The analysis of Youden squares proceeds in the same manner as that of balanced incomplete blocks, except that an additional component eliminating

Table 10.4.1 Youden square for 11 treatments

Position in block	Block										
	1	2	3	4	5	6	7	8	9	10	11
1	A	K	J	D	I	B	E	G	C	H	F
2	B	A	C	I	F	D	J	H	E	G	K
3	C	B	A	H	E	F	I	J	G	K	D
4	E	D	F	A	G	C	K	B	J	I	H
5	H	G	K	J	A	I	B	F	D	C	E

differences between positions is removed in the analysis. The formulae of **10.2** may therefore be applied as before, except that the number of degrees of freedom for the residual mean square will be reduced.

10.5 Resolvable designs

The balanced incomplete block design given in Table 10.2.1 has been constructed in such a way that the 30 blocks can be divided into six sets of five blocks each such that every treatment is replicated once in each set. The sets, or replicates, are given by blocks 1–5, 6–10, and so on. Designs of this type are called *resolvable*. It is often advantageous to be able to perform an experiment a replicate at a time. If the experiment has to be discontinued at any time then all treatments will have occurred equally often. Accuracy will also be increased if the experimental material can be arranged so that replicates are relatively homogeneous. For instance, in agricultural experiments, the land may be divided into a number of large areas corresponding to the replication sets, and then each area further subdivided into blocks.

The intra-block analysis of resolvable balanced incomplete block designs is similar to that given in **10.2**. Now the unadjusted block sum of squares can be subdivided into two components, namely the sum of squares between replicates with $r - 1$ degrees of freedom and the sum of squares between blocks within replicates with $b - r$ degrees of freedom. For the recovery of inter-block information, the equations given in **10.2** still hold, except that the estimate of ω' is changed. It is now based on the adjusted mean square between blocks within replicates, namely s''^2, where

$$(b - r)s''^2 = (b - 1)s'^2 - \text{s.s. } R,$$

and where s.s. R is the unadjusted sum of squares between replicates. The mean square s'^2 is obtained from Table 10.2.4. We then get

$$\omega' = \frac{rv - v - k(r - 1)}{k(b - r)s''^2 - (v - k)s^2}.$$

One class of resolvable balanced incomplete blocks are those constructed from complete sets of orthogonal Latin squares with $v = p^2$ treatments and $k = p$

treatments per block. They are called *balanced lattices*. For these designs, the weighting factor ω' simplifies to

$$\omega' = \frac{k}{rs''^2 - s^2}.$$

In Table 10.2.2, in addition to the balanced lattice for $v = 9$ and $k = 3$, the design with $v = 8$ and $k = 4$ is also resolvable.

Balanced lattices may be used to derive another type of design: *lattice squares*. The treatments may be arranged in a set of squares so that each square forms a complete replication and the rows and columns of the squares correspond to the blocks of a balanced incomplete block design. For p^2 treatments it is necessary to have $p + 1$ squares if p is even, but if p is odd, $\frac{1}{2}(p + 1)$ squares may be used. The latter type of design is particularly useful.

Lattice squares may be easily formed using the corresponding balanced lattice design. Thus, using Table 10.2.1, we may construct the set of 5×5 lattice squares shown in Table 10.5.1. The rows of these squares correspond to the first,

Table 10.5.1 Set of 5×5 lattice squares

1	2	3	4	5		1	10	14	18	22		1	8	15	17	24
6	7	8	9	10		23	2	6	15	19		25	2	9	11	18
11	12	13	14	15		20	24	3	7	11		19	21	3	10	12
16	17	18	19	20		12	16	25	4	8		13	20	22	4	6
21	22	23	24	25		9	13	17	21	5		7	14	16	23	5

third and fifth replications of Table 10.2.1, and the columns to the second, fourth and sixth replications. The design should be randomized before use by arranging the squares in random order, randomizing the rows and columns of each square, and assigning the numbers 1–25 to the treatments at random.

In the analysis of a set of lattice squares, it may be necessary to recover the information contained in the between-row and between-column comparisons. Thus, a set of three weighting factors has to be used. Apart from this, the methods are basically those used for balanced incomplete blocks. A full account of this analysis is given in, for example, the book by Kempthorne (1952).

10.6 Other incomplete block designs

The important feature of a balanced incomplete block design is that all treatment differences are estimated with the same accuracy. However, as was indicated in **10.2**, these balanced designs only exist for certain values of v, k and r, and other designs will be required when balanced designs of the required size are not available. Such designs will give rise to comparisons of differing accuracy. Another situation where designs of this type might be employed, even when balanced designs exist, arises when certain treatment comparisons are of particular interest and need to be estimated as accurately as possible. The choice, therefore, of an *unbalanced* design depends upon the purpose of the experiment. If an alternative to a balanced design is required, it would be best to choose a design, if one exists, where all differences are estimated with approximately the same accuracy. If, on the other hand, certain comparisons are of particular interest, a design which estimates these comparisons as accurately as possible and which, consequently, sacrifices information on other less important comparisons would be best.

There are two classes of unbalanced designs that are of considerable practical importance. First, there are the *partially balanced incomplete designs with two associate classes* (PBIB/2). One feature of these designs is that treatment differences are estimated with one of two degrees of accuracy. A second feature is that pairs of treatments occur together in either λ_1 or λ_2 blocks ($\lambda_1 \neq \lambda_2$). It should be noted that, whereas the first feature implies the second, a design with the second feature does not necessarily possess the first. PBIB/2 designs, in fact, belong to a much wider class of designs, first given by Bose and Nair in 1939. A considerable amount of work has been done since then in classifying and constructing them. An account of this work can be found in, for example, the books by P. W. M. John (1971) and Raghavarao (1971).

A catalogue of PBIB/2 designs has been compiled by Clatworthy (1973), in which more than 800 designs are listed. Full details of the intra-block analysis, and the recovery of inter-block information, are also given. In using these tables, particular attention should be given to the two different accuracies, or efficiencies, for estimating treatment differences, that are given with each design. Choice can then be based on these efficiencies and on the practical needs of the experiment. Some of these designs can also be used to eliminate position effects, as in the Youden squares of **10.4**. Other designs are resolvable, as in **10.5**. Designs possessing these additional properties are clearly indicated in the catalogue.

Although PBIB/2 designs add considerably to the choice of an incomplete block design, a design of a suitable size or with the required experimental properties may still not be available. A further class of designs are *cyclic designs*, consisting of sets of blocks obtained by cyclic development of one or more initial blocks. An important aspect of this class is its flexibility, which adds considerably to the experimenter's choice of designs. A catalogue of 460 designs has been compiled by John, Wolock and David (1972), together with details of analysis. These designs have been constructed so as to enable all treatment differences to be estimated as accurately as possible. The emphasis is on the range of efficiencies and not on the number of different efficiencies. However, because of the simple method of construction, it should not be difficult to construct cyclic designs satisfying different experimental criteria. An interesting recent example on the use of cyclic designs in seed orchard experiments was reported by Freeman (1967). Cyclic designs, in fact, belong to the wider class of PBIB designs given by Bose and Nair, and some have two associate classes.

In view of the method of construction, cyclic designs, with the number of treatments a multiple of the number of blocks, provide automatic elimination of heterogeneity in two directions, that is, are Youden-square type designs. Further, if v/k is an integer, David (1967) has shown that it is possible to construct designs that are resolvable.

One experimental situation which is of some interest occurs when the block size is restricted to two; for instance, when identical twins or when two halves of a leaf are used as a block. A difficulty arises in the construction of these *paired comparison* designs in that the balanced incomplete block designs correspond to all possible sets of the v treatments, taken two at a time. This necessitates the use of $v - 1$ replications if balance is to be achieved, and, in practice, this may be too many. It is therefore desirable to consider what other designs, involving fewer replications, might be used. Such designs must necessarily be unbalanced, but near-balance may be achieved by a suitable choice of design.

Table 10.6.1 gives two possible designs for twelve treatments in 36 and 48 blocks, respectively. In this instance, 66 blocks would be needed for full

Table 10.6.1 Designs in blocks of two

		Aa	Ba	Ca	Da	Ea	Fa				
		Ab	Bb	Cb	Db	Eb	Fb				
		Ac	Bc	Cc	Dc	Ec	Fc				
		Ad	Bd	Cd	Dd	Ed	Fd				
		Ae	Be	Ce	De	Ee	Fe				
		Af	Bf	Cf	Df	Ef	Ff				

Aa	Ba	Ca	Da	Aα	Bα	Cα	Dα	aα	bα	cα	dα
Ab	Bb	Cb	Db	Aβ	Bβ	Cβ	Dβ	aβ	bβ	cβ	dβ
Ac	Bc	Cc	Dc	Aγ	Bγ	Cγ	Dγ	aγ	bγ	cγ	dγ
Ad	Bd	Cd	Dd	Aδ	Bδ	Cδ	Dδ	aδ	bδ	cδ	dδ

balance. In the first design, the treatments are divided into two groups, and each member of one group occurs with each member of the other. In the second design, three groups are used, and each member of one group occurs with each member of the other two groups. Similar designs may, of course, be constructed using more than three groups, but then the number of blocks rapidly approaches that required for full balance.

In designs of this type, comparisons between treatments not occurring in the same block are less accurate than those between treatments occurring in the same block. However, their relative accuracy is in no case less than $1 - 1/v$ (which occurs when between-block variation is large). All comparisons are thus of comparable accuracy.

This type of design requires at least $\frac{1}{2}v$ replications and falls into the class of PBIB/2 designs with $k = 2$. Other PBIB/2 designs, some involving fewer replicates, can be constructed and have been extensively tabulated by Clatworthy (1955, 1973). Examples of PBIB designs for paired comparisons with more than two associate classes can be found in John (1967). Another important class of designs are the cyclic paired comparison designs, which were first studied in detail by David (1963, 1965). In the catalogue by John, Wolock and David (1972), 136 of these designs are listed for $6 \leqslant v \leqslant 30$ and $r \leqslant 10$.

11 Long-term Experiments

11.1 Problems of long-term policy

So far, we have been concerned with the problems of designing and analysing experiments to estimate treatment effects at a selected place at a particular time. These problems form, however, only part of those concerning the experimenter, and the solution of them still leaves certain important questions to be answered.

First, the experimenter may wish to know what effects his treatments may have over a long period of time, and how they may be most profitably applied during that time. For instance, initial experimentation may show that vaccination increases resistance to a virus and that the convalescent period of patients freshly vaccinated is so many days less than that of unvaccinated patients. It may then be asked how rapidly the effect of vaccination wears off, and how often it is worth while repeating it. Or, to provide an alternative illustration, an experiment may be conducted to estimate the cumulative effects of an insecticide and to determine whether initial treatments serve to make insects more, or less, susceptible over a period of time.

Secondly, the experimenter may want to vary the conditions under which the experiment is carried out, so that instead of one experiment under fixed conditions a series of experiments under different conditions will be planned and carried out. The resulting answers will show the general reliability and reproducibility of the estimated treatment effects.

Lastly, the experimenter may wish to correlate his results with those previously obtained, and possibly to summarize all the available experimental material. For this purpose he will have to use an analysis to combine the results from a number of different sources of varying accuracy and to test whether these results are compatible with one another.

All these problems are thus part of the experience of any research worker, and it is not irrelevant to deal with them here. In the next three chapters we shall consider different aspects of these problems, and in particular this chapter will deal with experiments involving several periods of observation—long-term experiments.

11.2 Short-term designs involving time as a factor

When it is desired to carry an experiment through several periods, it is sometimes possible to treat time as a factor in the design of a short-term experiment, and consequently to estimate or eliminate the effects of taking observations at different times in the final analysis. Thus, for instance, the blocks of observations in a randomized block experiment may be taken at different times, and in this way differences due to a general trend in time can be eliminated. Alternatively, one of the factors in a factorial experiment may be taken as time, and the variation in treatment effects at different times estimated from their interaction with time.

An illustration of a short-term experiment involving time as a factor is presented by the example of **2.9–2.11**, in which the same rabbits were used on four different dates. In this example there were found to be significant differences in the falls in blood-sugar on different dates, and these were removed from the comparisons between doses by the design adopted. (As shown in the analysis of these sections, these differences could in fact be ascribed in large part to daily variation in blood-sugar.) Much more involved and complex illustrations of the use of time as a factor may be found in the literature.

It must, however, be noted that the use of time as a factor in this manner is based upon two important assumptions that will often not be justified in long-term experiments. These are—

(1) that the results in any one period of the experiment do not affect those in later periods of the experiment, and
(2) that the conditions in the experiment do not change from one period to the next.

Where (1) is not true, it is important to adjust the main comparisons for any effects that may have been carried over from one period to the next. Usually also, it is one of the more important functions of most long-term experiments to obtain accurate estimates of such "carry-over" effects, and possibly to compare them with one another. For instance, consider a field trial in which fertilizers are applied over a period of several years. In any one year, it will be important to eliminate any fertility differences arising as a result of treatments in previous years, but it will also be important to estimate these carry-over or residual effects if the full consequences of applying fertilizers are to be known.

Where (2) is not true, it is often though not always necessary to arrange that estimates of effects and carry-over effects should be obtained in each period of the experiment separately, and possibly combined afterwards. Otherwise, if the variability of treatment effects alters from period to period, the results may be misleading and the analysis invalid. Thus, if there are large variations in crop yield from year to year, the treatment and residual effects should first be considered for each year in turn, especially in relation to the mean yield and the variability in each year; combination and full analysis of the results may subsequently be attempted.

In what follows, experiments that are designed to give estimates of direct and residual effects in each period, and consequently a series of different estimates, will be referred to as *serial experiments*. Those for which assumption (2) above is true, and which consequently give one single overall set of estimates based on observations taken in all periods, will be termed *long-term experiments with stable conditions*.

11.3 Adjustment for residual or carry-over effects

Residual effects of a treatment may occur in any period of the experiment after application of the treatment. Thus, for instance, in an agricultural experiment, the effect of a dressing of lime may be felt in diminishing degrees for many years after it is first applied. To help distinguish between residual effects, those occurring after one period of experiment are called "first residuals", after two periods "second residuals", and so on.

Usually, in most fields of experimentation, the first residuals, if any, will be the largest, and the second and subsequent residuals will be successively smaller and are often assumed to be negligible. Sometimes, however, the second and subsequent residuals may need to be estimated, and in some instances it may be assumed that any residual that exists in one period of an experiment is permanent in all subsequent periods.

Where an experiment of the type described in the last section is carried out, it is assumed that residual effects are non-existent. If they do exist, the direct effects will be biased, and the analysis will be invalid. It is therefore useful to be able to carry out an analysis to test and, if necessary, to adjust for the existence of residual effects. In the first instance, it is usually simpler to do this when it is assumed that the residual effects do not persist for more than one period after application. If these first residuals exist, then an extended examination to test and, if necessary, to adjust for the second residuals may be carried out. An example will demonstrate the form of analysis.

We might test whether, in the example of **2.9**, the previous doses of insulin affect the subsequent falls in blood-sugar (in the first instance ignoring the covariance on initial blood-sugar). The allowance for residual effects can be made by introducing additional constants for residual effects into the analysis. Thus if t_1, t_2, t_3 and t_4 represent the direct effect of the four dosages and r_1, r_2, r_3 and r_4 the residual effects, then the total effects of the dosages of, for example, the first rabbit are given by t_3 in the first period, $t_2 + r_3$ in the second period, $t_1 + r_2$ in the third period, and $t_4 + r_1$ in the fourth period.

One way of estimating the residual effects is to introduce four dummy variables d_1, d_2, d_3 and d_4. The first, d_1, takes the value 1 when it follows dose A, and zero

Table 11.3.1 Values of dummy variable d_1

Period	Rabbit								Total
	1	2	3	4	5	6	7	8	
1	0	0	0	0	0	0	0	0	0
2	0	1	0	0	0	1	0	0	2
3	0	0	0	1	0	0	0	1	2
4	1	0	0	0	1	0	0	0	2
Total	1	1	0	1	1	1	0	1	6

otherwise. The values of this variable are shown in Table 11.3.1. Similarly, the dummy variables d_2, d_3 and d_4 take a value 1 when they follow doses B, C and D respectively, and zero otherwise. If a permanent residual effect were being tested, the dummy variable would take the value 1 in all periods after any dose had been applied.

An analysis of covariance on the four dummy variables would then provide estimates of the residual effects and allow the treatment means to be adjusted. The regression equations for the estimation of the residual effects are

$$3\cdot0r_1 - 0\cdot25r_2 - 2\cdot5r_3 - 0\cdot25r_4 = \quad 2\cdot86$$

$$-0\cdot25r_1 + 3\cdot0r_2 - 0\cdot25r_3 - 2\cdot5r_4 = -5\cdot83$$

$$-2\cdot5r_1 - 0\cdot25r_2 + 3\cdot0r_3 - 0\cdot25r_4 = \quad 7\cdot66$$

$$-0\cdot25r_1 - 2\cdot5r_2 - 0\cdot25r_3 + 3\cdot0r_4 = -4\cdot70.$$

These equations do not, however, suffice to determine r_1, r_2, r_3 and r_4, since the mean residual effect is confounded between periods of the experiment; some arbitrary chosen restriction is necessary to make these constants determinate. It is most convenient to choose $r_1 + r_2 + r_3 + r_4 = 0$, in which case

$$r_1 = 4\cdot82, \quad r_2 = -5\cdot36, \quad r_3 = 5\cdot70, \quad r_4 = -5\cdot16,$$

and the sum of squares due to the residual effects is

$$(4\cdot82)(2\cdot86) + (-5\cdot36)(-5\cdot83) + (5\cdot70)(7\cdot66) + (-5\cdot16)(-4\cdot70)$$
$$= 112\cdot948,$$

with three degrees of freedom, since the mean has to be chosen to be zero.

The residual mean square in this analysis is $27\cdot7$, based on 15 degrees of freedom. It is clear that the differences between the residual effects are insignificant. If, however, these had been significant, it would have been necessary to adjust the direct effects accordingly. For instance, the mean fall for dose A would have been

$$16\cdot0 - 3(-5\cdot36)/8 - 3(-5\cdot16)/8 = 19\cdot945.$$

(The sum of squares due to treatments in the analysis of variance might also have been altered if an exact test of significance had been required.)

If, in this instance, it had been desired to carry out an analysis of covariance on initial blood-sugar at the same time, the five variables d_1, d_2, d_3, d_4 and i would have been used, giving a sum of squares 129, with four degrees of freedom. This is 85 more than the sum of squares 44, obtained by using blood-sugar alone, compared with a residual mean square of about 28, so that the residual effects again fail to reach significance.

11.4 Some designs for long-term experiments with stable conditions

Designs that permit the estimation of residuals as well as direct effects are known as *change-over designs*. The simplest type of change-over design is a Latin square, or set of squares, with rows representing periods of time and columns representing the replicates. The design in the last section was a change-over design with four treatments, four periods, and two Latin squares with four replicates per square. Generally, such designs will have t treatments, $p = t$ periods, and m Latin squares with $k = t$ replicates per square. An alternative design to the one used in the last section is given in Table 11.4.1. Again each treatment occurs twice in each period and once in each replicate. However, this

Table 11.4.1   Design for the estimation of first residuals

Period	Replicate							
	1	2	3	4	5	6	7	8
1	A	B	C	D	A	B	C	D
2	B	C	D	A	B	C	D	A
3	D	A	B	C	D	A	B	C
4	C	D	A	B	C	D	A	B

design is now balanced for first residuals, in that each treatment follows every other treatment twice during the whole experiment. A balanced change-over design thus means that comparisons among direct effects and among residual effects are made with the same precision. This allows the analysis of the last section to be considerably simplified and at the same time provides more precise estimates of the direct and residual treatment effects. For the design of Table 11.4.1, the variance of the difference between any two residual effects is $2\sigma^2/5$. The average variance of the difference between residual effects for the design in the previous section is $10\sigma^2/11$, with some differences considerably less accurately determined than others.

Cochran, Autrey and Cannon (1941) showed that complete sets of orthogonal Latin squares gave balanced change-over designs, with $m = t - 1$. Williams (1949) showed that, for an even number of treatments, balanced designs can be obtained using one Latin square. He further showed that squares of this type may be generated by permuting the letters occurring in the first column in order. Thus by replacing A by B, B by C, C by D and D by A in the first Latin square in Table 11.4.1 we get the second column from the first, the third from the second, and so on. All we need to know in constructing such designs is the first column; the remaining $t - 1$ columns may be filled in by cyclical permutation. The first columns of similar designs for six and eight treatments are given in Table 11.4.2.

For an odd number of treatments, Williams showed that at least two Latin squares are needed if balance is to be obtained. For instance, Table 11.4.3 gives a design for testing five treatments. The method of generating each square is exactly the same as described above. Table 11.4.4 gives pairs of first columns of designs of this type, testing three, five and seven treatments.

Table 11.4.2 Balanced designs for six and eight treatments

Six		Eight	
A	A	A	A
B	C	B	B
F	B	D	H
C	E	G	C
E	F	C	G
D	D	H	D
		F	F
		E	E

Table 11.4.3 Balanced design for five treatments

Period	Replicate									
	1	2	3	4	5	6	7	8	9	10
1	A	B	C	D	E	A	B	C	D	E
2	B	C	D	E	A	E	A	B	C	D
3	E	A	B	C	D	B	C	D	E	A
4	C	D	E	A	B	D	E	A	B	C
5	D	E	A	B	C	C	D	E	A	B

Table 11.4.4 Balanced designs for three, five and seven treatments

Three		Five				Seven							
A	A	A	A	A	A	A	A	A	A	A	A	A	A
B	C	B	C	B	E	B	G	B	F	B	G	B	G
C	B	D	B	E	B	E	D	E	C	G	B	D	E
		E	E	C	D	C	F	D	E	C	F	G	B
		C	D	D	C	G	B	C	G	F	C	C	F
						F	C	F	D	D	E	E	D
						D	E	G	B	E	D	F	C

These balanced Latin square designs have $p = t = k$. It is also possible to construct balanced designs for which p is less than t. Any number of rows can be omitted from a complete set of orthogonal Latin squares to give another balanced design. Table 11.4.5 gives an example of a design for four treatments in three periods, which has been constructed by eliminating the last row from

8—EDA * *

Table 11.4.5 Balanced design for four treatments in three periods

Period	Site											
	1	2	3	4	5	6	7	8	9	10	11	12
1	A	B	C	D	A	B	C	D	A	B	C	D
2	B	A	D	C	C	D	A	B	D	C	B	A
3	C	D	A	B	D	C	B	A	B	A	D	C

the complete set of orthogonal 4 × 4 Latin squares. We see that each treatment follows every other treatment twice in the design.

For some values of t, balance can also be obtained with fewer than $t - 1$ incomplete squares. Table 11.4.6 gives an example of such a design for seven treatments in four periods using two incomplete squares.

Table 11.4.6 Balanced design for seven treatments in four periods using two incomplete squares

Period	Site													
	1	2	3	4	5	6	7	8	9	10	11	12	13	14
1	A	B	C	D	E	F	G	A	B	C	D	E	F	G
2	B	C	D	E	F	G	A	G	A	B	C	D	E	F
3	D	E	F	G	A	B	C	E	F	G	A	B	C	D
4	G	A	B	C	D	E	F	B	C	D	E	F	G	A

Balanced designs are also available for k less than t both in complete and incomplete squares. These designs are based on the balanced incomplete block designs of **10.2**. Although orthogonality is now lost between treatments and periods, the designs are still balanced in that comparisons among the treatment effects and among the residual effects are made with the same precision. A catalogue of balanced designs has been given by Patterson and Lucas (1962).

Other change-over designs with k less than t have been based on the partially balanced designs of **10.6**. The analysis is slightly more complicated than that of the balanced designs, and some comparisons are made less precisely than others. A listing of such designs is given in Patterson and Lucas (1962) together with details of the analysis. Designs based on the cyclic incomplete block designs of **10.6** have been given by Davis and Hall (1969).

It should be noted that the designs given above allow for the estimation of the first residuals only. Other designs may, however, be constructed, and Williams (1950) gives designs for estimating the effects of the preceding two treatments and any possible interaction between them. Table 11.4.7 gives an example of such a design testing four treatments. In this design, every treatment follows every other treatment three times and every other pair of treatments

Table 11.4.7 Balanced design for estimation of first and second residuals and their interaction

Period	Replicate											
	1	2	3	4	5	6	7	8	9	10	11	12
1	A	B	C	D	A	B	C	D	A	B	C	D
2	B	A	D	C	C	D	A	B	D	C	B	A
3	C	D	A	B	D	C	B	A	B	A	D	C
4	D	C	B	A	B	A	D	C	C	D	A	B

once. This balanced arrangement thus facilitates the estimation of the residual effects.

11.5 Examples of the estimation of first residual effects in stable experiments

Where the balanced designs of the last section are used, the analytical procedure given in **11.3** simplifies greatly. For the designs with $p = t = k$ it may be shown that the first residual effects are given by—

$$mt(t^2 - t - 2)r_i = t^2 R_i + tT_i + tP_1 + tC_i - (t + 2)G,$$

where

R_i = total of observations preceded by the ith treatment,
T_i = total of observations of the ith treatment,
P_1 = total of first period,
C_i = total of columns or replications for which the ith treatment is the last,
G = overall total,
m = number of Latin squares in design,
t = number of treatments.

The corresponding sum of squares due to residual effects in the analysis of variance is $\Sigma\{mt(t^2 - t - 2)r_i\}^2/mt^3(t^2 - t - 2)$, and the standard error of the difference between two residual effects is

$$\sqrt{\left(\frac{2ts^2}{m(t^2 - t - 2)}\right)}.$$

The adjusted values of the treatment means are given by

$$\frac{T_i + mr_i}{mt}$$

and the sum of squares ascribable to direct effects after adjustment for residual effects is

$$\frac{t^2 - t - 2}{t^2 - t - 1}\left[\frac{\Sigma(T_i + mr_i)^2}{mt} - \frac{G^2}{mt^2}\right].$$

The standard error of the difference between two treatment means is correspondingly

$$\sqrt{\left[\frac{2s^2}{mt} \cdot \frac{t^2 - t - 1}{t^2 - t - 2}\right]}.$$

As an illustration of the analysis, consider the experiment given by Williams. This is shown in Table 11.5.1.

Table 11.5.1 Results of long-term balanced design

Period	Replication						Total
	1	2	3	4	5	6	
1	C 56·7	E 58·5	A 55·7	B 57·3	F 53·7	D 58·1	340·0
2	F 53·8	C 60·2	D 60·7	A 57·7	E 57·1	B 55·7	345·2
3	B 54·4	D 61·3	E 56·7	F 55·2	A 59·2	C 58·9	345·7
4	E 54·4	F 54·4	B 59·9	D 58·1	C 58·9	A 56·6	342·3
5	D 58·9	A 59·1	F 56·6	C 60·2	B 58·9	E 59·6	353·3
6	A 54·5	B 59·8	C 59·6	E 60·2	D 59·6	F 57·5	351·2
Total	332·7	353·3	349·2	348·7	347·4	346·4	2077·7

The experiment here gave the burst-factor results obtained by beating six concentrations, A–F, of pulp suspensions with six mills, i.e. replications 1–6. Certain concentrations were believed to affect the mill during the subsequent beating, so that this balanced design was adopted to allow the residual effects to be evaluated.

The first step in the analysis is to form the totals T_i, R_i, C_i, and hence $mt(t_2 - t - 2)r_i, r_i, T_i + mr_i$ and the treatment means. This is done in Table 11.5.2 using $m = 1, t = 6$.

Table 11.5.2 Analysis of burst factor experiment

Treatment	T_i	R_i	C_i	$168r_i$	Residual effect, r_i	$T_i + r_i$	Adjusted mean
A	342·8	294·2	332·7	62·6	0·37	343·17	57·20
B	346·0	287·2	353·3	—46·6	—0·28	345·72	57·62
C	354·5	290·8	349·2	109·4	0·65	355·15	59·19
D	356·7	281·5	347·4	—223·0	—1·33	355·37	59·23
E	346·5	295·7	348·7	234·8	1·40	347·90	57·98
F	331·2	288·3	346·4	—137·2	—0·82	330·38	55·06
Total	2077·7	1737·7	2077·7	0·0	—0·01	2077·69	
	P_1 = 340·0						
	Total	2077·7					

The analysis of variance may be carried out in the usual way, the treatment sum of squares being calculated from T_i as usual, the sum of squares due to residual effects being—

$$\frac{(62{\cdot}6)^2 + (-46{\cdot}6)^2 + (109{\cdot}4)^2 + (-223{\cdot}0)^2 + (234{\cdot}8)^2 + (-137{\cdot}2)^2}{6048}$$

$$= 23{\cdot}44.$$

This gives the analysis of variance shown in Table 11.5.3.

Table 11.5.3 Analysis of variance

	d.f.	s.s.	m.s.
Replications	5	41·56	
Period	5	21·71	
Direct effects	5	69·30	13·86
Residual effects	5	23·44	4·69
Unaccountable	15	9·05	0·603
Total	35	165·06	

The residual effects evidently account for a significant ($P < 0{\cdot}01$) portion of the total variation, while the differences between treatment totals appear highly significant. To test whether they are still significant when the residual effects have been taken into account, the sum of squares of $T_i + r_i$ has to be calculated and used in the above formulae. Since $T_i + r_i$ differs very little from T_i, the changes in the sum of squares and in the significance of direct effects are negligible, and the exact test is hardly worth while in this instance. (Actually, the sum of squares, 69·30, changes to 68·66.)

The analysis may be completed by calculating standard errors of differences. These are—

standard error of difference between adjusted means

$$= \sqrt{\left(\frac{1{\cdot}206}{6} \times \frac{29}{28}\right)} = \pm\ 0{\cdot}46;$$

standard error of difference between residual effects

$$= \sqrt{\left(1{\cdot}206 \times \frac{6}{28}\right)} = \pm\ 0{\cdot}51.$$

These may be used to examine the direct and residual effects more closely.

11.6 Complete balance for first residual effects

The characteristics of the designs in the last two sections are that differences between replicates and between periods can be excluded from treatment comparisons, and that the first residuals can be estimated without great difficulty.

However, since within any one replicate it is impossible for any treatment to follow itself, the direct and residual effects of these designs are confounded with each other. This results in a loss of information on treatment comparisons and a more complex analysis of the direct effects. The analysis of these effects is considerably simplified if the design is completely balanced for first residual effects in the sense that the treatments follow one another equally often.

Lucas (1957) suggested that the treatments in the last period of a basic change-over design should be repeated in an extra period. These designs are called "extra-period balanced designs", and a design for three treatments is given in Table 11.6.1.

Table 11.6.1   Extra-period change-over design for three treatments

Period	Site					
	1	2	3	4	5	6
1	A	B	C	A	B	C
2	B	C	A	C	A	B
3	C	A	B	B	C	A
4	C	A	B	B	C	A

A feature of this design is that each treatment follows every other treatment twice. Direct and residual effects are therefore orthogonal to each other, resulting in a simplified analysis and in an increase in precision for treatment and residual effects. A listing of such designs, together with details of their analysis, is given in Patterson and Lucas (1959).

For the extra-period designs, however, the treatments do not occur the same number of times in each site, so that treatments and sites are confounded. Table 11.6.2 gives a design for testing two treatments in which the direct and residual

Table 11.6.2   Completely balanced design for two treatments

Period	Site			
	1	2	3	4
1	A	B	B	A
2	A	A	B	B
3	B	A	A	B
4	B	B	A	A

effects are again orthogonal to each other, and further that each treatment occurs twice in each site and twice in each period. This design therefore permits the direct effects to be estimated in exactly the same way as if there were no residual effects. Moreover the elimination of confounding reduces the variances of treatment comparisons to a minimum.

It may be seen that this design is obtained by taking all possible cyclical arrangements of the treatments A, A, B, B. Designs for three or more treatments can be constructed by taking all possible cyclical arrangements of two or more series of treatments. Some possible designs of this type are shown in Table 11.6.3.

Table 11.6.3 Balanced designs for three and four treatments

Number of treatments	Use all cyclical arrangements of								
3	(1)					(2)			
	A	A	A			A	B	C	
	A	A	B			A	B	C	
	B	C	C			B	C	A	
	B	C	B			C	A	B	
	C	B	A			C	A	B	
	C	B	C			B	C	A	
4	(1)		(2)		(3)				
	A	A	A	A	A	C			
	A	C	A	C	A	C			
	B	B	B	C	B	A			
	B	A	B	B	C	D			
	C	D	C	D	D	B			
	C	B	D	A	D	B			
	D	D	D	D	C	D			
	D	C	C	B	B	A			

For three and four treatments, 18 and 16 sites respectively are necessary. Berenblut (1964) presents a class of completely balanced designs for t treatments requiring $2t$ periods and t^2 sites. The design for three treatments is given in Table 11.6.4. The analysis of such designs has been given in Berenblut (1967).

Table 11.6.4 Completely balanced design for three treatments

Period	Site								
	1	2	3	4	5	6	7	8	9
1	A	B	C	A	B	C	A	B	C
2	C	A	B	B	C	A	A	B	C
3	B	C	A	B	C	A	B	C	A
4	B	C	A	A	B	C	C	A	B
5	C	A	B	C	A	B	C	A	B
6	A	B	C	C	A	B	B	C	A

To obtain completely balanced designs for both first and second residuals, it is necessary to carry each treatment at least three times in each site. If both the first and second residuals and their interaction are to be estimated independently, the number of replications needed is very large (more than 81) for more than two treatments. For two treatments, the design shown in Table 11.6.5 may be used.

Table 11.6.5   Balanced design for estimating first and second residuals and their interaction

Period	Site			
	1	2	3	4
1	A	B	A	B
2	A	B	A	B
3	A	B	B	A
4	B	A	A	B
5	B	A	B	A
6	B	A	B	A

11.7   Some designs for serial experiments

The simplest type of serial experiment is that in which treatments are applied in the first period of the experiment and no treatment or uniform treatment is given thereafter. Comparison of values in the first period then gives estimates of direct effects, while comparisons in the second and subsequent periods estimate the first and subsequent residual effects

This type of experiment is easily carried out, and short-term designs may be used in laying it down. Its analysis can then be carried out as a series of short-term experiments, provided no comparisons are made between experiments. Further, it may be very simply modified, if a factorial design is used, by making some of the symbols refer to treatments applied in a later period of the experiment. Consider, for instance, the design shown in Table 11.7.1 for one basic treatment factor A at two levels. The levels are represented by 1 (A applied) and 0 (A not applied).

The basic design used is that of a 2^3 experiment in two blocks, confounding the

Table 11.7.1   Design for serial experiment with one treatment at two levels

Period	Block 1				Block 2			
	(1)	ab	ac	bc	a	b	c	abc
1	0	1	1	0	1	0	0	1
2	0	1	0	1	0	1	0	1
3	0	0	1	1	0	0	1	1
4	0	0	0	0	0	0	0	0
5	. . .				. . .			

second-order interaction. However, *a* may be taken as referring to *A* applied in the first period, *b* as *A* applied in the second period, and *c* as *A* applied in the third period. That is, each period is regarded as a separate factor at two levels (0, 1). This gives rise to the design shown.

The analysis of such a design is quite straightforward. In the first period, only the direct effect of *A* need be considered; in the second period the direct effect, its first residual, and their interaction need to be considered; and in the third period the direct effect, its first and second residuals, and their interactions in pairs can be estimated. Thereafter, various residuals and their interactions in pairs may be estimated.

Table 11.7.2 gives a second example of an experiment for one basic treatment factor at three levels 0, 1 and 2. In the first period the direct effect can be estimated. All combinations of the three levels have been included in the first two

Table 11.7.2 Design for a serial experiment with one treatment at three levels

	Plot								
Period	1	2	3	4	5	6	7	8	9
1	0	1	2	0	1	2	0	1	2
2	0	0	0	1	1	1	2	2	2
3	0	2	1	1	0	2	2	1	0

periods. Consequently, in the second period the direct effects, its first residual, and their interaction can be estimated. The levels in the third period have been chosen so that the nine combinations can be regarded as constituting a one-third replicate of a 3^3 design, with defining contrast $I = AB^2C$. Then, if the interactions of the direct effect and residuals can be ignored, the direct effect and its residuals can be estimated in the third period.

Of course the factors in the basic experiment need not be taken as referring to the same treatment, and any number of treatments may be used and introduced at any time. For instance, in Table 11.7.2 the three levels could equally well refer to three separate factors *A*, *B* and *C*.

In general, however, designs obtained in this way are restricted in their uses by the fact that estimates of relevant effects are often made in only one period of the experiment; and that estimates made in one period of the experiment are not comparable with estimates made in another. Thus, for instance, in estimating the rates of decay of the effects of fertilizers, if the fertilizers are applied in the first year, and the subsequent years are used to estimate the residual effects, the comparison of the direct and residual effects is made between years and is consequently liable to be influenced by changes in weather conditions during the course of the experiment. To put it another way, since the direct effects and residual effects may change in the different periods of the experiment, it is often necessary to ensure that estimates of all are obtained in the same period of an experiment.

To do this it is necessary to ensure that the design has essentially the same structure in any group of successive periods. For instance, the design in Table 11.7.3, for one treatment factor at two levels (0, 1), can be used if third and

Table 11.7.3 Serial factorial design for one basic treatment at two levels

Period	Plot			
	1	2	3	4
1	1	0	0	1
2	0	1	0	1
3	0	0	1	1
4	1	0	0	1
5	0	1	0	1
6	0	0	1	1
.	.	.	.	.
.	.	.	.	.
.	.	.	.	.

subsequent residuals are assumed to be zero. In any two successive periods, all combinations of the two levels have been included. In any three successive periods, the design can be regarded as a one-half replicate of a 2^3 experiment with defining contrast $I = ABC$. If first-order interactions can be assumed negligible, third and subsequent periods will provide estimates of the direct effect and its first and second residuals. Alternatively, if residual effects are zero three years after application, it will provide estimates of the direct effects, its first residual, and their interaction. A design with these same properties is given in Table 11.7.4. In any three successive periods the one-half replicate has defining contrast $I = AC$. In addition, this design is *balanced for plots* for any four successive periods, i.e. each level of the treatment occurs twice in each plot. Such a design is better for eliminating the influence of any persistent plot differences.

In the designs of Tables 11.7.3 and 11.7.4 it is not until the third and subsequent periods of the experiment that the residuals can be estimated, and therefore the experiment cannot be considered to be fully operative before this period. Similarly, if designs are constructed from those given in Tables 11.7.1 and 11.7.2 by applying the same treatments in periods 4, 5, 6 . . ., as were applied in periods 1, 2, 3, . . . , it is not until the third and subsequent periods that the experiments become fully operative.

The construction of these serial factorial designs has been considered by Patterson (1968). He also considers designs for experiments with one basic treatment at more than two levels and for experiments with more than one basic treatment.

Table 11.7.4 Serial factorial design balanced for plots

Period	Plot 1	2	3	4
1	1	0	0	1
2	0	1	0	1
3	0	1	1	0
4	1	0	1	0
5	1	0	0	1
6	0	1	0	1
.	.	.	.	.
.	.	.	.	.
.	.	.	.	.

11.8 Example of a serial experiment

Table 11.8.1 gives the treatments in the first four periods of a design for a serial factorial experiment on grass, carried out by D. Reid and designed by R. Henderson and H. D. Patterson. Four levels of nitrogen were applied on each occasion. The four levels, which are coded in Table 11.8.1, were at 0, 33, 66 and

Table 11.8.1 Design for a serial experiment

Block	Cut	Plot 1	2	3	4	5	6	7	8	9	10	11	12	13	14	15	16
1	1	3	0	3	2	1	1	0	1	0	3	3	0	2	2	1	2
	2	3	2	2	3	0	1	1	3	0	0	1	3	1	2	2	0
	3	3	2	0	0	3	0	3	2	0	2	1	1	2	3	1	1
	4	3	3	1	2	1	3	2	0	0	2	0	1	1	0	2	3
2	1	0	0	1	3	3	2	2	2	1	1	0	2	1	3	0	3
	2	3	0	1	3	2	1	3	2	0	2	2	0	3	0	1	1
	3	3	2	2	1	2	0	2	1	1	3	0	3	0	0	1	3
	4	0	1	2	2	0	0	3	1	0	3	2	2	1	3	3	1
3	1	3	1	2	1	2	0	0	2	2	3	0	1	3	0	3	1
	2	3	2	0	0	3	3	1	1	2	0	2	1	2	0	1	3
	3	2	0	0	2	1	0	2	3	2	3	3	1	1	1	0	3
	4	1	0	1	3	0	3	0	3	2	0	1	1	3	2	2	2
4	1	1	3	2	2	1	2	0	3	1	3	0	2	1	0	0	3
	2	3	2	2	0	1	1	3	3	0	1	0	3	2	1	2	0
	3	1	3	0	2	3	1	2	0	0	2	3	3	2	0	1	1
	4	3	2	3	0	0	2	2	0	2	3	3	1	1	1	0	1

99 kg per ha. About one month after application the grass was cut and dry matter yields (in kg/ha) obtained. Nitrogen was again applied and after a further month yields at the second cut obtained. The process was repeated to give yields at a third and fourth cutting.

Yields at cut 1 can be used to estimate the direct effects of nitrogen, with each level of nitrogen occurring four times on each occasion, i.e. block. For the first two cuts all combinations of the levels occur once in each block, and hence the design can be seen to be four replicates of a complete 4^2 experiment. Yields at cut 2 provide estimates of the direct effects, its first residual, and their interaction. The first three cuts give rise to a design corresponding to a 4^3 experiment in four blocks of sixteen plots, where the interactions $A''B''C'''$, $A'''B'C'$ and $A'B''C''$ are confounded with blocks. Here, the factors A, B and C refer to nitrogen for cuts 1, 2 and 3 respectively, while the comparisons A', A'', ... are as defined in 7.5. Cut 3 yields, therefore, can provide estimates of the direct effects, first and second residuals and their interactions in pairs. Finally, the levels at cut 4 give rise to the one-quarter replicate of a 4^4 experiment in four blocks of sixteen given in 7.5. If the first-order interactions involving third residuals and all second- and third-order interactions can be assumed to be negligible, then the direct effects, first and second residuals, their interactions in pairs, and the third residual effects can be estimated.

Table 11.8.2   Dry matter yields at cut 4 (kg/ha)

Plot	Block 1	2	3	4
1	25126	10468	15789	23163
2	22842	14811	2013	21921
3	7847	19158	5963	16400
4	14289	17818	24868	6500
5	18800	6947	5137	7697
6	15579	2067	18016	17039
7	22853	22595	5732	19011
8	7168	9900	25126	4311
9	1258	3900	20495	11842
10	20487	26858	7971	24116
11	3979	13116	17179	26342
12	11163	21711	10089	19100
13	15553	7663	22816	14013
14	9558	16421	17053	7442
15	16763	20532	13189	3916
16	20463	16337	20037	10842
Total	233728	230311	231473	233655

Table 11.8.2 gives the dry matter yields at cut 4. These data can now be analysed as an ordinary fractional factorial experiment where, for instance, the main effects now correspond to the direct effects and first, second and third residuals, respectively. Table 11.8.3 gives the two-way table of total yields for the calcula-

Table 11.8.3   Total yields for direct × first residual effects

Level of nitrogen at cut 3	Level of nitrogen at cut 4				Total
	0	1	2	3	
0	9658	28915	52436	66416	157425
1	16932	41994	68673	86974	214573
2	26347	60166	79151	94421	260085
3	35694	71416	86522	103452	297084
Total	88631	202491	286782	351263	929167

tion of direct effects, first residual effects, and their interaction. Similarly, tables can be constructed for the calculation of the other effects. The analysis of variance is shown in Table 11.8.4. First-order interactions involving third resid-

Table 11.8.4   Analysis of variance

	d.f.	s.s.	m.s.
Blocks	3	5321·87	1773·96
Direct effects	3	24156150·91	8052050·30
First residual effects	3	6805927·98	2268642·66
Second residual effects	3	72711·71	24237·24
Third residual effects	3	12993·45	4331·15
Direct × first residuals	9	333321·05	37035·67
Direct × second residuals	9	82883·82	9209·31
First residuals × second residuals	9	103347·81	11483·09
Error	21	203128·55	9672·79
Total	63	31775787·15	

uals and the second and higher-order interactions are included in the error term. Only the direct effects, first residual effects, and their interaction reach significance.

Estimates of the linear, quadratic and cubic components of the effects can be obtained along the lines of 4.4. The subdivision of the sum of squares for the direct effects, first residuals, and their interaction is shown in Table 11.8.5.

Table 11.8.5 Further subdivision of sum of squares

	d.f.	s.s.
Direct (D):		
Linear D	1	23772192·59
Quadratic D	1	380982·13
Cubic D	1	2976·19
First residual (F):		
Linear F	1	6742188·47
Quadratic F	1	63434·72
Cubic F	1	304·79
Interaction:		
Linear D ×		
Linear F	1	22617·90
Linear D ×		
Quadratic F	1	71511·83
Quadratic D ×		
Linear F	1	85585·72
Remainder	6	153605·60

The linear and quadratic components of the direct effects and the first residuals reach significance. A table of means for these effects can be calculated directly from Table 11.8.3. The standard error of the means in the main body of the table will be ±49·17, whilst the standard error of the marginal means will be ±24·59.

The data from the other cuts can be analysed in a similar way. Because of the nature of this serial experiment it is essential that each cut be analysed separately. Ultimately, however, an estimate of the combined direct and residual effects would be needed. This presents considerable difficulties since the results may not be completely independent of one another. In this experiment, cuts taken from the same plot will tend to be positively correlated due to persistent features in the plot. On the other hand, there will be a negative component also because a plot that gives a poor yield at one cut may make up for it at the next. This problem is considered further in Chapter 13 and in particular in **13.9**.

11.9 Rotation experiments

A particular type of serial experiment which occurs frequently in practice is the crop rotation experiment. In this, in accordance with usual agricultural practice, plots receive different crops in successive years, a rotation of crops being maintained over a series of years. It should be noted that the design of rotation experiments is a very specialized field, with no simple analogy outside crop experimentation. Yates (1954) gave two main classes of rotation experiments—

(a) Fixed-rotation experiments, which are experiments comparing the effects of treatments on the crops of a single rotation. The treatments may be repeated year after year or may be varied in some manner.

(b) Multi-rotation experiments, which are experiments in which different crop rotations are to be compared. The different crops now act as treatments, and it becomes necessary to ensure that the plots to be compared carry the same crop in a sufficient number of years for the necessary comparisons to be made.

These classes of experiments will be considered in turn.

(a) *Fixed-rotation experiments*

The simplest type of fixed-rotation experiment is where the plots receive the same treatments throughout. Table 11.9.1 gives a design for comparing four levels (0, 1, 2, 3) of a treatment on three crops. In this three-course experiment

Table 11.9.1 Three-course rotation experiment

		Plot			
Year	Crop	1	2	3	4
1	A	0	1	2	3
2	B	0	1	2	3
3	C	0	1	2	3
4	A	0	1	2	3
5	B	0	1	2	3
.	.	.	.	.	.
.	.	.	.	.	.
.	.	.	.	.	.

each crop will occur only once every three years. However, the effects of treatments will normally vary from year to year, and, in order to ensure that all crops are exposed to the same experimental conditions, it will be necessary for all crops to be represented in any year. Each crop is therefore grown in each year and is followed by the next crop in the order of the rotation. The three-course experiment is thus divided into three *series*, each of which is at a different stage of rotation. Each series consists of four plots and each plot receives the same treatment each year. The design given in Table 11.9.1 constitutes one series of the full experiment.

In an analysis, treatment comparisons will have to be made for each crop separately. The design of Table 11.9.1 will enable estimates of the direct effects to be calculated but will not provide any information on residual effects. Table 11.9.2 provides an example of a design which enables information to be obtained on first residuals. It represents a three-course experiment with two treatments *a* and *b*. Non-application of the treatments is represented by –. The 24 plots

Table 11.9.2 Three-course rotation experiment for estimating first residuals

Year	Series 1	2	3	Plot 1	2	3	4	5	6	7	8
1	*A*	*B*	*C*	*a*	*a*	–	–	*b*	*b*	–	–
2	*B*	*C*	*A*	–	–	*a*	*a*	–	–	*b*	*b*
3	*C*	*A*	*B*	*a*	*a*	–	–	*b*	*b*	–	–
4	*A*	*B*	*C*	–	–	*a*	*a*	–	–	*b*	*b*
5	*B*	*C*	*A*	*a*	*a*	–	–	*b*	*b*	–	–
6	*C*	*A*	*B*	–	–	*a*	*a*	–	–	*b*	*b*
.	.	.	.	.	.	.	.	.	.	.	.
.	.	.	.	.	.	.	.	.	.	.	.
.	.	.	.	.	.	.	.	.	.	.	.

are set out in three randomized blocks of eight plots each. Within each block or series, two levels, presence and absence, are associated with each treatment, so that there are four treatment-level combinations, each replicated twice. Direct effects and first residuals can now be estimated, the experiment commencing in effect with the second year. The direct and residual effects of a treatment on a particular crop in a given year are estimated from the plots receiving that crop in that year. The direct effect is estimated from the plots receiving the treatment in that year, and the residual effect from those plots which had the treatment applied to a different crop in the previous year. For instance, in year 5, effects are estimated on crop *A* in series 3, with the direct effect of treatment *a* from plots 1 and 5 and the residual effect from plots 3 and 4.

Table 11.9.3 gives an example of one series of a four-course experiment with

Table 11.9.3 Four-course experiment for estimating first and second residuals

Year	Crop	Plot 1	2	3	4	5	6
1	*A*	*a*	–	–	*b*	–	–
2	*B*	–	*a*	–	–	*b*	–
3	*C*	–	–	*a*	–	–	*b*
4	*D*	*a*	–	–	*b*	–	–
5	*A*	–	*a*	–	–	*b*	–
6	*B*	–	–	*a*	–	–	*b*
7	*C*	*a*	–	–	*b*	–	–
8	*D*	–	*a*	–	–	*b*	–
.	.	.	.	.	.	.	.
.	.	.	.	.	.	.	.
.	.	.	.	.	.	.	.

two treatments, which provides estimates of direct effects and both first and second residuals. The treatment cycle of this experiment is three years. Consequently each plot will receive its treatment whilst growing each crop in a complete cycle of 12 years. If the number of crops is equal to the length of the treatment cycle then the same plot always receives its treatment when under the same crop. This can be seen if the designs in Table 11.9.2 or 11.9.3 are extended to provide estimates of second or third residuals respectively. Such designs would be best avoided, especially if persistent plot differences are possible.

Further examples of fixed-rotation experiments and further details of the analyses can be found in Yates (1949) and Patterson (1953, 1959).

(b) *Multi-rotation experiments*

The simplest type of experiments which compare the same crops in different rotations are best treated as if each rotation represented a distinct treatment. Each phase of every rotation has then to be represented in any design, and comparisons between rotations can be made in turn upon each crop represented in any year of the experiment. For instance, the design of Table 11.9.4 might be used to compare the crop rotations *A*, *B*, *C* and *A*, *C*, *B*. The rotations are then compared in each year on each crop.

Table 11.9.4 Design for a crop-rotation experiment

| | Rotations | | | | | |
| | I | | | II | | |
Year	1	2	3	4	5	6
1	*A*	*B*	*C*	*A*	*B*	*C*
2	*B*	*C*	*A*	*C*	*A*	*B*
3	*C*	*A*	*B*	*B*	*C*	*A*
4	*A*	*B*	*C*	*A*	*B*	*C*

Different crops can be used in the rotations. For instance, some of the crops of the basic crop rotation can be varied. The crops common to all rotations would be regarded as test crops and the crops that are varied as treatment crops. Different rotations can be compared in any year in which they are growing the same test crops. Test crops need not be common to all rotations of an experiment. For instance, Table 11.9.5 gives a design for comparing two crops *A* and *B* grown continuously. Rotations I and III have no crops in common and cannot be compared directly. However, they can be compared using rotation II. Crop *A* is the test crop for comparing rotation I and II, and crop *B* is the test crop for comparing rotations II and III.

The design given in Table 11.9.6 provides an example of an experiment in

Table 11.9.5 Design for the comparison of the effects of two crops

	Rotations			
	I	II		III
Year	1	2	3	4
1	A	A	B	B
2	A	B	A	B
3	A	A	B	B
4	A	B	A	B
5	A	A	B	B
.	.	.	.	.
.	.	.	.	.
.	.	.	.	.

Table 11.9.6 Design for a crop-rotation experiment

	Rotations								
	I			II			III		
Year	1	2	3	4	5	6	7	8	9
1	A	E_1	E_2	B	C	E_3	D	E_4	E_5
2	E_1	E_2	A	C	E_3	B	E_4	E_5	D
3	E_2	A	E_1	E_3	B	C	E_5	D	E_4
.	.	.	.	.	.	.	.	.	.
.	.	.	.	.	.	.	.	.	.
.	.	.	.	.	.	.	.	.	.

which one of the crops is repeated in a rotation. The experiment compares the three rotations—

$$I : A, E, E$$
$$II : B, C, E$$
$$III : D, E, E$$

The crops A, B, C and D are treatment crops and crop E is a test crop. The different E crops that may be compared in this experiment are distinguished by suffixes. The different rotations can be assessed in each year by comparing the yields of $\frac{1}{2}(E_1 + E_2)$, E_3 and $\frac{1}{2}(E_4 + E_5)$. Since rotations I and III contain the same crop more than once, other comparisons can be made, namely between E_1 and E_2 and between E_4 and E_5. These are comparisons between the different phases of the same crop and are known as *phase differences*.

The design given in Table 11.9.6 requires nine plots to be set out in a randomized block design. Reduction of block size is possible by grouping together all the plots of the basic rotations to form one series, and the plots in the second phase of the basic rotations to form the second series, and so on. The design of Table 11.9.6 has been rearranged into three series of three plots each in Table 11.9.7. Comparisons between E_1 and E_4 and between E_2, E_3 and E_5 can still be made, but phase differences and differences between different phases of different rotations have been confounded between series.

Table 11.9.7 Design of Table 11.9.6 in series

	Series								
	1			2			3		
	Rotations			Rotations			Rotations		
Year	I	II	III	I	II	III	I	II	III
1	A	B	D	E_1	C	E_4	E_2	E_3	E_5
2	E_1	C	E_4	E_2	E_3	E_5	A	B	D
3	E_2	E_3	E_5	A	B	D	E_1	C	E_4
.	.	.	.	.	.	.	.	.	.
.	.	.	.	.	.	.	.	.	.
.	.	.	.	.	.	.	.	.	.

As we have already seen in Table 11.9.5, experiments can be designed when the rotations are of differing length. Yates (1954) provides an example of a design for comparing rotations of rice (R) and grass (G). The three rotations were

    I : 1 year rice, 2 years grass
    II : 2 years rice, 2 years grass
    III : 1 year rice, 3 years grass.

Table 11.9.8 gives the design for one replicate of the experiment. There are eleven phases altogether in the three rotations, so that the experiment involves eleven plots. The full experiment continues for a period of twelve years, the first three years being regarded as preliminary years.

In each year after the fourth, comparison of the mean yields of rice from each rotation will provide an assessment of the three rotations. In addition, the phase difference R_2 with R_3 provides information on the relative yields of rice in rotation II one and two years after grass. Grass yields can also be compared if necessary.

Designs with rotations of unequal length cannot be arranged in series in the same way as the design of Table 11.9.7. The block size can, however, be reduced by using the reduced and phase-confounded designs proposed by Patterson (1964). Further details of the designs and of their analyses can be found in Patterson's paper.

Table 11.9.8   One replicate of a rice–pasture rotation experiment

	Rotations										
	I			II				III			
Years	1	2	3	4	5	6	7	8	9	10	11
1	R_1	G	G	R_2	G	G	R_3	R_4	G	G	G
2	G	R_1	G	R_3	R_2	G	G	G	R_4	G	G
3	G	G	R_1	G	R_3	R_2	G	G	G	R_4	G
4	R_1	G	G	G	G	R_3	R_2	G	G	G	R_4
5	G	R_1	G	R_2	G	G	R_3	R_4	G	G	G
6	G	G	R_1	R_3	R_2	G	G	G	R_4	G	G
7	R_1	G	G	G	R_3	R_2	G	G	G	R_4	G
8	G	R_1	G	G	G	R_3	R_2	G	G	G	R_4
9	G	G	R_1	R_2	G	G	R_3	R_4	G	G	G
10	R_1	G	G	R_3	R_2	G	G	G	R_4	G	G
11	G	R_1	G	G	R_3	R_2	G	G	G	R_4	G
12	G	G	R_1	G	G	R_3	R_2	G	G	G	R_4

12   Planning of Groups of Experiments

12.1   General considerations

In many fields of experimentation, the treatment effects obtained vary with the time and place of observation, and results obtained in one experiment, however accurate in themselves, are of no use for the purpose of predicting what is likely to happen in future work. In consequence, to obtain estimates of treatment effects which may be generally applied, and to investigate the manner in which these estimates may change with the conditions under which the treatments are applied, more than one experiment has to be carried out.

A group of experiments, if carried out correctly, will provide values for treatment effects which may be generally used. Further, careful planning should give the maximum accuracy in these estimates for the minimum of work. However, the procedure to be followed in planning such a group of experiments involves more than a consideration of the individual designs: a number of special questions merit attention. These questions will be dealt with in this chapter.

In setting up a group of experiments, many things need to be decided. These are—

(1) the number of experiments,
(2) the location of the experiments in time and space,
(3) the number of treatments and size of the experiments,
(4) the design(s) of the experiments.

The answers to these questions will obviously depend upon the experimental situation, which will usually play a main part in deciding the final set-up. Nevertheless, it is possible to assess the relative advantages of different approaches, thereby guiding the experimenter in making his final decisions, and to point out pitfalls and short-cuts which might not otherwise be noticed. This will be done in the following sections.

12.2   Size and number of experiments

In setting up a series of experiments, a first question that will normally have to be considered is the likely accuracy of the estimates that will be obtained, and how this may be made as high as possible for the smallest cost in material and work.

The error variance of any estimate of a treatment effect will consist of two parts. In the first place, there will be the variance per replication, σ^2, of the treatment effects in each experiment. This represents the variation at one particular location during the course of any one experiment. In the second place, there will be the variance, σ_0^2, of the treatment effect from experiment to experiment.

If the treatment effect changes greatly from experiment to experiment in relation to the variation within experiments, and the amount of extra work or cost involved in repeating experiments is small (i.e. two experiments cause very little more work than one experiment of double the size), it is obviously preferable to have a large number of small experiments. On the other hand, if the variation in the treatment effects is small and the cost of setting up new experiments is large, it will be preferable to have a small number of large experiments.

As a rough guide to the optimum number of replications per experiment, the following formula may be used. If c is the cost of setting up an experiment in terms of the cost of taking a single replication, the optimum number of replications, r, per experiment is roughly

$$r = \frac{\sigma \sqrt{c}}{\sigma_0}.$$

This formula is very crude, especially since it requires an estimation of the variation, which can only be made very approximately. Further it assumes that σ will not increase with the size of the experiment, although this is probably not true. Nevertheless, it will act as a guide to the number of replications that will give optimum efficiency. For example, suppose there is roughly a 20 percent variation in the estimate of treatment effects per replication in any one experiment, and that there is a 10 percent variation in the treatment effects from experiment to experiment. Suppose also that the cost of setting up an experiment is four replications, so that, for instance, three experiments of six replications cost as much in work and expense as one experiment of 26 replications or two experiments of 11 replications. The optimum number of replications per experiment is roughly

$$\frac{20}{10} \sqrt{4} = 4.$$

Of course, if it is desired to examine closely the results from each experiment or to ascertain the existence of a treatment effect, more replications may be needed, but values obtained by this method provide a guide to the number of replications required in general.

The number of experiments to be carried out will depend upon the same considerations as the number of replications needed in an individual experiment. Tables 1.7.1 and 1.7.2 may therefore be used to estimate roughly the number of experiments required for specific purposes. In entering these tables, however, it is necessary to use, as a value for the error in the individual observations, the expression

$$\sqrt{\left(\frac{\sigma^2 + r\sigma_0^2}{2r}\right)}.$$

For instance, to estimate the above treatment effect to within 10 percent with 95 percent certainty, Table 1.7.1 is used with a coefficient of variation

$$\sqrt{\left(\frac{20^2 + 4 \times 10^2}{2 \times 4}\right)} = 10 \text{ percent.}$$

We should conclude that nine experiments, each with four replications, were needed for this purpose. Alternatively, if it had been decided to use eight replications per experiment, a coefficient of variation of 8·7 percent would have been used, and the use of eight experiments would have been indicated.

12.3 Locating the experiments

An important point to be noted in using the formulae of the last section is that the same principles apply to groups of experiments as to the individual experiment. Replication and randomization are both required if valid conclusions are to be drawn for the population of conditions under consideration. The experiments thus need to be randomly located if the estimates obtained are to be generally applicable. For instance, to test a medical treatment in a series of experiments, the co-operation of a number of hospitals and doctors, chosen to provide a random (or stratified random) sample of the whole, should be used.

In practice, it is unfortunately not always possible to select on a random basis the location of the experiments in time and space. It is then necessary to restrict the investigation to a narrower field and to accept the fact that the results may not be generally applicable. For example, if some hospitals refused to co-operate in setting up a series of experiments, the results can be taken as applying only to the population attending "co-operative" hospitals. This may be the same as the general population, but on the other hand it may not. The unco-operative hospitals may be those which are busier and which are dealing with a less healthy group of the population, or alternatively, they may be less efficient hospitals in which the treatment effect may be greater or less than usual.

Thus, in selecting a group of experiments it may be necessary to limit the generality of their results because of practical considerations. In such cases, it is usually better to aim at limiting experiments to a definable population than to obtain results applicable to a wider but undefined population.

12.4 Choosing the number of treatments

Often the number of treatments to be used in the experiments will be determined by prior considerations, but sometimes the experimenter will have a large number of treatments and will need to decide how many he should include in his experiments.

Obviously, if a large number of treatments is used, the number of replications of each will be small, and the variation in each replication of the experiment may be increased. Treatment effects will be less accurately estimated in consequence. On the other hand, if a small number of treatments is used, the treatment effects may be more accurately estimated, but there is a chance of some good treatment being rejected without trial.

The decision then as to how many treatments should be used will depend upon how conclusive the group of experiments is intended to be—the alternative results being the accurate estimation of a small number of treatment effects or the less accurate estimation of a large number. In general, the use of a large number of treatments is to be recommended, with certain reservations mentioned in the next section, since it will in the long run lead to a more rapid selection of the best treatments. However, if the purpose of the experiments is to select a good treatment but not necessarily the best, and to estimate its effect within the period of the experiments, some limitation of the number of treatments must be carried out. Preferably this should be done with the aid of initial "pilot" experiments, but if these cannot be carried out, the experimenter will have to use whatever information is available for the purpose of deciding what are likely to be the best treatments.

To decide the exact number of treatments to be employed in any series of experiments, it is necessary to consider (with the aid of the formulae of the last section) the effects of using differing numbers of treatments. This must necessarily give a very crude answer, but it serves to act as a guide to the number that should be used. For example, suppose it is decided to take a total of 1000 observations in a group of experiments for which it is gauged that $\sigma = 20$ percent per replication and $\sigma_0 = 10$ percent in terms of an arbitrary estimate of any treatment effect. The optimum number of replications per experiment is, by the methods of the last section, roughly four, and the value of 10 percent should be used in entering Table 1.7.1.

If it decided to estimate the treatment effects to within 10 percent with 99 percent certainty, Table 1.7.1 shows that at least sixteen experiments are required. Consequently, the largest possible number of treatments that can be used in each replication is

$$\frac{1000}{4 \times 16} = 15.$$

This value thus indicates the sort of number that may be used.

12.5 Choosing the designs

The choice of designs must be conditioned by the experiences of the experimenter in the particular field in which he works, and by the relative ease with which the different designs may be carried out. What the statistician can do to help the experimenter in his choice of design is to indicate the relative efficiencies of different types of design. If this is done, the experimenter may know that, by using one design rather than another, he obtains estimates of treatment effects which are more accurate by so many percent. The experimenter will then have to weigh the relative advantages to be gained by the use of any one design against the extra work that is likely to be entailed by its use.

Of course, the relative efficiencies of different designs will depend upon the prevailing conditions in the field to which they are being applied, and only by examining the results of a number of earlier experiments in that field may any conclusions be reached. Thus all that can be done here is to examine methods of estimating the efficiency of different types of design. These methods will then have to be applied to practical data to determine the most suitable designs for any purpose.

The basic methods that should be employed have already been demonstrated in **2.8**. All that is required, then, is an extension of these methods to other designs.

For confounded factorial and split-plot designs, the methods of **2.8** should be applied. However, the degrees of freedom corresponding to the confounded interactions should, if possible, be isolated and replaced by the residual mean square for blocks. For instance, to determine the efficiency of the use of litter-mates in the design of **5.2**, an overall mean square needs to be calculated from the residual within-litter and residual between-litter mean squares, 0·0419 and 0·00715. This may be done as shown in Table 12.5.1.

Table 12.5.1   Estimating the efficiency of confounding

	d.f.	s.s.	m.s.
Litters	7	0·2933	0·0419
Treatments	14	0·1001	0·00715
Residual	42	0·3001	0·00715
Total	63	0·6935	0·01101

In estimating all effects other than $CFM\male$, the gain in efficiency resulting from the confounding is thus

$$100 \left(\frac{1101}{715} - 1 \right) = 54 \text{ percent.}$$

For the effect $CFM\male$, the loss in efficiency is

$$100 \left(1 - \frac{715}{4190} \right) = 83 \text{ percent.}$$

The advantage of the confounding is obvious.

To demonstrate a more complicated application of the same principles, we may consider an experiment similar to that of **4.9** in which chicks are stratified by weight before placing them together in the cages. We shall suppose in this instance that there are significant differences between cages and that the cage treatments are applied *after* the stratification is employed.[*] The (hypothetical) analysis of this experiment is shown in Table 12.5.2. From it, we shall calculate

---

[*] If they are applied *before*, the stratification has no effect on between-cage comparisons and has the same effect as is indicated here on the within-cage comparisons.

the increase in efficiency of estimation of treatment effects as a result of the stratification.

Table 12.5.2　Analysis of variance of split-plot experiment

	d.f.	s.s.	m.s.
Treatments	3	17257·8	
Between-cage residual	4	4000·0	1000·0
Between cages	7	21257·8	
Treatments	12	118710·8	
Strata	12	26106·5	2175·5
Within-cage residual	96	53884·2	561·3
Total	127	219959·3	

As a first step we may replace both the between-cage and treatment mean squares by the within-cage mean square and use this to estimate what the mean square would have been if the stratification had not been employed. This gives the analysis shown in Table 12.5.3.

Table 12.5.3　Adjusted analysis of variance

	d.f.	s.s.	m.s.
Between cages	7	3929·1	561·3
Treatments	12	6735·6	561·3
Strata	12	26106·5	2175·5
Within-cage residual	96	53884·2	561·3
Total	127	90655·4	713·8

The percentage gain in efficiency in the within-cage comparisons is thus $100(713\cdot8/561\cdot3 - 1) = 27\cdot2$ percent.

The gain in efficiency in the between-cage comparisons is found simply by multiplying this value by the ratio of the variances, $561\cdot3/1000\cdot0$. Thus, for between-cage comparisons, the gain in efficiency is $27\cdot2 \times 0\cdot5613 = 15\cdot3$ percent.

The same method also provides the basis for testing the efficiency of incomplete block designs of the type described in Chapter 10, but the analysis is complicated by the recovery of inter-block information and by the use of weighting factors. Yates (1940) gives details of the procedure appropriate for a resolvable balanced incomplete block design.

The standard error of the difference between treatment effects can be used to calculate an efficiency factor for incomplete block designs. For instance, this standard error for a balanced incomplete block design is

$$\sqrt{\left(\frac{2ks^2}{\lambda v}\right)}.$$

If this is compared with the standard error for a randomized block design, $\sqrt{(2s^2/r)}$, a measure of efficiency can be defined by

$$E = \frac{2s^2}{r} \bigg/ \frac{2ks^2}{\lambda v} = \frac{\lambda v}{rk}.$$

Hence the standard error of a balanced incomplete block design is $1/\sqrt{E}$ times that of a randomized block design. For the example of **10.3**, $E = 0 \cdot 8$ and $1/\sqrt{E} = 1 \cdot 12$. This means that the use of a balanced incomplete block design will be advantageous if there is a reduction of at least 12 percent in the error variation. This does not take into account the additional gain in precision that would result from the recovery of inter-block information. It also ignores differences due to changes in the number of residual degrees of freedom; this point is discussed in the next section.

12.6   Degrees of freedom of the residual mean square

One other quantity needs to be considered in deciding the designs of a group of experiments: the number of degrees of freedom of the residual mean square.

It was pointed out in Chapter 1 that in designing an experiment it is necessary to aim not only for accurate estimation of treatment effects but also for a measure of the accuracy. The residual mean square provides the method of measuring this accuracy, and it is therefore necessary by replication and randomization to ensure that its value can be estimated.

Failure to obtain an estimate of the residual mean square does not, of course, change the accuracy of the estimates of treatment effects, but it severely limits their usefulness. Similarly an inaccurate estimation of the residual mean square (i.e. an estimation based upon few degrees of freedom) makes the assessment and testing of treatment effects difficult to carry out. The accuracy of the estimated effects remains the same, but it cannot be closely gauged and, in consequence, confidence limits for the effect may be wide.

The ability of an experiment to gauge the accuracy of estimated treatment effects may be termed its "sensitivity"; or, alternatively, the "information" contained in the estimated effects varies with the degrees of freedom of the residual mean square. Various measures may be made of the sensitivity or information contained in an experiment. One of these, already used in **5.5**, is to use the significant levels in the variance-ratio table as a guide to the effect of changing the degrees of freedom of the residual.

A second method, due to R. A. Fisher, indicates that the amount of information in estimates based upon f degrees of freedom is proportional to

$(f+1)/(f+3)$, so that, for instance, the relative information obtainable from say, estimates based on 19 and 32 degrees of freedom are 20/22 : 33/35 or 1·00 : 1·04.

Other methods may also be used, but these two will normally provide a sufficient basis for deciding when the number of degrees of freedom of any estimate is large enough.

As a general practice, more than ten degrees of freedom are usually regarded as adequate, and five or less as being rather low if significance tests are to be carried out. This rate should not, however, be followed too strictly, since different experimental conditions may easily make less than five degrees of freedom adequate or more than ten inadequate.

One further point might be noted. If a group of experiments is being carried out in which the treatment effect varies considerably from experiment to experiment, accurate estimation of the errors of effects in individual experiments is often unnecessary. Sometimes, as will be seen in the next chapter, accurate estimation allows a weighting analysis to be carried out if the experiments differ appreciably in accuracy. Usually, however, it is more important to obtain a good estimate of the variation in the treatment effect from experiment to experiment than it is to get good estimates of the variation in each individual experiment.

12.7 Sampling the experiments

In setting up a series of experiments, it is advisable to consider what measurements will best reflect the treatment effects that are being investigated. Often it is possible to save a great deal of time and trouble by using less accurate measurements and sacrificing information which might be obtained with more care. It is then necessary to consider what loss of information might result from the use of the less accurate observations and whether this loss is balanced by the gains in time and labour.

In particular, in many fields of experimentation, it is possible to sample the experiments by measuring only a proportion of the possible total in each observation. For example, in a field-plot experiment, the yield of a sample from each plot may be measured instead of the yield of the whole plot, or, in an industrial experiment, part of the production of a number of machines during a specified time might be measured. In this instance, it is necessary to consider what loss of information might result as a consequence of the sampling.

The procedure for estimating the loss of information is basically the same in both these cases: the comparison of the residual mean square in the analysis of the accurate or full measurements with that in the analysis of the inaccurate or sampled measurements. For the comparison of two different sets of measurements, this is most simply done by carrying out a distinct analysis for each set. The relative efficiencies of the two measurements may then be gauged from a comparison of the two residual mean squares, the two measurements being corrected, if necessary, to the same scale. If no direct conversion between the two scales of measurement is possible, the values of the treatment variance ratio minus one should be compared, the larger value indicating the more sensitive measurement.

The same procedure may be adopted to estimate the efficiency due to sampling an experiment, but if initial experiments are conducted so that each major experimental unit or plot is broken into a number of sub-units each of which is measured, one overall analysis can be carried out to estimate the loss in efficiency. If s_1^2 and s^2 are the mean squares between and within major sampling units, the percentage loss in efficiency when a fraction f of the sub-units are measured is given by—

$$100(1 - f)\,\frac{s^2}{s_1^2}.$$

To demonstrate the method by which the efficiency of sampling may be investigated in any particular experiment, we may consider figures given by Hudson (1939) on the weights of wheat obtained in a uniformity trial in 1934–5. The total area was divided into five strips or blocks, each containing six equal-sized plots. The plots were further divided into 20 samples. The analysis of variance for this subdivision proceeds as shown in Table 12.7.1.

Table 12.7.1 Analysis of variance for sampled plots

	d.f.	s.s.	m.s.
Blocks	4	7990	
Plots	25	6655	266·20
Samples	570	13859	24·31
Total	599	28504	

The percentage loss in efficiency resulting from the use of two samples instead of the whole plot is given by

$$100\left(1 - \frac{2}{20}\right)\frac{24\cdot31}{266\cdot20} = 8\cdot2 \text{ percent.}$$

Thus, in this instance, the use of two samples would not give an appreciable loss in efficiency. It must, however, be emphasized that this is an isolated experiment and that the results obtained from it refer only to plots of the size used and to conditions similar to those in this experiment. Further experiments and analysis would be needed to establish results of any generality.

12.8 Grouping of experimental results

In many types of experiments, a large part of the work results from the individual measurements and might be avoided if the observations could be taken in groups. For example, where chemical analyses of the treatment results are being undertaken, it would reduce the amount of work if results of each treatment could be analysed together in one analysis. If there were no experimental error in the analysis, the estimates of treatment effects obtained from the analysis of the combined measurements would be as accurate as estimates obtained from the analysis of individuals.[*] However, as a result of this combination, the number of degrees of freedom available for estimating the residual mean square will be reduced or lost altogether, with a corresponding reduction or loss in the sensitivity of the experiment.

If this loss in sensitivity is not very large, or if the experiment is one of a group for which a combined analysis is to be carried out later, the saving in time and labour may be considerable. It is therefore worth while to consider before the start of any experiment or group of experiments whether such a combination can be easily and validly carried out.

The grouping of experimental results is easily carried out for randomized block experiments. The results of the same treatment may be taken together from pairs, trios, or higher numbers of blocks and analysed as an ordinary randomized block design. For instance, if chemical analyses were to be carried out in the experiment of **2.2**, pairs of animals receiving the same diets may be taken from litters 1–2, 3–4, 5–6 and 7–8. The analysis could then be conducted as four randomized blocks of five pairs, leaving 12 degrees of freedom for the residual mean square instead of the 28 obtainable by the full analysis.

Using Fisher's formula (**12.6**), the percentage loss in sensitivity as a result of grouping would be—

$$100 \left(1 - \frac{13/15}{29/31}\right) = 7 \text{ percent.}$$

This is likely to be easily outweighed by the 50 percent reduction (from 40 to 20) in the number of chemical analyses required and by the subsequent saving in numerical analysis.

A similar procedure may be adopted for Latin square designs, provided the choice of design was restricted at the outset of the experiment. Only Latin square designs which consist of a series of Latin squares placed in Latin square formation should be used if grouping of the experimental results is planned. Table 12.8.1 gives an example of such a design.

Each compartment of this square represents a randomly chosen Latin square on two treatments, and the squares are placed in a randomly chosen 3×3 Latin square. The rows, columns and treatments of this final design should be randomized before application.

In analysing this design, pairs of results on the same treatment arising from the same compartments should be combined, and the analysis of variance partitioned as in Table 12.8.2.

Here, eight degrees of freedom are available in the residual as compared with

---

[*] This is not true for incomplete block designs since an adjustment to the treatment mean based upon the block totals is required in this case.

Table 12.8.1 Latin square for grouping results

A	B	C	D	E	F
B	A	D	C	F	E
C	D	F	E	B	A
D	C	E	F	A	B
E	F	A	B	D	C
F	E	B	A	C	D

20 in the full design, a loss of 10 percent in information on Fisher's formula. Again, however, a reduction of 50 percent in the number of samples measured is achieved, with no loss of accuracy.

Factorial experiments may be treated in a similar manner to randomized blocks, but if very few replicates are available, a second method that may be used

Table 12.8.2 Partition of analysis of variance

	d.f.
Between pairs of rows	2
Between pairs of columns	2
Treatments	5
Residual	8
Total	17

is to sacrifice all information on one or more treatment effects and their interaction. Thus, for instance, (1) may be combined with a, b with ab, c with ac and so on, thus sacrificing all information on A and its interactions.

This method is most useful when, say, chemical analyses are being carried out after the numerical analysis of a main series of observations. Comparisons which have proved to be of no importance in the main series might then be sacrificed in the subsequent work.

13 Combination of Experimental Results

13.1 General considerations

The combination of experimental results is an important, and often neglected, part of any experimental program. By combining results from a series of experiments conducted over a number of years in different situations, more accurate estimates of treatment effects may be obtained. More important than this is the fact that estimates of treatment effects of a wider applicability may be obtained For instance, by combining results from a series of fertilizer trials, an estimate of the effect of a fertilizer on several varieties and on soil types may be obtained. Also it may be studied how the fertilizer effect tends to change, if at all, with climate, soil, variety, etc. The importance of obtaining both accurate and generally applicable results has, in fact, been emphasized in several previous chapters and need not be discussed further here.

One important reservation affecting estimates obtained by combining experimental results must, however, be appreciated. This is the fact that the validity of the estimates and of their errors depends upon the random location of the experiments. Obviously no conclusions can be drawn about any population unless all members stand a chance of being included in any sample; similarly, the conditions under which a series of experiments are conducted should be a random sample of the possible conditions. For instance, the sites of a series of agricultural experiments should be chosen at random in the population of soil types to which the results of the experiments would be applied.

If this condition of random location of experiments is satisfied, then the methods of this chapter may be applied without qualms. Where, as is often true, practical considerations influence the conditions under which the experiments are carried out, the methods described may be used, but any results so obtained should be accepted with reservation.

13.2 Methods of combination

In general, in combining a series of estimates $x_1, x_2, \ldots, x_n$ of a treatment effect, two possible forms of combination may be considered. These are the simple or unweighted mean

$$\bar{x} = \frac{x_1 + x_2 + \ldots + x_n}{n},$$

and the weighted mean

$$\bar{x}_w = \frac{w_1 x_1 + w_2 x_2 + \ldots + w_n x_n}{w_1 + w_2 + \ldots + w_n}.$$

This latter quantity will be used in preference to the former when the estimates are of widely differing accuracy, and it is therefore desired to lay greater emphasis on certain of the estimates. This is done by giving the more accurate estimates larger weights. In order, however, for this mean to be a valid and useful estimate, the weights that are adopted must not be associated in any way with the estimated effects, otherwise the weighted mean will be biased. Thus, if the less accurate experiments tend to give lower estimates of treatment effects, an unweighted mean has to be used in combining their results. Further, unless accurate estimates of the weights can be obtained, this weighted mean may in fact be less accurate than the simple unweighted mean.

In the simplest case, when the true effect, μ, of the treatment may be considered to be constant over the whole series of results, and $s_1, s_2, \ldots, s_n$ are the estimated standard errors with degrees of freedom $f_1, f_2, \ldots, f_n$, the weights $w_1, w_2, \ldots, w_n$, may be estimated from

$$w_i = \frac{f_i - 2}{f_i s_i^2},$$

or more exactly from

$$w_i = \frac{f_i + 1}{f_i s_i^2 + (x_i - \mu_0)^2},$$

where μ_0 is a first approximation to the true effect. The standard error of the estimated mean is then given roughly by

$$\sqrt{\left[\frac{1 + 2/\bar{f}}{w_1 + w_2 + \ldots + w_n} \right]},$$

where $\bar{f}$ is the mean number of degrees of freedom of the estimated standard error.

However, when the degrees of freedom of the estimates tend to be small (less than ten), this approach may give unsatisfactory results. In part, this difficulty will be due to too great an emphasis being placed upon results of an apparently high accuracy when no such accuracy has been achieved, and may be overcome by setting an upper limit to the weights used in any analysis. More generally, this can be done by setting a lower limit for the standard deviations of each individual experiment, any individual falling below this limit being replaced by it. If $w'_1, w'_2, \ldots, w'_n$ are the revised weights, the standard error of the mean is then approximately

$$\frac{\sqrt{\left[\left(\frac{w'^2_1}{w_1} + \frac{w'^2_2}{w_2} + \ldots + \frac{w'^2_n}{w_n} \right) \left(1 + \frac{2}{\bar{f}} \right) \right]}}{w'_1 + w'_2 + \ldots + w'_n}.$$

The calculation of this expression requires only the alteration of the affected terms.

As an illustration, we shall consider an example first analysed by Yates and Cochran (1938). The data given in Table 13.2.1 are the average linear responses to

Table 13.2.1   Responses to fertilizers in a series of experiments

Site	Linear response to N	P	K	s_i	f_i	w_i
1	−0·24	0·63	0·57	±0·519	15	3·2
2*	1·23	0·35	0·01	±0·285	22	11·2
3*	0·11	−0·38	−0·21	±0·603	22	2·5
4	2·08	−0·05	−0·22	±0·351	15	7·0
5	0·20	0·32	0·14	±0·453	15	4·2
6	1·05	0·87	−0·07	±0·287	15	10·5
7	−1·14	0·80	−0·08	±0·886	15	1·1
8	3·34	0·11	0·23	±0·356	15	6·8
9	1·64	0·57	0·34	±0·344	15	7·3
10	0·52	0·12	−0·57	±0·481	15	3·7
11	1·37	0·54	−0·33	±0·198	15	22·1
12	0·00	−0·14	0·40	±0·622	15	2·2
13	−0·14	1·02	−1·34	±0·618	15	2·3
14*	2·72	−0·21	−0·18	±0·357	22	7·1
15	3·32	0·19	0·38	±0·443	15	4·4
Mean	1·07	0·32	−0·06	±0·125	16·4	95·6

nitrate, phosphate and potash of the weights of washed roots of sugar-beet in a series of 3^3 factorial designs. In three of the fifteen centres, indicated with asterisks, two replicates were carried out. In the other twelve, only one replicate was used. Simple means are given at the bottom of the table.

If a weighted mean is calculated for, say, the phosphate effects, we get

$$\bar{P}_w = \frac{32 \times 0·63 + 11·2 \times 0·35 - \ldots + 4·4 \times 0·19}{95·6}$$

$$= 0·363,$$

with an approximate standard error of

$$\sqrt{\left(\frac{1 + 0·122}{95·6}\right)} = \pm 0·108.$$

In this instance, however, the mean is largely determined by the results on sites 2, 6 and 11, and therefore it would seem advisable to set an upper limit to the weights to be given. For example, a standard deviation of 0·5 corresponds to standard errors of ±0·236 and ±0·167 and weights of 15·6 and 32·7 for the experiments with one and two replicates respectively. We might therefore replace the weight 22·1 by 15·6 to give a fresh estimate for the weighted mean—

$$\bar{P}_w = 0·350,$$

with an approximate standard error of

$$\frac{\sqrt{[(95 \cdot 6 - 22 \cdot 1 + 11 \cdot 0)(1 \cdot 122)]}}{95 \cdot 6 - 22 \cdot 1 + 15 \cdot 6} = \pm 0 \cdot 109.$$

It will be seen in subsequent sections that a number of considerations will influence the decision to use a weighted mean and will often make a simple mean a preferable measure of a treatment effect. A weighted mean may sometimes be useful, but some care is necessary to ensure that an estimate of treatment effects more accurate than the simple mean is really being obtained, and not an estimate with spuriously high accuracy.

13.3 Tests of homogeneity of variance and consistency of treatment effect

Before carrying out any combination of estimates of a treatment effect, it is normally necessary to decide two things—

(1) whether the experiments upon which the results are based are of comparable precision, and
(2) whether the estimates are consistent with one constant overall value for the treatment effect, or whether it is necessary to assume that the treatment effect varies from experiment to experiment.

The decisions on these two questions will naturally influence the type of analysis to be carried out, since, for example, there is no point in using a weighted mean if the estimates of treatment effects are of comparable precision. Methods of examining these two questions will thus be considered before proceeding to the general consideration of the combination of experimental results.

We shall use Bartlett's test to test whether a set of n estimated variances $s_1{}^2, s_2{}^2, \ldots, s_n{}^2$, based on $f_1, f_2, \ldots, f_n$ degrees of freedom respectively, are homogeneous, i.e. likely to have the same *true* value. Other tests are available; see, for example, Hall (1972). To carry out Bartlett's test, the quantity

$$(f \log s^2 - f_1 \log s_1{}^2 - f_2 \log s_2{}^2 - \ldots - f_n \log s_n{}^2)/C$$

is calculated, where

$$f = f_1 + f_2 + \ldots + f_n$$

$$s^2 = \frac{f_1 s_1{}^2 + f_2 s_2{}^2 + \ldots + f_n s_n{}^2}{f_1 + f_2 + \ldots + f_n},$$

and

$$C = 0 \cdot 4343 \left[1 + \frac{1}{3(n-1)} \left(\frac{1}{f_1} + \frac{1}{f_2} + \ldots + \frac{1}{f_n} - \frac{1}{f} \right) \right].$$

(The logarithms in this expression are to base 10.) The significance of this may then be approximately tested using a χ^2-test with $n - 1$ degrees of freedom, a significant value indicating real differences in the variances.

As an example of the use of this test, we shall consider observations taken by Lee, Robbins and Chen (1942). Table 13.3.1 gives the logarithms of the uterine weights of 34 immature rats after treatment with 0.4 μg of stilbestrol given orally. The observations were taken on four different dates as indicated, but on animals of the same age in each instance.

Table 13.3.1 Uterine weights of treated rats

	Day			
	1	2	3	4
	1·657	1·619	1·696	1·656
	1·640	1·670	1·732	1·664
	1·732	1·581	1·796	1·663
	1·671	1·737	1·706	1·616
	1·620	1·650	1·762	1·609
	1·716	1·542	1·836	
	1·556	1·623	1·725	
	1·697	1·560	1·672	
	1·683	1·638	1·818	
		1·583	1·718	
Mean	1·664	1·620	1·746	1·642
s_i^2	0·002 881	0·003 333	0·003 004	0·000 721
f_i	8	9	9	4

For these observations, we have $f = 30$, $s^2 = 0.002\,766$, $C = 0.4615$ and

$$\chi^2_{(3)} = \frac{30 \log 0.002\,766 - 8 \log 0.002\,881 - \ldots - 4 \log 0.000\,721}{0.4615},$$

$$= 2.48.$$

The low value of the variance ratio ($P > 0.40$) indicates that the variability in the observations of the four days is of comparable magnitude and hence that an analysis of the four days' observations together may be validly carried out.

When, as here, the variances are homogeneous, an analysis of variance may be used in the normal fashion to test the differences between the estimates of the uterine weights on different days. In this case, this gives the analysis shown in Table 13.3.2. The differences between the uterine weights are highly significant.

It should be noted that "days" in this analysis corresponds to what in a normal analysis would be the "days $\times$ treatment effect" interaction, and that this term naturally provides a test of the consistency of any effect.

If, however, the variances are not homogeneous, two alternatives present themselves: either a change has to be made in the scale of measurement, as described in Chapter 14, to make the variances homogeneous, or if this cannot be done, a

Table 13.3.2 Analysis of variance testing treatment effects

	d.f.	s.s	m.s.	Variance ratio
Days	3	0·086 90	0·028 97	10·47
Residual	30	0·082 97	0·002 766	
Total	33	0·169 87		

different test of the consistency of the treatment effect has to be applied. In this latter case, the procedure in testing is more complicated and needs to be carried out in three steps as follows—

(1) A first estimate, μ_0, of the treatment mean effect is obtained.
(2) This is used to calculate normal scores

$$y_i = \pm \left(\frac{8f_i + 1}{8f_i + 3}\right) \sqrt{\left\{f_i \log_e \left[1 + \left(\frac{x_i - \mu_0}{s_i \sqrt{f_i}}\right)^2\right]\right\}},$$

where the sign is that of the difference $x_i - \mu_0$.

(3) The homogeneity of the scores is tested using the quantity $y_1^2 + y_2^2 + \ldots + y_n^2$. This is distributed approximately as a χ^2 with $n - 1$ degrees of freedom.

The transformation to normal scores given above is due to Wallace (1959). A comparison by Prescott (1974) indicates that this transformation is more accurate than other available transformations.

To demonstrate this procedure, we may consider the responses of Table 13.2.1. The corresponding normal scores for the values of this table are given in Table 13.3.3, using the unweighted means for μ_0. The sums of squares of these scores are given at the bottom of this table.

It may be seen that, whereas the response to N varies significantly ($P < 0.01$) from site to site, the responses to P and K vary no more than would be expected by chance ($P > 0.50$).

13.4 Combination of estimates of a single treatment effect

We may now consider the principles governing the combination of estimates of a single treatment effect. The method adopted will, as pointed out previously, depend upon whether the experiments are of comparable precision and whether the treatment response varies from experiment to experiment.

If the treatment response does not vary significantly from experiment to experiment, the weighted mean may be used, the weights being determined simply from the number of observations used in estimating the effects if the experiments are of comparable precision. The validity of the use of the weighted

Table 13.3.3   Normal scores for fertilizer responses

Site	Linear response to		
	N	P	K
1	−2·27	0·58	1·17
2	0·55	0·10	0·24
3	−1·53	−1·13	−0·25
4	2·53	−1·02	−0·45
5	−1·79	0·00	0·43
6	−0·07	1·78	−0·03
7	−2·24	0·53	−0·02
8	4·36	−0·58	0·79
9	1·56	0·71	1·12
10	−1·10	−0·41	−1·02
11	1·44	1·07	−1·30
12	−1·62	−0·72	0·72
13	−1·82	1·09	−1·91
14	3·82	−1·43	−0·33
15	3·81	−0·29	0·96
$\chi^2_{(14)}$	82·19	12·13	11·70

mean must, however, depend on the usual reservation—that the weights and size of response must be unrelated.

If the treatment response varies significantly from experiment to experiment, then the use of the unweighted mean of the estimated effects is usually preferable. The standard error of this is then

$$\sqrt{\left(\frac{s_1^2 + s_2^2 + \ldots + s_n^2}{n}\right)}.$$

However, if the differences between the variances of the estimated effects are large compared with the variation in the effect from experiment to experiment, it may still be profitable to use a weighted mean. The weights then have to be altered to include an estimate, s_0^2, of the variance of the treatment effect. The revised weights are then approximately

$$w_i = \frac{1}{s_0^2 + s_i^2}.$$

The quantity s_0^2 may be estimated from an analysis of variance of the observed effects.

To demonstrate the practical application of these rules, consider again the data of Table 13.2.1. The analysis of Table 13.3.3 indicated that the phosphate and potash responses did not differ significantly from experiment to experiment.

Their weighted means may therefore be used (with an upper limit for the weights) in the manner described in **13.1**. This gives

$$P = 0.350 \pm 0.109 \text{ and } K = -0.060 \pm 0.109.$$

Since the nitrate responses varied significantly from experiment to experiment, it is necessary to gauge the extent of this variation. The estimated variance of the responses is

$$\frac{1}{14}\left[(-0.24)^2 + (1.23)^2 + \ldots + (3.32)^2 - \frac{(16.06)^2}{15}\right] = 1.8278.$$

Of this, the part due to normal variability is estimated from

$$\frac{s_1^2 + s_2^2 + \ldots + s_n^2}{n} = 0.2345.$$

The difference between these two values thus estimates the variance of the response

$$s_0^2 = 1.8278 - 0.2345 = 1.59.$$

The revised weights may now be calculated. These range between 0.61 for site 11 and 0.42 for site 7—a 46 percent change at most. This is, in fact, too small a change to make a weighting analysis worth while, so that the simple mean $N = 1.07 \pm 0.125$ should be used.

13.5 Series of similar experiments of comparable precision

We may now consider how the results of a series of similar experiments of comparable precision may be combined, the main point being to extend the results of the last three sections to the combination of the results of experiments including a number of treatments.

If the results are of comparable precision, then the simple arithmetic mean may be used to combine the experiments. The main difficulty then is the assignment of standard errors to the comparisons to be made. A further difficulty may be the overall test of significance of treatment differences. Both these difficulties result, in fact, from the possibility of the treatment effects varying from experiment to experiment, and it is this possibility that needs to be investigated in any analysis.

It was shown in **13.3** that, in combining a series of estimates of a single treatment effect from a series of experiments of comparable accuracy, a test of the consistency of the effect could be made by testing the sum of squares for the "experiment $\times$ treatment" interaction against the residual in the analysis. A similar test is therefore suggested for the general analysis and might be used to test whether the effects of treatments vary significantly from experiment to experiment.

Such a test, however, has certain disadvantages. A significant "experiment $\times$ treatment" interaction may be taken as indicating a real change in the treatment effects from experiment to experiment, but the reverse is unfortunately not true: a non-significant value does not show that *all* comparisons that may be made do not change from experiment to experiment. To decide this point, a further analysis is required, partitioning the "experiment × treatment" interaction into components, each of which has to be tested. Unless such components are insignificant, the assumption of invariable treatment effects cannot be justified. An example will serve to demonstrate this point.

Stoate and Lane Poole (1938) reported the results of a set of three pruning experiments upon Monterey pine arranged in 5 × 5 Latin squares in different parts of a plantation.

The five treatments were an unpruned control A, and four prunings, B–E, to heights of 4, 6, 8 and 10 ft, respectively. Table 13.5.1 gives the totals of the annual increments in square inches of basal area for the five treatments and the analysis of variance for the three experiments.

Table 13.5.1   Treatment totals and analysis of variance

Experiment	A	B	C	D	E	Total
1	22·2	22·5	23·2	21·5	19·9	109·3
2	28·6	28·5	25·6	26·3	24·4	133·4
3	22·4	22·9	22·7	21·4	21·5	110·9
Total	73·2	73·9	71·5	69·2	65·8	353·6

	d.f.	Experiment 1 s.s.	m.s.	Experiment 2 s.s.	m.s.	Experiment 3 s.s.	m.s.
Treatments	4	1·258		2·702		0·382	
Rows	4	1·478		1·326		0·378	
Columns	4	0·634		1·394		0·150	
Residual	12	0·680	0·057	1·276	0·106	2·248	0·187
Total	24	4·050		6·698		3·158	

A test of the homogeneity of the residual variances gives $\chi^2_{(2)} = 3{\cdot}94$, $P > 0.10$, so that the experiments may be taken to be of comparable accuracy. One overall analysis may now be performed as shown in Table 13.5.2.

The interaction "experiments × treatments" is not significant, but this does not necessarily mean that a component of some importance is not hidden. For instance, it may be that the treatment effects are different for different mean rates of growth. Such a state of affairs may be of great practical importance, since it would mean that the best pruning procedure depends upon the rate of growth and would be different for different stands.

To test this, the experiment × treatment interaction may be subdivided into

Table 13.5.2 Overall analysis of variance

	d.f.	s.s.	m.s.	Variance ratio
Experiments	2	14·528		
Rows	12	3·182		
Columns	12	2·178		
Treatments	4	2·893		
Experiments × Treatments	8	1·449	0·181	1·55
Residual	36	4·204	0·117	
Total	74	28·434		

two parts, one comparing the fast-growing second experiment with the other two, and the other comparing the first and third experiments. This gives the subdivision shown in Table 13.5.3.

Table 13.5.3 Subdivision of experiment × treatment interaction

	d.f.	s.s.	m.s.	Variance ratio
Experiment 2 v. 1 + 3	4	1·198	0·300	2·56
Experiment 1 v. 3	4	0·251	0·063	0·54
Total	8	1·449		

The first component in this subdivision is nearly significant, indicating that there is a suggestion that the yield affects the response to different levels of pruning. Further subdivision such as that shown in Table 13.5.4 might therefore be adopted. Here, both the linear and quartic components (assuming the

Table 13.5.4 Further subdivision of experiment × treatment interaction

	d.f.	s.s.	Variance ratio
Linear component	1	0·5043	4·31
Quadratic component	1	0·1562	1·34
Cubic component	1	0·0065	0·06
Quartic component	1	0·5312	4·54
Experiment 2 v. 1 + 3	4	1·1982	

rates to be equally spaced) reach significance at the 5 percent levels, so that it appears that constancy of the treatment effects cannot be assumed.

Various procedures might now be adopted. One possibility is to change the scale on which the measurements are made. For instance, by using the logarithms of the growth increments, differences between means reflect proportional changes in the increment, and these do not change significantly with the yield. The analysis of the logarithms may therefore be completed in the usual manner, one overall residual mean square being calculated by pooling the residual and experiment × treatment sums of squares. More commonly, however, it would be necessary to use the interaction in assigning errors to any comparisons that may be made, the procedure being equivalent to testing each comparison separately. A further example will be needed to demonstrate this procedure.

13.6　Example of the analysis of a series of similar experiments

S. E. A. McCullen and F. Wilcoxon have reported the results of three 4×4 experiments on the germination of spores of *Sclerotinia fructicola* from four

Table 13.6.1　Results and analysis of variance for three experiments

Experiment	Dose	Isolate D.A. 1	2	Isolate D.K. 1	2	Isolate E.E. 1	2	Isolate F.D. 1	2
1	1	70	76	64	72	65	70	56	57
	2	56	61	57	49	46	42	48	43
	3	31	35	20	21	45	24	38	36
	4	16	21	8	8	15	12	8	15
2	1	68	57	71	68	74	69	65	71
	2	49	38	52	54	59	51	57	46
	3	32	33	31	31	30	36	47	34
	4	12	20	18	21	24	15	28	21
3	1	71	72	59	55	70	63	64	67
	2	66	63	59	42	63	50	55	50
	3	36	35	41	44	30	25	26	20
	4	26	25	32	39	16	15	16	13

	d.f.	Experiment 1 s.s.	m.s.	Experiment 2 s.s.	m.s.	Experiment 3 s.s.	m.s.
Treatments	15	13856		10744		10939	
Residual	16	400	25·0	455	28·4	349	21·8
Total	31	14256		11199		11288	

single-spore isolates at four concentrations of copper sulphate. The four concentrations were applied to two transfers from the same stock shoot in each of the three experiments, and the percentage germination in 100 spore counts observed in each case. Table 13.6.1 gives the results of these experiments transformed to degrees by the $\sin^{-1}\sqrt{p}$ transformation, and the analysis of variance for the three experiments. An explanation of the purpose of this transformation is given in **14.5**.

The three experiments are obviously of comparable accuracy, so that one overall analysis may be carried out as in Table 13.6.2.

Table 13.6.2   Overall analysis of variance

	d.f.	s.s.	m.s.
Experiments	2	263	131·5
Treatments	15	32617	2174·5
Experiments × Treatments	30	2922	97·4
Residual	48	1204	25·1
Total	95	37006	

The interaction "experiment × treatments" here is highly significant, so that its mean square, rather than the residual mean square, should be used in assigning errors to the estimated effects.

One reservation is, however, necessary. If certain components of this interaction are much higher than others, the corresponding effects will be more variable. In such a case, the appropriate method is to estimate the error in each effect individually by its interaction with experiments—a constant repetition of the procedure used in **13.2**. Only if the separate components of the interaction sum of squares are homogeneous will the use of an overall mean square be justified.

In this instance the interaction may be subdivided as shown in Table 13.6.3. The mean squares in either subdivision are homogeneous, and it would seem

Table 13.6.3   Subdivision of experiment × treatment interaction

		d.f.	s.s.	m.s.		d.f.	s.s.	m.s.
Experiment ×	Doses	6	381	63·5	Linear	2	164	82·0
					Other	4	217	54·2
	Strains	6	976	162·7				
	Strains × Doses	18	1565	86·9	Linear	6	1061	176·8
					Other	12	504	42·0
	Treatments	30	2922					

reasonable to use the overall mean square, 97·4, in estimating the errors of the treatment means. However, for any specific comparisons that may subsequently prove to be of importance, it would still be advisable to check that the corresponding component in the interaction is not significantly greater than this value.

13.7   Series of experiments of differing precision

The example of **13.5** serves to show that there is no uniform answer to the best way of combining a series of experiments of differing precision. If the interaction between experiments and effects is high compared with the variation in the experimental errors, the simple mean may be used. Otherwise, a weighted mean is required.

If, therefore, the comparisons of interest can be split into orthogonal components as in **13.5**, each component should be dealt with separately; in fact, any comparison that proves to be of interest should be treated in the manner of that section. However, if general comparisons between a series of treatments are first desired, an analysis is necessary to show what comparisons are likely to be of interest.

An initial analysis might therefore be carried out using treatment means of the different experiments. With e experiments and t treatments, the analysis of variance would then partition as shown in Table 13.7.1.

Table 13.7.1   Subdivision of analysis of variance

	d.f.
Experiments	$e - 1$
Treatments	$t - 1$
Experiments $\times$ Treatments	$(e - 1)(t - 1)$
Total	$et - 1$

The components in this analysis would certainly be heterogeneous, but the interaction mean square might nevertheless be compared with

$$\frac{s_1^2 + s_2^2 + \ldots + s_n^2}{n},$$

where s_i is the standard error of the means in the ith experiment. No exact test is available for this purpose; all that is required in this instance is some guidance as to whether the treatment effects vary from experiment to experiment and, if so, whether they are likely to vary so much that the differing accuracies of the experiments may be ignored.

If the interaction mean square is large, the analysis may be continued as in **13.6**; the interaction mean square may be examined for homogeneity, and if no components are outstanding, the overall mean square may be used to estimate the errors of any comparisons. If some components are outstanding, they should be used in estimating the errors of the appropriate comparisons. In any case, the components corresponding to any comparison of interest should be removed and examined.

If the interaction mean square is small, it is again necessary to examine it to see if it contains any large components and, if so, to use these in estimating the errors of the appropriate comparisons. If not, then σ_0^2, the variation in the treatment effect, may be estimated by subtracting $(s_1^2 + s_2^2 + \ldots + s_n^2)/n$ from the interaction mean square. Weighted means may then be used with weights $w_i = 1/(s_i^2 + \sigma_0^2)$.

It is necessary to realize that, whatever analysis is employed in this instance, it must be of an approximate and exploratory nature. The main purpose of such an analysis should be to provide a basis for further investigation. An example will demonstrate how this is done.

Watson (1939) reported the results of a series of experiments testing the effects on wheat yield of applying 25 kg of nitrate fertilizer per hectare, both early and late in the year. These results are shown in Table 13.7.2.

Table 13.7.2 Mean yields of a series of fertilizer experiments

Year of harvest	No N	N early	N late	s_i^2	w_i
1926	16·3	17·9	19·8	0·49	1·4
1927	25·2	26·6	26·5	0·79	1·0
1928	25·1	25·7	27·2	0·27	2·1
1929	17·6	19·4	19·4	1·31	0·7
1930 (a)	15·1	15·0	15·4	0·17	2·6
(b)	26·7	24·6	26·7	1·14	0·7
1931	21·2	22·4	21·4	0·05	3·8
Mean	21·0	21·7	22·3	0·60	12·3

If an analysis of variance is carried out on the mean yields of these experiments, the values shown in Table 13.7.3 are obtained. The experiments × treatments

Table 13.7.3 Analysis of variance of mean yields

	d.f.	s.s.	m.s.
Experiments	6	363·36	
Treatments	2	6·05	3·02
Experiments × Treatments	12	9·67	0·81
Total	20	379·08	

interaction exceeds the mean variance by 0·21, and this might therefore be used as an estimate of σ_0^2. However, before doing so, it is advisable to check the homogeneity of the experiments × treatments interaction. This is done in Table 13.7.4, which shows that for the three partitions most worthy of consideration there is no large component in the interaction sum of squares.

Table 13.7.4 Partitions of the experiments × treatments interaction

	d.f.	s.s.
Early N v. No N	6	5·61
Late N v. (No N + Early N)	6	4·06
Late N v. No N	6	4·81
Early N v. (No N + Late N)	6	4·85
Early N v. Late N	6	4·07
No N v. (Early N + Late N)	6	5·59

The value 0·21 may therefore be taken as an estimate of σ_0^2, and weights $w_i = 1/(\sigma_0^2 + s_i^2)$ calculated as in the last column of Table 13.7.2. This gives means of 20·45, 21·18 and 21·54 for the three applications, the standard error of the difference between any pair being roughly

$$\sqrt{\left(\frac{2}{12\cdot3}\right)} = \pm\, 0\cdot40.$$

To carry out an overall test of significance in this instance is slightly more difficult. The analysis of variance of Table 13.7.3 provides an approximate method of doing so, but since the variance ratio, 3·73, is of borderline significance, a more exact test is needed. A more exact estimate of the variance ratio can be obtained by multiplying the mean square of the weighted means by the overall weight. This is likely to be an overestimate. Since this gives a value of 3·79, which is not significant, we may conclude that the differences between the estimated means are not significant.

13.8 Combination of estimates obtained at different times and places

The analysis of experiments carried out at different places and at different times introduces two new complications into the procedure for combining and testing a series of estimates.

First, if the experiments differ in accuracy, a weighting factor may have to be adopted in which the amounts of the variation of the treatment effects from place to place, from year to year, and independent of places and years, have to be estimated. The weighting factor is then of the form

$$\omega_i = \frac{1}{\sigma_0'^2 + \sigma_0''^2 + \sigma_0'''^2 + s_i^2}.$$

In practice, however, this will usually give estimates differing but little from those obtained using one overall value $\sigma_0{}^2$ for the variation in the treatment effects.

Secondly, the test of significance of the treatment effects will have to be modified to take into account the different sources of variation. To demonstrate how this situation arises, we may consider an experiment carried out by Greenwood and Salerno (1949). In this experiment, sixteen judges placed in order of preference six dishes (three varieties of kale cooked for two different lengths of time) on each of five dates. To carry out an analysis, normal scores (see **14.6**) were used. The variabilities in scores for different judges and on different days were comparable, so that one overall analysis could be a carried out as shown in Table 13.8.1.

Table 13.8.1 Overall analysis of variance

	d.f.	s.s.	m.s.
Dishes	5	17·80	3·56
Days × Dishes	20	32·23	1·61
Judges × Dishes	75	99·84	1·33
Days × Judges × Dishes	300	180·13	0·60
Total	400	330·00	

There is evidently a significant variation in the relative ranks on different days and with different judges. To test whether the differences between dishes are significant, it is necessary to take both these facts into account. This can be done by testing the variance ratio

$$\frac{3·56 + 0·60}{1·61 + 1·33} = 1·41,$$

using f_1 and f_2 degrees of freedom, where

$$\frac{(3·56 + 0·60)^2}{f_1} = \frac{(3·56)^2}{5} + \frac{(0·60)^2}{300}, \text{ i.e. } f_1 = 7,$$

$$\frac{(1·61 + 1·33)^2}{f_2} = \frac{(1·61)^2}{20} + \frac{(1·33)^2}{75}, \text{ i.e. } f_2 = 56.$$

The variance ratio thus fails to reach the 5 percent significance level, 2·18.

As usual, in applying this test it is necessary to ensure that the components of interaction are homogeneous. Here, this was not so, and the component testing the differences between varieties of kale was markedly larger than the remainder. The separation of the components corresponding to the comparisons between kale gave a revised variance ratio $F = (8·61 + 0·68)/(2·87 + 1·89) = 1·95$ with roughly 2 and 19·5 degrees of freedom. This also fails to reach significance.

13.9 Combination of results in serial experiments

Some care is needed in combining results from different periods of a long-term experiment since the results may not be completely independent of one another. For instance, in a field trial, plots with a high fertility in one year usually tend also to have fertility in succeeding years. The treatment, then, of results in successive years as if they were independent may lead to an incorrect conception of the precision of the whole experiment.

If correlations exist between responses from the same plot in different periods, it will be possible to obtain more precise estimates of the effects in a given period by utilizing the responses obtained in previous periods. Curnow and Sharpe (1962) have shown how this can be achieved in two-period experiments, and a more general discussion of the problem can be found in Patterson and Henderson (1973). Using these improved estimates, combined estimates can then be obtained using the methods given earlier in this chapter.

It is important, however, in combining results in serial and other experiments that the use of external factors should not be overlooked. It may be that the results of such experiments should be combined with weights which depend on external factors. For instance, in the grass-cutting experiment of **11.8** the dry matter yield in the early part of the season may be of more economic value than the yield in the latter part of the season, and hence the results of such experiments may best be combined according to their economic worth.

14 Scaling of Observations

14.1 Reasons for scaling observations

A difficulty which sometimes occurs in the analysis of experimental results is that the observations do not satisfy the assumptions underlying the analysis. In consequence, the treatment effects and their standard errors may be incorrectly estimated, and the tests of significance may be vitiated. It is therefore important to ensure that the assumptions underlying the analysis are at least roughly satisfied. Fortunately, in most instances, the analysis is insensitive to deviations from the basic assumptions, and results obtained in the normal manner will be only slightly affected by these deviations.

As was indicated in **1.6**, there are three assumptions that are commonly made—

(1) that the observations are normally distributed about their true or expected values;
(2) that the observations are independent;
(3) that the variance of the observations is constant, or, if not, that it varies in some known manner.

The validity of these assumptions ensures that efficient estimates of treatment effects and their errors are obtained. If any one of these assumptions is untrue, biased or inefficient estimates may be obtained.

One other important assumption which is commonly made may be mentioned. This is

(4) that the treatment effect is constant within the experiment and does not vary at different points of the scale of measurement.

This assumption is in part tested in the factorial experiment, by determining whether the changes caused by one set of treatments influence the effect of another treatment. Again, as pointed out in **13.5**, it is usually necessary to test this assumption in combining the results of a group of experiments. It is equally necessary to do so in the individual experiment.

If any of the assumptions (1)–(4) is incorrect, the estimates of effects and their errors may be biased or inaccurate. The analysis of variance, although algebraically correct, will no longer be a valid procedure, since the variance ratios will be biased (usually upwards) and will therefore give incorrect conceptions of the significance of the treatment effects.

These assumptions will be examined in this chapter. In particular, it will be shown how, by altering the scale on which the observations are taken, these assumptions can be made roughly true, so that the normal statistical procedures and tests may be applied.

14.2 Scaling for additivity

Scaling is often important when the range of values of observations on a particular treatment is large. For instance, an experiment which used insect counts made in different months would normally give a wide range of counts. In consequence, the treatment effects might be expected to be largest in those months in which the insects were greatest in numbers. In any analysis, then, it would be necessary either to consider the treatment effects as varying at different points on the scale of measurement, or to adopt a different scale on which the treatment effects were constant. Which of these alternatives would be adopted would depend in part upon other considerations, such as homogeneity of variance, but usually the latter alternative would be preferable.

To consider a more concrete illustration, the figures in Table 14.2.1 represent

Table 14.2.1   Counts of insects in ten blocks

| Treatment | Block | | | | | | | | | |
	1	2	3	4	5	6	7	8	9	10
1	32	38	27	7	13	14	26	25	22	30
1	18	40	39	12	19	26	30	19	18	28
2	6	23	8	4	3	18	26	27	17	19
2	9	14	20	13	15	14	15	19	19	10
3	10	21	25	10	13	20	33	48	28	27
3	4	21	26	4	9	14	30	18	27	18
4	2	17	11	3	10	10	26	13	22	17
4	24	13	13	10	6	14	28	11	34	7
5	13	2	5	0	18	10	33	23	20	34
5	17	22	23	8	14	16	26	22	15	34
6	13	10	21	4	10	8	17	15	13	16
6	17	9	29	5	18	15	19	16	27	23
7	37	58	28	11	24	44	30	44	56	45
7	44	71	55	20	26	27	43	52	39	58
Total	246	359	330	111	198	250	382	352	357	366

the counts of an insect, *Pyrausta nubilalis*, in ten blocks each consisting of 14 plots, two plots of each of seven treatments being included in each block. This is part of the data reported by Beall (1942).

Inspection of these figures shows that treatment effects tend to be largest in the blocks with high counts. For instance, the differences between the total counts on treatments 7 and 1 vary between 12 in the fourth block and 55 in the ninth block.

This same effect is shown more clearly in Table 14.2.2, where the mean $\bar{x}$ and treatment mean square s_t^2 are shown for each block. With one replicate in each

Table 14.2.2   Means and treatment mean squares

					Block					
	1	2	3	4	5	6	7	8	9	10
x	17·6	25·6	23·6	7·9	14·1	17·9	27·3	25·1	25·5	26·1
s_t^2	276·1	773·6	244·4	30·1	66·3	139·5	80·1	290·5	225·0	368·6
$s_t/\bar{x}$	0·94	1·09	0·66	0·69	0·58	0·66	0·33	0·68	0·59	0·74

block the treatment mean square would be the same as the ordinary within-block mean square. It may be seen from Table 14.2.2 that there is a distinct tendency for the blocks with higher mean yields to give higher treatment differences.

The significance of this tendency may be approximately tested by using the fact that log s^2 tends to be normally distributed with variance $0.3772/(f-1)$, where f is the number of degrees of freedom of s^2, here 6. A regression analysis testing the dependence of log s_t^2 on log $\bar{x}$ may thus be converted into a partition of χ^2 in the manner shown in Table 14.2.3. The final column of this table gives the ratio of the sum of squares in the analysis of variance to the variance of log s_t^2. This analysis shows quite clearly that the overall variation in s_t^2 is significant ($P < 0.05$) and may be accounted for by its association with the mean level $\bar{x}$.

Table 14.2.3   Analysis of variation

	d.f.	s.s.	χ^2
Regression	1	0·851	11·28
Residual	8	0·678	8·99
Total	9	1·529	20·27

The main problem then is to decide on what scale the observations should be measured, i.e. what transformation should be applied to make the treatment effects constant. The most common solution is to use a logarithmic scale, i.e. the logarithms of the observations, but the usefulness of this scale is restricted to cases where the treatment effects increase proportionally with the mean. Then, the use of logarithms makes proportional changes take the same value at any level.

To test whether the logarithmic transformation is likely to be useful, it may be noted that in such cases $s_t/\bar{x}$ will be roughly constant. This may be tested by inspection of the observations; the value of $s_t/\bar{x}$ are given in Table 14.2.2. Alternatively, if an analysis similar to that in Table 14.2.3 has been carried out, the regression coefficient of log s_t^2 on log $\bar{x}$ should be approximately equal to 2. In this instance, its value is 1·81, so that the use of the logarithmic transformation is suggested.

Where small numbers and zeros occur in the observations, it is necessary to employ some modification of the logarithmic transformation. The most common modification is to use the logarithms of one plus the numbers, i.e. $\log (x + 1)$. Using this transformation, a fresh analysis may be carried out. This gives the values of $\bar{x}$ and s_t^2 and the partition of χ^2 shown in Table 14.2.4.

Table 14.2.4 Means, treatment mean squares, and the analysis of variation

	1	2	3	4	5	6	7	8	9	10
$\bar{x}$	1·16	1·31	1·33	0·86	1·14	1·24	1·44	1·37	1·39	1·38
s_t^2	0·153	0·197	0·092	0·102	0·063	0·051	0·022	0·068	0·045	0·097

	d.f.	s.s.	χ^2
Regression	1	0·082	1·09
Residual	8	0·596	7·90
Total	9	0·678	8·99

No significant variation in the treatment effects exists from block to block, nor is the variation associated with the mean level. It would therefore appear that the use of logarithms of 1 plus the observations makes the treatment effects constant. Further examination of the individual effects is nevertheless advisable before final conclusions are drawn.

One other simple transformation might be noted here, namely the square-root transformation. This transformation is likely to be useful where $s_t^2/\bar{x}$ is roughly constant, i.e. where the regression coefficient of $\log s_t^2$ on $\log \bar{x}$ is approximately equal to 1. Where small numbers are experienced, the alternatives of $\sqrt{(x + \frac{3}{8})}$ and $\sqrt{x} + \sqrt{(x + 1)}$ should be considered.

14.3 Testing for additivity

Usually it is unnecessary to carry out rigorous tests of the assumptions that are made in any analysis, since any suggestion, significant or otherwise, that these do not hold, requires investigating. Nevertheless, it is often useful to be able to gauge the likelihood of any observed changes in treatment effects having arisen by chance.

This may be done quite simply if estimates of error are available which are independent of the treatment effects. For instance, each treatment was repeated twice in each block of the last section, and therefore analyses of variance may be carried out as shown in Table 14.3.1.

It may be seen that the treatment $\times$ blocks interaction is highly significant ($P < 0.01$) for the untransformed counts, but is insignificant ($P > 0.50$) for the transformed values. This gives the same conclusion as was obtained in the last section: that there are significant changes in treatment effects from block to block for the untransformed counts, but not for the transformed counts.

It must, however, be noted that the same objections raised in 13.5 may also

Table 14.3.1 Analyses of variance

| | d.f. | Untransformed counts | | | Transformed counts | |
		s.s.	m.s.		s.s.	m.s.
Treatments	6	10327			3·2813	
Blocks	9	5194			3·7282	
Blocks × treatments	54	4637	85·9		2·0487	0·0379
Residual	70	3354	47·9		2·7907	0·0399
Total	139	23512			11·8489	

apply here. In particular, the treatment × blocks interaction, although insignificant, may contain a significant component. For that reason it is often advisable to partition an insignificant interaction into components likely to be of interest. If no specific comparisons are of interest, this should be carried out on the basis of the total yields of each block–treatment combination, i.e. on a regression basis. For instance, the deviations of the transformed block totals from the mean block total are nearly proportional to

$$-1, 1, 1, -6, -2, 0, 2, 1, 2, 2,$$

and the deviations of the treatment totals from the mean treatment total are nearly proportional to

$$2, -2, 0, -3, -2, -2, 7.$$

The components corresponding to these deviations may be extracted as shown in Table 14.3.2. For example,

$$-2·80 + 3·20 + 3·05 - 6 \times 2·01 - \ldots + 2 \times 2·95 = \quad 6·22$$
$$2 \times 6·22 - 2 \times 6·09 + \qquad \ldots + 7 \times 6·76 = -9·69, \text{etc.}$$

These values may then be used to calculate the sums of squares shown. These give the final analysis of Table 14.3.3, e.g. $0·1688 - 0·0113 = 0·1575$ and $0·3521 - 0·0113 = 0·3408$.

It may be seen that none of these components is large, and that the assumption of no interaction is reasonable. The transformation seems therefore to be successful.

Two points may now be noted. In the first place, an independent estimate of error is often not available, since the residual in any analysis is usually composed of the blocks × treatment interaction. For such situations, Tukey (1949, 1955) proposed a test which extracts one degree of freedom from the residual to test for non-additivity.

Secondly, the design may not allow the independent estimation of the treatment mean square to be carried out under a number of conditions. For instance, in the investigation of observations of a Latin square design, the treatment mean

Table 14.3.2 Calculation of components of interaction

Treatment	Score	Block 1 −1	2 1	3 1	4 −6	5 −2	6 0	7 2	8 1	9 2	10 2	Scored total
1	2	2·80	3·20	3·05	2·01	2·45	2·61	2·92	2·71	2·64	2·95	6·22
2	−2	1·85	2·56	2·27	1·85	1·80	2·46	2·63	2·75	2·56	2·34	6·09
3	0	1·74	2·68	2·84	1·74	2·15	2·50	3·02	2·97	2·91	2·73	9·33
4	−3	1·88	2·41	2·23	1·64	1·89	2·22	2·89	2·23	2·90	2·16	7·27
5	−2	2·41	1·84	2·16	0·95	2·46	2·27	2·96	2·74	2·52	3·08	10·83
6	−2	2·41	2·04	2·82	1·48	2·32	2·15	2·56	2·43	2·60	2·61	6·90
7	7	3·23	3·63	3·21	2·40	2·83	3·10	3·13	3·37	3·36	3·43	6·76
Scored total		9·23	11·70	7·38	7·34	5·88	6·50	2·78	6·48	4·74	7·37	−9·69

Scored total (treatments) = 53·40

69·40

$$(-1)^2 + (1)^2 + (1)^2 + \ldots + (2)^2 \qquad = 56$$
$$(2)^2 + (-2)^2 + (0)^2 + \ldots + (7)^2 \qquad = 74$$

$$\frac{(-9.69)^2}{2 \times 56 \times 74} \qquad = 0.0113$$

$$\frac{(6.22)^2 + (6.09)^2 + \ldots + (6.76)^2}{2 \times 56} - \frac{(53.40)^2}{2 \times 56 \times 7} = 0.1688$$

$$\frac{(9.23)^2 + (11.70)^2 + \ldots + (7.37)^2}{2 \times 74} - \frac{(69.40)^2}{2 \times 74 \times 10} = 0.3521$$

Table 14.3.3 Partition of blocks × treatments interaction

	d.f.	s.s.	m.s.
Linear blocks × linear treatments	1	0·0113	0·0113
Linear blocks × non-linear treatments	5	0·1575	0·0315
Non-linear blocks × linear treatments	8	0·3408	0·0426
Non-linear blocks × non-linear treatments	40	1·5391	0·0385
Blocks × treatments	54	2·0487	

square may be estimated within rows or within columns but not within both, unless the whole design is used, in which case only one estimate is available. Therefore it is necessary to investigate either the mean square for treatments plus rows or that for treatments plus columns. This procedure will, however, often suffice. Alternatively, Tukey's procedure may be used to partition the residual sum of squares and test for additivity.

14.4 The scaling of percentages—the probit transformation

One particular transformation to make treatment effects additive is worth noting—the probit transformation. This transformation is useful for dealing with the analysis of percentages based upon counts. For example, if the proportions of animals dying after different treatments are observed in an experiment, the probit transformation may be required if constant effects are to appear so at all points on the scale of measurement.

To see why this should be so, consider a treatment whose effect is to reduce the percentage mortality from a particular cause on one batch of animals from, say, 60 per cent to 20 per cent. On another batch of animals, the percentage mortality may be only 30 percent, so that at best the reduction due to the treatment would appear to be less than previously. This state of affairs arises owing to the limitations in the values that can be taken by percentages (from 0 to 100), but also as a consequence of the fact that a change from, say, 20 percent to 10 percent cannot usually be regarded as comparable to a change from 10 percent to 0 percent, the latter change representing the more significant improvement.

To understand the probit transformation, it is necessary to employ the concept of an individual "tolerance" or "stress" distribution which is normal. That is, there is considered to be an underlying normal distribution of "tolerance" of the individuals. Any one set of experimental conditions will impose certain stresses on the individuals, and individuals whose tolerance is low will succumb to these stresses and thus give rise to the experimental percentages. The purpose of the probit transformation is to transform these percentages into the corresponding "stress" or "tolerance" values which may then be used in an analysis.

This situation is pictured graphically in Fig. 14.4.1, which shows how the

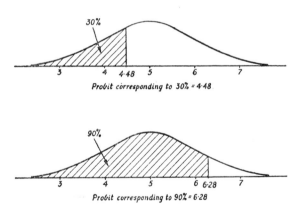

Fig. 14.4.1   Normal tolerance distributions

value of probits may be determined for different percentages. If should be noted that a normal distribution with mean equal to 5 and standard deviation equal to 1 is used as the basis of the transformation. Tables of this transformation may be found in Fisher and Yates' *Statistical Tables*.

In a probit analysis it will be necessary to attach weights to the probits, since the accuracy of the percentages and their corresponding probits will vary; it is easier to determine a probit near to 5·0 accurately than one with a high or low value. This raises complications in any analysis, since it means that each transformed value will have a different weight and that the orthogonality of comparisons in the analysis will be destroyed. Full details of the methods of probit analysis can be found in Finney (1971).

14.5 Scaling to attain variance homogeneity

It is characteristic of many types of observations that their reliability or variability changes with their mean level. Such observations need to be transformed if the condition of variance homogeneity, or constancy or variation, is to be met. As explained previously, if this condition is not met, tests of significance based upon the analysis of variance will no longer be valid, and confidence limits will be incorrectly estimated.

The example used in **14.2** provides a typical illustration of observations for which the variation might be expected to increase with the mean level, i.e. higher infestation might be expected to give more variable counts. This can in fact be investigated either graphically, by plotting the differences between replicate pairs in the same block against their sums, or, alternatively, by a numerical test, possibly of the kind described in **14.2**.

If residual mean squares are calculated for each block–treatment combination in turn, a regression of $\log s^2$ on $\log \bar{x}$ may be calculated and tested in the manner described above. An alternative approximate numerical test can be carried out by taking a regression of the differences between pairs, signs being ignored, on the sums of pairs. This allows the residual sums of squares of Table 14.3.1 to be partitioned as shown in Table 14.5.1.

Table 14.5.1 Partition of the residual sum of squares

	Untransformed counts $b = 0.08$			Transformed counts $b = -0.11$	
	d.f.	s.s.	m.s.	s.s.	m.s.
Mean difference	1	2029		1·3752	
Regression	1	109	109	0·4609	0·4609
Remainder	68	1216	17·9	0·9547	0·0140
Residual	70	3354		2·7908	

This analysis shows that neither the untransformed nor the transformed counts succeed in stabilizing the variance. In one case the variance increases with the mean, and in the other it decreases, implying that some transformation less drastic than the logarithmic might succeed in stabilizing the variance. The use of the square-root transformation is thus suggested.

For the data of Table 14.2.1, the logarithmic transformation is proposed to achieve additivity, whilst the square-root transformation is proposed to stabilize the variance. In general it may not be possible to obtain a transformation which will achieve both additivity and variance homogeneity, in which case it will be necessary to sacrifice one property to attain the other.

To investigate this further, the methods proposed by Box and Cox (1964) for examining the family of transformations

$$y = \begin{cases} [(x + a)^b - 1]/b, & b \neq 0 \\ \log (x + a), & b = 0 \end{cases}$$

for various values of a and b could be employed. Alternatively, the simpler but effective approach of Draper and Hunter (1969) can be used. This involves carrying out analyses corresponding to those given in Tables 14.3.1 and 14.5.1 for a number of transformations. An appropriate transformation for achieving additivity and variance stability may then be suggested from an inspection of the variance ratios of the blocks × treatments interaction and of the regression component of the residual. These ratios are given for $a = 1$ and for various values of b in Table 14.5.2. The g_2 values given in the last line of this table are considered in the next section.

Table 14.5.2 Analysis of transformations

Variance ratio	Values of b								
	-0.4	-0.2	0.0	0.2	0.4	0.5	0.6	0.8	1.0
Blocks × treatments	0.80	0.86	0.95	1.08	1.25	1.34	1.43	1.62	1.79
Regression	101.4	59.5	32.8	15.6	5.1	2.1	0.4	0.9	6.1
g_2		9.21	5.24	2.95	1.62	0.82	0.57	0.41	0.37	0.70

As we have already seen, the untransformed counts ($b = 1.0$) fail to achieve additivity ($P < 0.01$) and fail to stabilize the variance ($P < 0.02$). Also, the logarithmic transformation ($b = 0.0$) achieves additivity ($P > 0.50$) but does not stabilize the variance ($P < 0.01$). However, the square-root transformation ($b = 0.5$) appears to achieve both objectives, with $P > 0.10$ in both cases. Before accepting this transformation, however, further analyses of the type described in **14.3** should be carried out.

The above procedure for looking at various transformations can easily be incorporated into standard regression and analysis of variance computer programs.

For the example of **14.2** it has been possible to find a transformation of the counts which will stabilize the variance and give additivity of treatment effects. In other situations it may not be possible to achieve both of these objectives. In particular, it has already been noted that the probit transformation for percentages requires the use of weighting factors, since homogeneity of variance is not obtained using this transformation. In fact, homogeneity of variance cannot be obtained unless the percentages are based upon equal numbers of observations, in which case the transformation $y = \sin^{-1} \sqrt{p}$ (where p is a proportion) should be used.

This transformation has been tabulated in degrees in Fisher and Yates' *Statistical Tables*, and its use has already been demonstrated in the example of **13.6.** When each percentage is the result of a large number, n, of independent observations, the theoretical value of the residual mean square obtained after the transformation is $821/n$. This value may be used in the analysis if the assumption that the observations are independent is reasonable and consistent with the observed value of the residual mean square.

In the analyses of Table 13.6.1, the individual mean squares ranged from $21 \cdot 8$ to $28 \cdot 4$, while their theoretical value, on the assumption that the spores acted independently, was $8 \cdot 21$. It is obvious that in this instance the assumption of independence is invalid and that the calculated mean squares should be used in preference to the theoretical value.

Here, it should be noted, the loss of additivity is not likely to have serious effects, since the range of values taken by any one treatment is not very large. It does, however, mean that the linear components used in this analysis no longer have any exact meaning, but simply represent a comparison that is likely to be large.

In the normal investigation of the stability of the variance, replicate observations will not be available to estimate the manner in which the variability may change with the mean level. If this situation is thought to be likely, it may be necessary to adopt a design which allows independent estimates of variability to be obtained. Alternatively, an independent investigation may be carried out to determine a suitable transformation. If no situation of this kind is visualized, it may be necessary to carry out a rough analysis of the type employed in Tables 14.3.2 and 14.3.3 to decide whether a transformation is likely to be necessary and, if so, what form it should take.

14.6 Scaling for non-normality

Transformations may also be used to ensure that the distribution of observations is fairly normal. However, unless the deviations from normality are fairly large, this effect may often be neglected in subsequent analysis. This is because the mean of a number of observations tends to be normally distributed whether the individual observations are normally distributed or not. Consequently, if the groups are large, the variance-ratio test for testing the difference between group means is valid for most of the commonly met distributions. For this reason, achieving normality is usually a secondary consideration after achieving homogeneity of the residual mean square. Also, it is often the case in practice that the transformation which tends to stabilize the variance is also the one which achieves normality, so that both objectives can be attained simultaneously.

In order to investigate normality, the residuals from the analysis need to be calculated. The use of residuals has been considered previously in **2.12** with regard to estimating missing observations. Anscombe (1961) has given expressions for coefficients of skewness and kurtosis, based on simple unweighted sums of third and fourth powers of the residuals, which can be used to examine normality. For the example of Table 14.2.1, an equivalent procedure would be to study the differences, d_i, between the replicate observations. For instance, a coefficient of kurtosis may be calculated from

$$g_2 = \frac{n \Sigma d_i^4}{2(\Sigma d_i^2)^2} - 3.$$

If the distribution is normal, g_2 takes the value 0 with a standard error of $\sqrt{(12/n)}$ or ± 0.29. The calculation of such statistics can again be incorporated into a computer analysis of the family of transformations described in **14.5**. In Table 14.5.2, the values of g_2 are given for a number of different transformations. Using a standard error of ± 0.29 as a rough guide, we can see that the kurtosis of the untransformed counts is barely significant, but it is highly significant for the logarithmic transformation. For the square-root transformation the value of g_2 is not significant, so that, in this instance, this transformation achieves all three objectives: namely, additivity, variance stability, and normality.

An alternative procedure is to plot the residuals on standard, i.e. normal, probability paper. The points should lie approximately on a straight line. The use of half-normal plots to examine the treatment comparisons in 2^m factorial experiments is discussed in the next section.

The residuals can also be examined by looking for signs of abnormal patterns, such as an excessive number of large positive and negative residuals. Table 14.6.1 gives the residuals for the experiment of Table 2.2.1. The method of calculating these residuals is given in **2.12**. It should be noted that the treatment and block totals are roughly zero in this table.

Table 14.6.1   Residuals of randomized block experiment

Litter	A	B	Diet C	D	E	Total
1	−7·65	−2·69	4·39	2·89	3·06	0·00
2	−6·81	1·95	−4·07	4·53	4·40	0·00
3	−3·53	1·03	−2·79	2·71	2·58	0·00
4	3·43	−12·81	1·27	0·87	7·24	0·00
5	0·95	3·21	−8·91	4·09	0·66	0·00
6	−2·71	4·25	9·43	−1·17	−9·80	0·00
7	10·81	5·27	0·25	−8·05	−8·28	0·00
8	5·51	−0·23	0·45	−5·85	0·12	0·00
Total	0·00	−0·02	0·02	0·02	−0·02	0·00

A full and exact examination of the normality of a series of residuals of this type involves rather complicated analysis since the residuals are not independent, but a rapid examination may be carried out on the assumption of independence.

The sum of squares of the residuals, obtained from Table 2.2.2, is 1137·7, so that the mean square of these deviations is $1137\cdot7/40 = 28\cdot44$, and their standard deviation is $\sqrt{(28\cdot44)} = \pm\ 5\cdot33$. Ninety-five percent, or 38, of the residuals would be expected to fall within $\pm\ 1\cdot96 \times 5\cdot33 = \pm\ 10\cdot45$, and 99 percent, or $39\cdot6$, to fall within $\pm\ 2\cdot58 \times 5\cdot33 = \pm\ 13\cdot75$. Actually, 38 and 40 residuals respectively fall within these limits, so that the agreement with the normal distribution is good. No further investigation of the normality of the residuals is called for in this instance. If, however, 34 and 37 residuals fell within these limits, the use of a transformation would have been suggested.

One particular transformation to achieve normality that is often used should be noted: the use of normal scores. These scores give the average values of the largest, next largest, third largest, . . . observations in a series of n observations taken at random from a normal distribution. They are particularly useful for assigning values to observations of rank or order of preference. These scores have been tabulated in Fisher and Yates' *Statistical Tables*.

The example of **13.8** illustrates the type of problem to which these scores may be applied. In this example, six dishes were placed in order of preference by sixteen judges on each of five days. Thus the values given by any one judge on any one day consisted of an ordering of the numbers 1–6. These are obviously not normally distributed and, for the purposes of analysis, need to be replaced by the corresponding normal scores. These are $1\cdot27$, $0\cdot64$, $0\cdot20$, $-0\cdot20$, $-0\cdot64$, $-1\cdot27$. The analysis carried out with these scores then indicates whether consistent differences exist between the dishes.

14.7 The half-normal plot

In a factorial experiment in which each factor is at two levels, the half-normal plot technique proposed by Daniel (1959) is particularly valuable in aiding an examination of the observations. It is suitable for deciding which effects are significant in small experiments where there are very few degrees of freedom available for error. It is also useful in indicating whether the residuals are normally distributed or whether observations which can in some sense be regarded as outliers are likely to be present.

The example of **5.2** will be used to illustrate the technique. First, the absolute values of the treatment effects are arranged in order of magnitude, as given in

Table 14.7.1 Absolute values of treatment effects

Effect	$\male$	F	$F\male$	$CFM\male$	CF
Total	9·40	1·78	1·68	0·84	0·64
Effect	$M\male$	C	CM	FM	CFM
Total	0·34	0·32	0·22	0·20	0·18
Effect	$CF\male$	$CM\male$	M	$C\male$	$FM\male$
Total	0·14	0·08	0·04	0·02	0·02

Table 14.7.1. It should be noted that the $CFM\mathring{\delta}$ effect has been confounded with blocks.

These values are now plotted on half-normal probability paper, i.e. on normal probability paper which has been folded in half and whose probability values P greater than 50 percent have been replaced by the corresponding values $P' = 2P - 100$. The relation

$$P' = (i - \tfrac{1}{2})/n, \quad i = 1, 2, \ldots n,$$

where n is the number of treatment effects, is used for plotting the empirical distribution. Alternatively it is possible to construct special purpose paper, with rank values replacing the probabilities, for $n = 2^m - 1$ and for various values of m.

In Fig. 14.7.1 the effects given in Table 14.7.1 are plotted in rank order on half-normal probability paper. For instance, the largest effect, $\mathring{\delta}$, is plotted on the line numbered 15, the next largest, F, on the line numbered 14, and so on.

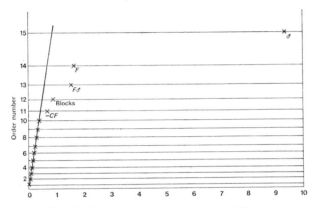

Fig. 14.7.1   Half-normal plot of a confounded 2^5 experiment

If no effects were significant and if the effects were normally distributed, the points in Fig. 14.7.1 would all fall on a straight line passing through the origin. However, it is clear in this example that the normal distribution does not provide a close fit to a number of the points in the tail of the distribution. This would indicate that either these effects are significant or that the observations need further examination. The presence of a large number of high-order interactions in the tail of the distribution may indicate that there exist outliers amongst the observations or that the underlying normality assumption is invalid. The problem of detecting outliers is discussed in the next section. A transformation of the observations may be necessary if the effects are non-normal. The length of the tail of the distribution in the half-normal plot will give a guide to the type of transformation necessary. The square-root transformation is the least drastic, but a long tail would indicate the need for a logarithmic or, even more drastic, a reciprocal transformation. After replacing or excluding outliers or after transforming the observations, the half-normal plot can be used again to examine the new effects.

In the example of Fig. 14.7.1 it would seem reasonable, however, to accept the two main effects δ and F and their interaction $F\delta$ as being real, and that the underlying normality assumption is valid.

Half-normal plots have been advocated by Draper and Stoneman (1964) as a method of checking on possible bias introduced when missing observations are estimated in 2^m experiments; see **3.5**.

Such graphical procedures can be included, without too much difficulty, as part of a computer analysis. Sparks (1970) gives an algorithm which plots the treatment effects on a half-normal probability scale using line-printer output. Of course, special graph-plotting computer equipment could be used, but the accuracy of most line-printers will be more than adequate.

14.8   Rejection of outliers

In experimentation, observations are sometimes recorded which conflict with the pattern exhibited by the other observations. Frequently, they are extreme observations, or "outliers", in the sense that they are much larger or much smaller than the other observations. The residuals corresponding to these observations will be large and hence considerable doubt will be thrown on their validity. The possibility of errors in recording the observations, perhaps in the instruments, and of disturbing factors from outside then needs to be considered. If the existence of such possibilities is proved, outliers may be rejected. Otherwise it needs to be considered whether these observations are likely to have arisen by chance, and if not, to modify or altogether reject them.

An example of a case where there is some doubt about the validity of an observation has already been provided in **4.3**. The extreme observation on the p_0l_0 treatment in the third block in Table 4.3.2 was in fact retained without any test of its significance being carried out. However, such a test will often be required to gauge how extreme any one observation may be and to provide a basis for deciding about the rejection of the observation.

To carry out a test, it is necessary to estimate by how much the residual sum of squares would be reduced if the outlier were rejected, i.e. were treated as being missing. Using an estimated value of 274, obtained by any of the methods in **2.12**, for the observation on the p_0l_0 treatment leads to the partition of the original residual sum of squares shown in Table 14.8.1. The sum of squares due to the outlier is obtained by subtraction.

Table 14.8.1   Analysis of variance for testing an outlier

	d.f.	s.s.	m.s.
Due to outlier	1	23296	23296
New residual	33	43332	1313
Original residual	34	66628	1960

It may be seen that this one outlier accounts for more than one-third of the residual sum of squares, the variance ratio being $23296/1313 = 17\cdot74$. By the ordinary test, this would be highly significant, but this test is not appropriate in this instance, since the observation has been selected as being the most extreme out of 54 possible choices. Some allowance for this fact has to be made in carrying out the test of significance.

As an approximate test, the probability of a variance ratio as large as $17\cdot74$ should be assessed using the variance-ratio table. This should then be multiplied by the number of observations to estimate the probability of an outlier arising by chance. Here the variance ratio reaches significance at approximately the $0\cdot02$ percent level, so that the probability may be taken as $54 \times 0\cdot0002 \approx 0\cdot01$. This indicates that the extreme observation of the $p_0 l_0$ treatment is an outlier and should have been rejected. In the new analysis this observation could be replaced by the missing value estimate of 274. Fuller details of this test can be found in John and Prescott (1975).

A check on outliers can be included as a routine part of the statistical analysis of an experiment. Again, such an analysis would be based on the residuals. In calculating Table 14.8.1 the mean square due to the outlier is equivalent to the square of the largest residual, signs being ignored, multiplied by n/r, where n is the total number of observations and r is the number of degrees of freedom associated with the original residual. If the observation corresponding to the largest absolute residual is rejected, the new residuals can be calculated and the procedure repeated.

14.9   Presentation of scaled observations

When an analysis has been carried out using transformed observations, it is usually a problem to decide how the results should be presented. If the scale has been chosen for additivity, then the only suitable summary of treatment effects is provided on this scale. To present them on any other scale might require the consideration of several different sets of means. For example, a difference of 1 between mean probits corresponds to changes from $2\cdot22$ percent to $15\cdot9$ percent, from $15\cdot9$ percent to 50 percent, from 50 percent to $84\cdot1$ percent, etc., and each of these changes is representative of the treatment effect.

If only one set of means is to be used, obviously the values corresponding to the overall mean of the experiment are suggested, but here again there is a difficulty: the values obtained by taking the means of the transformed values and transforming them back to the original scale are likely to be widely different from means obtained directly. In part, this will be the consequence of extreme observations which occur in the untransformed measurements and, in part, the result of bias introduced by the transformation. It is therefore often desirable to carry out a rough adjustment to make them roughly comparable to means obtained directly.

As an example, consider the treatment means of the experiment of 14.2, where the counts are transformed using a square-root transformation, i.e. $y = \surd(x + \frac{3}{8})$. The means of the untransformed and transformed counts are given in Table 14.9.1, together with the derived means obtained by transforming back to the original scale.

Table 14.9.1   Table of means

	Treatment						
	1	2	3	4	5	6	7
Untransformed	24·15	14·95	20·30	14·55	17·75	15·25	40·60
Transformed	4·86	3·80	4·38	3·71	4·04	3·86	6·28
Derived	23·24	14·10	18·84	13·36	15·92	14·52	39·09

The derived means are considerably less than the untransformed means, due to bias introduced by scaling. To overcome this bias, it is necessary to add $(n-1)s^2/n$ to the derived means, where n is the number of observations in each mean and s^2 is the residual mean square. In this instance, $n = 20$ and $s^2 = 0.67$. Thus, $0.95 \times 0.67 = 0.64$ should be added to the derived means. This gives the revised values shown in Table 14.9.2.

Table 14.9.2   Table of means

	Treatment						
	1	2	3	4	5	6	7
Untransformed	24·15	14·95	20·30	14·55	17·75	15·25	40·60
Transformed back	23·88	14·74	19·48	14·00	16·56	15·16	39·73

These values are in much better agreement with the untransformed values, although they are all still less than the original means.

For other transformations, different adjustments should be made. For the log $(x+1)$ transformation, where the logarithms are taken to base 10, an approximate adjustment can be made by multiplying each derived mean by $1 + 2.65(n-1)s^2/n$. For the $\sin^{-1}\sqrt{p}$ transformation the derived means should be multiplied by $1 - 2(n-1)s^2/n$ and this product added to $(n-1)s^2/n$. These adjustments should be sufficiently accurate, especially if the number of degrees of freedom of s^2 is large. Details of more exact adjustments for these and other transformations are given in Neyman and Scott (1960); see also Hoyle (1973).

Appendix

Table A.1   Table of t

Degrees of freedom	Percentage of trials in which deviate, t, is exceeded							
	50	25	10	5	2·5	1·0	0·5	0·1
1	1·00	2·41	6·31	12·71	25·45	63·66	127·32	636·62
2	0·82	1·60	2·92	4·30	6·20	9·92	14·09	31·60
3	0·76	1·42	2·35	3·18	4·18	5·84	7·45	12·94
4	0·74	1·34	2·13	2·78	3·50	4·60	5·60	8·61
5	0·73	1·30	2·01	2·57	3·16	4·03	4·77	6·86
6	0·72	1·27	1·94	2·45	2·97	3·71	4·32	5·96
7	0·71	1·25	1·89	2·36	2·84	3·50	4·03	5·40
8	0·71	1·24	1·86	2·30	2·75	3·35	3·83	5·04
9	0·70	1·23	1·83	2·26	2·68	3·25	3·69	4·78
10	0·70	1·22	1·81	2·23	2·63	3·17	3·58	4·59
11	0·70	1·21	1·80	2·20	2·59	3·11	3·50	4·44
12	0·70	1·21	1·78	2·18	2·56	3·05	3·43	4·32
13	0·69	1·20	1·77	2·16	2·53	3·01	3·37	4·22
14	0·69	1·20	1·76	2·14	2·51	2·98	3·32	4·14
15	0·69	1·20	1·75	2·13	2·49	2·95	3·29	4·07
16	0·69	1·19	1·74	2·12	2·47	2·92	3·25	4·01
17	0·69	1·19	1·74	2·11	2·46	2·90	3·22	3·96
18	0·69	1·19	1·73	2·10	2·44	2·88	3·20	3·92
19	0·69	1·19	1·73	2·09	2·43	2·86	3·17	3·88
20	0·69	1·18	1·72	2·09	2·42	2·84	3·15	3·85
22	0·69	1·18	1·72	2·07	2·40	2·82	3·12	3·79
24	0·68	1·18	1·71	2·06	2·39	2·80	3·09	3·75
26	0·68	1·17	1·71	2·06	2·38	2·78	3·07	3·71
28	0·68	1·17	1·70	2·05	2·37	2·76	3·05	3·67
30	0·68	1·17	1·70	2·04	2·36	2·75	3·03	3·65
40	0·68	1·17	1·68	2·02	2·33	2·70	2·97	3·55
50	0·68	1·16	1·68	2·01	2·31	2·68	2·93	3·50
60	0·68	1·16	1·67	2·00	2·30	2·66	2·91	3·46
∞	0·67	1·15	1·64	1·96	2·24	2·58	2·81	3·29

10—EDA * *

Table A.2 Variance-ratio table, 5 percent points giving the values of the ratio exceeded by pure chance in 5 percent of trials

Degrees of freedom of denominator	Degrees of freedom of numerator									
	1	2	3	4	5	6	7	8	9	10
1	161	200	216	225	230	234	237	239	241	242
2	18·51	19·00	19·16	19·25	19·30	19·33	19·35	19·37	19·38	19·40
3	10·13	9·55	9·28	9·12	9·01	8·94	8·89	8·84	8·81	8·78
4	7·71	6·94	6·59	6·39	6·26	6·16	6·09	6·04	6·00	5·96
5	6·61	5·79	5·41	5·19	5·05	4·95	4·88	4·82	4·77	4·74
6	5·99	5·14	4·76	4·53	4·39	4·28	4·21	4·15	4·10	4·00
7	5·59	4·74	4·35	4·12	3·97	3·87	3·79	3·73	3·68	3·64
8	5·32	4·46	4·07	3·84	3·69	3·58	3·50	3·44	3·39	3·35
9	5·12	4·26	3·86	3·63	3·48	3·37	3·29	3·23	3·18	3·14
10	4·96	4·10	3·71	3·48	3·33	3·22	3·14	3·07	3·02	2·98
11	4·84	3·98	3·59	3·36	3·20	3·09	3·01	2·95	2·90	2·85
12	4·75	3·88	3·49	3·26	3·11	3·00	2·91	2·85	2·80	2·75
13	4·67	3·80	3·41	3·18	3·02	2·92	2·83	2·77	2·71	2·67
14	4·60	3·74	3·34	3·11	2·96	2·85	2·76	2·70	2·65	2·60
15	4·54	3·68	3·29	3·06	2·90	2·79	2·71	2·64	2·59	2·54
16	4·49	3·63	3·24	3·01	2·85	2·74	2·66	2·59	2·54	2·49
17	4·45	3·59	3·20	2·96	2·81	2·70	2·61	2·55	2·49	2·45
18	4·41	3·55	3·16	2·93	2·77	2·66	2·58	2·51	2·46	2·41
19	4·38	3·52	3·13	2·90	2·74	2·63	2·54	2·48	2·42	2·38
20	4·35	3·49	3·10	2·87	2·71	2·60	2·51	2·45	2·39	2·35
21	4·32	3·47	3·07	2·84	2·68	2·57	2·49	2·42	2·37	2·32
22	4·30	3·44	3·05	2·82	2·66	2·55	2·46	2·40	2·34	2·30
23	4·28	3·42	3·03	2·80	2·64	2·53	2·44	2·37	2·32	2·27
24	4·26	3·40	3·01	2·78	2·62	2·51	2·42	2·36	2·30	2·25
25	4·24	3·38	2·99	2·76	2·60	2·49	2·40	2·34	2·28	2·24
26	4·22	3·37	2·98	2·74	2·59	2·47	2·39	2·32	2·27	2·22
27	4·21	3·35	2·96	2·73	2·57	2·46	2·37	2·30	2·25	2·20
28	4·20	3·34	2·95	2·71	2·56	2·44	2·36	2·29	2·24	2·19
29	4·18	3·33	2·93	2·70	2·54	2·43	2·35	2·28	2·22	2·18
30	4·17	3·32	2·92	2·69	2·53	2·42	2·33	2·27	2·21	2·16
40	4·08	3·23	2·84	2·61	2·45	2·34	2·25	2·18	2·12	2·08
50	4·03	3·18	2·79	2·56	2·40	2·29	2·20	2·13	2·07	2·02
60	4·00	3·15	2·76	2·52	2·37	2·25	2·17	2·10	2·04	1·99
70	3·98	3·13	2·74	2·50	2·35	2·23	2·14	2·07	2·01	1·97
80	3·96	3·11	2·72	2·48	2·33	2·21	2·12	2·05	1·99	1·95
100	3·94	3·09	2·70	2·46	2·30	2·19	2·10	2·03	1·97	1·92
150	3·91	3·06	2·67	2·43	2·27	2·16	2·07	2·00	1·94	1·89
200	3·89	3·04	2·65	2·41	2·26	2·14	2·05	1·98	1·92	1·87
∞	3·84	3·00	2·60	2·37	2·21	2·09	2·01	1·94	1·88	1·83

Table A.2 Variance-ratio table, 5 percent points giving the values of the ratio exceeded by pure chance in 5 percent of trials (*continued*)

			Degrees of freedom of numerator							
12	16	20	24	30	40	50	60	75	100	∞
244	246	248	249	250	251	252	252	253	253	254
19·41	19·43	19·45	19·45	19·46	19·47	19·47	19·48	19·48	19·49	19·50
8·74	8·69	8·66	8·64	8·62	8·59	8·58	8·57	8·57	8·56	8·53
5·91	5·84	5·80	5·77	5·74	5·72	5·70	5·69	5·68	5·66	5·63
4·68	4·60	4·56	4·53	4·50	4·46	4·44	4·43	4·42	4·40	4·36
4·00	3·92	3·87	3·84	3·81	3·77	3·75	3·74	3·72	3·71	3·67
3·57	3·49	3·44	3·41	3·38	3·34	3·32	3·30	3·29	3·28	3·23
3·28	3·20	3·15	3·12	3·08	3·04	3·03	3·00	3·00	2·98	2·93
3·07	2·98	2·94	2·90	2·86	2·82	2·80	2·79	2·77	2·76	2·71
2·91	2·82	2·77	2·74	2·70	2·66	2·64	2·62	2·61	2·59	2·54
2·79	2·70	2·65	2·61	2·57	2·53	2·50	2·49	2·47	2·45	2·40
2·69	2·60	2·54	2·50	2·47	2·42	2·40	2·38	2·36	2·35	2·30
2·60	2·51	2·46	2·42	2·38	2·34	2·32	2·30	2·28	2·26	2·21
2·53	2·44	2·39	2·35	2·31	2·27	2·24	2·22	2·21	2·19	2·13
2·48	2·39	2·33	2·29	2·25	2·20	2·18	2·16	2·15	2·12	2·07
2·42	2·33	2·28	2·24	2·19	2·15	2·13	2·10	2·09	2·07	2·01
2·38	2·29	2·23	2·19	2·15	2·10	2·08	2·06	2·04	2·02	1·96
2·34	2·25	2·19	2·15	2·11	2·06	2·04	2·02	2·00	1·98	1·92
2·31	2·21	2·16	2·11	2·07	2·03	2·00	1·98	1·96	1·94	1·88
2·28	2·18	2·12	2·08	2·04	1·99	1·96	1·95	1·92	1·90	1·84
2·25	2·15	2·10	2·05	2·01	1·96	1·93	1·92	1·89	1·87	1·81
2·23	2·13	2·07	2·03	1·98	1·94	1·91	1·89	1·87	1·84	1·78
2·20	2·10	2·05	2·06	1·96	1·91	1·88	1·86	1·84	1·82	1·76
2·18	2·09	2·03	1·98	1·94	1·89	1·86	1·84	1·82	1·80	1·73
2·16	2·06	2·01	1·96	1·92	1·87	1·84	1·82	1·80	1·77	1·71
2·15	2·05	1·99	1·95	1·90	1·85	1·82	1·80	1·78	1·76	1·69
2·13	2·03	1·97	1·93	1·88	1·84	1·80	1·78	1·76	1·74	1·67
2·12	2·02	1·96	1·91	1·87	1·82	1·78	1·77	1·75	1·72	1·65
2·10	2·00	1·94	1·90	1·85	1·80	1·77	1·75	1·73	1·71	1·64
2·09	1·99	1·93	1·89	1·84	1·79	1·76	1·74	1·72	1·69	1·62
2·00	1·90	1·84	1·79	1·74	1·69	1·66	1·64	1·61	1·59	1·51
1·95	1·85	1·78	1·74	1·69	1·63	1·60	1·58	1·55	1·52	1·44
1·92	1·81	1·75	1·70	1·65	1·59	1·56	1·53	1·50	1·48	1·39
1·89	1·79	1·72	1·67	1·62	1·56	1·53	1·50	1·47	1·45	1·35
1·88	1·77	1·70	1·65	1·60	1·54	1·51	1·48	1·45	1·42	1·32
1·85	1·75	1·68	1·63	1·57	1·51	1·48	1·45	1·42	1·39	1·28
1·82	1·71	1·64	1·59	1·54	1·47	1·44	1·41	1·37	1·34	1·22
1·80	1·69	1·62	1·57	1·52	1·45	1·42	1·39	1·35	1·32	1·19
1·75	1·64	1·57	1·52	1·46	1·39	1·35	1·32	1·28	1·24	1·00

Table A.3 Variance-ratio table, 1 percent points giving the values of the ratio exceeded by pure chance in 1 percent of trials

Degrees of freedom of denominator	Degrees of freedom of numerator									
	1	2	3	4	5	6	7	8	9	10
1	4052	4999	5403	5625	5764	5859	5928	5982	6022	6056
2	98·50	99·00	99·17	99·25	99·30	99·33	99·36	99·36	99·39	99·40
3	34·12	30·82	29·46	28·71	28·24	27·91	27·67	27·49	27·34	27·23
4	21·20	18·00	16·69	15·98	15·52	15·21	14·98	14·80	14·66	14·55
5	16·26	13·27	12·06	11·39	10·97	10·67	10·46	10·29	10·16	10·05
6	13·74	10·92	9·78	9·15	8·75	8·47	8·26	8·10	7·98	7·87
7	12·25	9·55	8·45	7·85	7·46	7·19	6·99	6·84	6·72	6·62
8	11·26	8·65	7·59	7·01	6·63	6·37	6·18	6·03	5·91	5·81
9	10·56	8·02	6·99	6·42	6·06	5·80	5·61	5·47	5·35	5·26
10	10·04	7·56	6·55	5·99	5·64	5·39	5·20	5·06	4·94	4·85
11	9·65	7·20	6·22	5·67	5·32	5·07	4·89	4·74	4·63	4·54
12	9·33	6·93	5·95	5·41	5·06	4·82	4·64	4·50	4·39	4·30
13	9·07	6·70	5·74	5·20	4·86	4·62	4·44	4·30	4·19	4·10
14	8·86	6·51	5·56	5·04	4·69	4·46	4·28	4·14	4·03	3·94
15	8·68	6·36	5·42	4·89	4·56	4·32	4·14	4·00	3·89	3·80
16	8·53	6·23	5·29	4·77	4·44	4·20	4·03	3·89	3·78	3·69
17	8·40	6·11	5·18	4·67	4·34	4·10	3·93	3·79	3·68	3·59
18	8·28	6·01	5·09	4·58	4·25	4·01	3·84	3·71	3·60	3·51
19	8·18	5·93	5·01	4·50	4·17	3·94	3·76	3·63	3·52	3·43
20	8·10	5·85	4·94	4·43	4·10	3·87	3·70	3·56	3·46	3·37
21	8·02	5·78	4·87	4·37	4·04	3·81	3·64	3·51	3·40	3·31
22	7·94	5·72	4·82	4·31	3·99	3·76	3·59	3·45	3·36	3·26
23	7·88	5·66	4·76	4·26	3·94	3·71	3·54	3·41	3·30	3·21
24	7·82	5·61	4·72	4·22	3·90	3·67	3·50	3·36	3·26	3·17
25	7·77	5·57	4·68	4·18	3·86	3·63	3·46	3·32	3·22	3·13
26	7·72	5·53	4·64	4·14	3·82	3·59	3·42	3·29	3·18	3·09
27	7·68	5·49	4·60	4·11	3·78	3·56	3·39	3·26	3·15	3·06
28	7·64	5·45	4·57	4·07	3·75	3·53	3·36	3·23	3·12	3·03
29	7·60	5·42	4·54	4·04	3·73	3·50	3·33	3·20	3·09	3·00
30	7·56	5·39	4·51	4·02	3·70	3·47	3·30	3·17	3·07	2·98
40	7·31	5·18	4·31	3·83	3·51	3·29	3·12	2·99	2·89	2·80
50	7·17	5·06	4·20	3·72	3·41	3·18	3·02	2·88	2·78	2·70
60	7·08	4·98	4·13	3·65	3·34	3·12	2·95	2·82	2·72	2·63
70	7·01	4·92	4·08	3·60	3·29	3·07	2·91	2·77	2·67	2·59
80	6·96	4·88	4·04	3·56	3·25	3·04	2·87	2·74	2·64	2·55
100	6·90	4·82	3·98	3·51	3·20	2·99	2·82	2·69	2·59	2·51
150	6·81	4·75	3·91	3·44	3·14	2·92	2·76	2·62	2·53	2·44
200	6·76	4·71	3·88	3·41	3·11	2·90	2·73	2·60	2·50	2·41
∞	6·63	4·60	3·78	3·32	3·02	2·80	2·64	2·51	2·41	2·32

Table A.3 Variance-ratio table, 1 percent points giving the values of the ratio exceeded by pure chance in 1 percent of trials (*continued*)

			Degrees of freedom of numerator							
12	16	20	24	30	40	50	60	75	100	∞
6106	6169	6209	6235	6261	6287	6302	6313	6323	6334	6366
99·42	99·44	99·45	99·46	99·47	99·47	99·48	99·48	99·49	99·49	99·50
27·05	26·83	26·69	26·60	26·50	26·41	26·35	26·32	26·27	26·23	26·12
14·37	14·15	14·02	13·93	13·84	13·74	13·69	13·65	13·61	13·57	13·46
9·89	9·68	9·55	9·47	9·38	9·29	9·24	9·20	9·17	9·13	9·02
7·72	7·52	7·40	7·31	7·23	7·14	7·09	7·06	7·02	6·99	6·88
6·47	6·27	6·16	6·07	5·99	5·91	5·85	5·82	5·78	5·75	5·65
5·67	5·48	5·36	5·28	5·20	5·12	5·06	5·03	5·00	4·96	4·86
5·11	4·92	4·81	4·73	4·65	4·57	4·51	4·48	4·45	4·41	4·31
4·71	4·52	4·40	4·33	4·25	4·16	4·12	4·08	4·05	4·01	3·91
4·40	4·21	4·10	4·02	3·94	3·86	3·80	3·78	3·74	3·70	3·60
4·16	3·98	3·86	3·78	3·70	3·62	3·56	3·54	3·49	3·46	3·36
3·96	3·78	3·66	3·59	3·51	3·42	3·37	3·34	3·30	3·27	3·16
3·80	3·62	3·50	3·43	3·35	3·27	3·21	3·18	3·14	3·11	3·00
3·67	3·48	3·37	3·29	3·21	3·13	3·07	3·05	3·00	2·97	2·87
3·55	3·37	3·26	3·18	3·10	3·02	2·96	2·93	2·89	2·86	2·75
3·45	3·27	3·16	3·08	3·00	2·92	2·86	2·83	2·79	2·76	2·65
3·37	3·19	3·08	3·00	2·91	2·84	2·78	2·75	2·71	2·68	2·57
3·30	3·12	3·00	2·92	2·84	2·76	2·70	2·67	2·63	2·60	2·49
3·23	3·05	2·94	2·86	2·78	2·69	2·63	2·61	2·56	2·53	2·42
3·17	2·99	2·88	2·80	2·72	2·64	2·58	2·55	2·51	2·47	2·36
3·12	2·94	2·83	2·75	2·67	2·58	2·53	2·50	2·46	2·42	2·31
3·07	2·89	2·78	2·70	2·62	2·54	2·48	2·45	2·41	2·37	2·26
3·03	2·85	2·74	2·66	2·58	2·49	2·44	2·40	2·36	2·33	2·21
2·99	2·81	2·70	2·62	2·54	2·45	2·40	2·36	2·32	2·29	2·17
2·96	2·77	2·66	2·58	2·50	2·42	2·36	2·33	2·28	2·25	2·13
2·93	2·74	2·63	2·55	2·47	2·38	2·33	2·29	2·25	2·21	2·10
2·90	2·71	2·60	2·52	2·44	2·35	2·30	2·26	2·22	2·18	2·06
2·87	2·68	2·57	2·49	2·41	2·32	2·27	2·23	2·19	2·15	2·03
2·84	2·66	2·55	2·47	2·39	2·30	2·24	2·21	2·16	2·13	2·01
2·66	2·49	2·37	2·29	2·20	2·11	2·05	2·02	1·97	1·94	1·80
2·56	2·39	2·26	2·18	2·10	2·00	1·94	1·91	1·86	1·82	1·68
2·50	2·32	2·20	2·12	2·03	1·94	1·87	1·84	1·79	1·74	1·60
2·45	2·28	2·15	2·07	1·98	1·88	1·82	1·79	1·74	1·69	1·53
2·41	2·24	2·11	2·03	1·94	1·84	1·78	1·74	1·70	1·65	1·49
2·36	2·19	2·06	1·98	1·89	1·79	1·73	1·69	1·64	1·59	1·43
2·30	2·12	2·00	1·91	1·83	1·72	1·66	1·62	1·56	1·51	1·33
2·28	2·09	1·97	1·88	1·79	1·69	1·62	1·58	1·53	1·48	1·28
2·18	1·99	1·88	1·79	1·70	1·59	1·52	1·47	1·41	1·36	1·00

Table A.4   Table of χ^2 distribution

Degrees of freedom	Percentage of trials in which χ^2 is exceeded							
	50	25	10	5	2·5	1·0	0·5	0·1
1	0·45	1·32	2·70	3·84	5·02	6·63	7·88	10·83
2	1·39	2·77	4·60	5·99	7·38	9·21	10·60	13·82
3	2·36	4·11	6·25	7·81	9·35	11·34	12·84	16·27
4	3·36	5·38	7·78	9·49	11·14	13·28	14·86	18·46
5	4·35	6·62	9·24	11·07	12·83	15·09	16·75	20·52
6	5·35	7·84	10·64	12·59	14·45	16·81	18·55	22·46
7	6·34	9·04	12·02	14·07	16·01	18·48	20·28	24·32
8	7·34	10·22	13·36	15·51	17·53	20·09	21·96	26·12
9	8·34	11·39	14·68	16·92	19·02	21·67	23·59	27·88
10	9·34	12·55	15·99	18·31	20·48	23·21	25·19	29·59
11	10·34	13·70	17·28	19·68	21·92	24·72	26·76	31·26
12	11·34	14·84	18·55	21·03	23·34	26·22	28·30	32·91
13	12·34	15·98	19·81	22·36	24·74	27·69	29·82	34·53
14	13·34	17·12	21·06	23·68	26·12	29·14	31·32	36·12
15	14·34	18·24	22·31	25·00	27·49	30·58	32·80	37·70
16	15·34	19·37	23·54	26·30	28·84	32·00	34·27	39·25
17	16·34	20·49	24·77	27·59	30·19	33·41	35·72	40·79
18	17·34	21·60	25·99	28·87	31·53	34·80	37·16	42·31
19	18·34	22·72	27·20	30·14	32·85	36·19	38·58	43·82
20	19·34	23·83	28·41	31·41	34·17	37·57	40·00	45·32
22	21·34	26·04	30·81	33·92	36·78	40·29	42·80	48·27
24	23·34	28·24	33·20	36·42	39·36	42·98	45·56	51·18
26	25·34	30·43	35·56	38·88	41·92	45·64	48·29	54·05
28	27·34	32·62	37·92	41·34	44·46	48·28	50·99	56·89
30	29·34	34·80	40·26	43·77	46·98	50·89	53·67	59·70

Table A.5 Table of the studentized range: upper 5 percent points

Degrees of freedom for error (f)	Number of treatments (t)																		
	2	3	4	5	6	7	8	9	10	11	12	13	14	15	16	17	18	19	20
1	17·97	26·98	32·82	37·08	40·41	43·12	45·40	47·36	49·07	50·59	51·96	53·20	54·33	55·36	56·32	57·22	58·04	58·83	59·56
2	6·08	8·33	9·80	10·88	11·74	12·44	13·03	13·54	13·99	14·39	14·75	15·08	15·38	15·65	15·91	16·14	16·37	16·57	16·77
3	4·50	5·91	6·82	7·50	8·04	8·48	8·85	9·18	9·46	9·72	9·95	10·15	10·35	10·52	10·69	10·84	10·98	11·11	11·24
4	3·93	5·04	5·76	6·29	6·71	7·05	7·35	7·60	7·83	8·03	8·21	8·37	8·52	8·66	8·79	8·91	9·03	9·13	9·23
5	3·64	4·60	5·22	5·67	6·03	6·33	6·58	6·80	6·99	7·17	7·32	7·47	7·60	7·72	7·83	7·93	8·03	8·12	8·21
6	3·46	4·34	4·90	5·30	5·63	5·90	6·12	6·32	6·49	6·65	6·79	6·92	7·03	7·14	7·24	7·34	7·43	7·51	7·59
7	3·34	4·16	4·68	5·06	5·36	5·61	5·82	6·00	6·16	6·30	6·43	6·55	6·66	6·76	6·85	6·94	7·02	7·10	7·17
8	3·26	4·04	4·53	4·89	5·17	5·40	5·60	5·77	5·92	6·05	6·18	6·29	6·39	6·48	6·57	6·65	6·73	6·80	6·87
9	3·20	3·95	4·41	4·76	5·02	5·24	5·43	5·59	5·74	5·87	5·98	6·09	6·19	6·28	6·36	6·44	6·51	6·58	6·64
10	3·15	3·88	4·33	4·65	4·91	5·12	5·30	5·46	5·60	5·72	5·83	5·93	6·03	6·11	6·19	6·27	6·34	6·40	6·47
11	3·11	3·82	4·26	4·57	4·82	5·03	5·20	5·35	5·49	5·61	5·71	5·81	5·90	5·98	6·06	6·13	6·20	6·27	6·33
12	3·08	3·77	4·20	4·51	4·75	4·95	5·12	5·27	5·39	5·51	5·61	5·71	5·80	5·88	5·95	6·02	6·09	6·15	6·21
13	3·06	3·73	4·15	4·45	4·69	4·88	5·05	5·19	5·32	5·43	5·53	5·63	5·71	5·79	5·86	5·93	5·99	6·05	6·11
14	3·03	3·70	4·11	4·41	4·64	4·83	4·99	5·13	5·25	5·36	5·46	5·55	5·64	5·71	5·79	5·85	5·91	5·97	6·03
15	3·01	3·67	4·08	4·37	4·59	4·78	4·94	5·08	5·20	5·31	5·40	5·49	5·57	5·65	5·72	5·78	5·85	5·90	5·96
16	3·00	3·65	4·05	4·33	4·56	4·74	4·90	5·03	5·15	5·26	5·35	5·44	5·52	5·59	5·66	5·73	5·79	5·84	5·90
17	2·98	3·63	4·02	4·30	4·52	4·70	4·86	4·99	5·11	5·21	5·31	5·39	5·47	5·54	5·61	5·67	5·73	5·79	5·84
18	2·97	3·61	4·00	4·28	4·49	4·67	4·82	4·96	5·07	5·17	5·27	5·35	5·43	5·50	5·57	5·63	5·69	5·74	5·79
19	2·96	3·59	3·98	4·25	4·47	4·65	4·79	4·92	5·04	5·14	5·23	5·31	5·39	5·46	5·53	5·59	5·65	5·70	5·75
20	2·95	3·58	3·96	4·23	4·45	4·62	4·77	4·90	5·01	5·11	5·20	5·28	5·36	5·43	5·49	5·55	5·61	5·66	5·71
24	2·92	3·53	3·90	4·17	4·37	4·54	4·68	4·81	4·92	5·01	5·10	5·18	5·25	5·32	5·38	5·44	5·49	5·55	5·59
30	2·89	3·49	3·85	4·10	4·30	4·46	4·60	4·72	4·82	4·92	5·00	5·08	5·15	5·21	5·27	5·33	5·38	5·43	5·47
40	2·86	3·44	3·79	4·04	4·23	4·39	4·52	4·63	4·73	4·82	4·90	4·98	5·04	5·11	5·16	5·22	5·27	5·31	5·36
60	2·83	3·40	3·74	3·98	4·16	4·31	4·44	4·55	4·65	4·73	4·81	4·88	4·94	5·00	5·06	5·11	5·15	5·20	5·24
120	2·80	3·36	3·68	3·92	4·10	4·24	4·36	4·47	4·56	4·64	4·71	4·78	4·84	4·90	4·95	5·00	5·04	5·09	5·13
∞	2·77	3·31	3·63	3·86	4·03	4·17	4·29	4·39	4·47	4·55	4·62	4·68	4·74	4·80	4·85	4·89	4·93	4·97	5·01

Table A.6 Table of the studentized range: upper 1 percent points

Degrees of freedom for error (f)	Number of treatments (t)																		
	2	3	4	5	6	7	8	9	10	11	12	13	14	15	16	17	18	19	20
1	90·03	135·0	164·3	185·6	202·2	215·8	227·2	237·0	245·6	253·2	260·0	266·2	271·8	277·0	281·8	286·3	290·4	294·3	298·0
2	14·04	19·02	22·29	24·72	26·63	28·20	29·53	30·68	31·69	32·59	33·40	34·13	34·81	35·43	36·00	36·53	37·03	37·50	37·95
3	8·26	10·62	12·17	13·33	14·24	15·00	15·64	16·20	16·69	17·13	17·53	17·89	18·22	18·52	18·81	19·07	19·32	19·55	19·77
4	6·51	8·12	9·17	9·96	10·58	11·10	11·55	11·93	12·27	12·57	12·84	13·09	13·32	13·53	13·73	13·91	14·08	14·24	14·40
5	5·70	6·98	7·80	8·42	8·91	9·32	9·67	9·97	10·24	10·48	10·70	10·89	11·08	11·24	11·40	11·55	11·68	11·81	11·93
6	5·24	6·33	7·03	7·56	7·97	8·32	8·61	8·87	9·10	9·30	9·48	9·65	9·81	9·95	10·08	10·21	10·32	10·43	10·54
7	4·95	5·92	6·54	7·01	7·37	7·68	7·94	8·17	8·37	8·55	8·71	8·86	9·00	9·12	9·24	9·35	9·46	9·55	9·65
8	4·75	5·64	6·20	6·62	6·96	7·24	7·47	7·68	7·86	8·03	8·18	8·31	8·44	8·55	8·66	8·76	8·85	8·94	9·03
9	4·60	5·43	5·96	6·35	6·66	6·91	7·13	7·33	7·49	7·65	7·78	7·91	8·03	8·13	8·23	8·33	8·41	8·49	8·57
10	4·48	5·27	5·77	6·14	6·43	6·67	6·87	7·05	7·21	7·36	7·49	7·60	7·71	7·81	7·91	7·99	8·08	8·15	8·23
11	4·39	5·15	5·62	5·97	6·25	6·48	6·67	6·84	6·99	7·13	7·25	7·36	7·46	7·56	7·65	7·73	7·81	7·88	7·95
12	4·32	5·05	5·50	5·84	6·10	6·32	6·51	6·67	6·81	6·94	7·06	7·17	7·26	7·36	7·44	7·52	7·59	7·66	7·73
13	4·26	4·96	5·40	5·73	5·98	6·19	6·37	6·53	6·67	6·79	6·90	7·01	7·10	7·19	7·27	7·35	7·42	7·48	7·55
14	4·21	4·89	5·32	5·63	5·88	6·08	6·26	6·41	6·54	6·66	6·77	6·87	6·96	7·05	7·13	7·20	7·27	7·33	7·39
15	4·17	4·84	5·25	5·56	5·80	5·99	6·16	6·31	6·44	6·55	6·66	6·76	6·84	6·93	7·00	7·07	7·14	7·20	7·26
16	4·13	4·79	5·19	5·49	5·72	5·92	6·08	6·22	6·35	6·46	6·56	6·66	6·74	6·82	6·90	6·97	7·03	7·09	7·15
17	4·10	4·74	5·14	5·43	5·66	5·85	6·01	6·15	6·27	6·38	6·48	6·57	6·66	6·73	6·81	6·87	6·94	7·00	7·05
18	4·07	4·70	5·09	5·38	5·60	5·79	5·94	6·08	6·20	6·31	6·41	6·50	6·58	6·65	6·73	6·79	6·85	6·91	6·97
19	4·05	4·67	5·05	5·33	5·55	5·73	5·89	6·02	6·14	6·25	6·34	6·43	6·51	6·58	6·65	6·72	6·78	6·84	6·89
20	4·02	4·64	5·02	5·29	5·51	5·69	5·84	5·97	6·09	6·19	6·28	6·37	6·45	6·52	6·59	6·65	6·71	6·77	6·82
24	3·96	4·55	4·91	5·17	5·37	5·54	5·69	5·81	5·92	6·02	6·11	6·19	6·26	6·33	6·39	6·45	6·51	6·56	6·61
30	3·89	4·45	4·80	5·05	5·24	5·40	5·54	5·65	5·76	5·85	5·93	6·01	6·08	6·14	6·20	6·26	6·31	6·36	6·41
40	3·82	4·37	4·70	4·93	5·11	5·26	5·39	5·50	5·60	5·69	5·76	5·83	5·90	5·96	6·02	6·07	6·12	6·16	6·21
60	3·76	4·28	4·59	4·82	4·99	5·13	5·25	5·36	5·45	5·53	5·60	5·67	5·73	5·78	5·84	5·89	5·93	5·97	6·01
120	3·70	4·20	4·50	4·71	4·87	5·01	5·12	5·21	5·30	5·37	5·44	5·50	5·56	5·61	5·66	5·71	5·75	5·79	5·83
∞	3·64	4·12	4·40	4·60	4·76	4·88	4·99	5·08	5·16	5·23	5·29	5·35	5·40	5·45	5·49	5·54	5·57	5·61	5·65

Table A.7 Random orderings of numbers 1–9

1 4 1 5 7 5 4 8 5 9	1 8 3 7 2 5 9 9 3 7	2 4 9 7 3 8 8 6 9 5	9 3 6 4 8 2 3 7 2 2
2 1 3 4 5 6 5 3 4 3	3 5 5 4 4 3 5 2 8 9	6 1 1 8 5 7 4 4 1 1	3 7 7 1 4 4 5 3 5 1
5 3 8 7 1 7 1 9 1 1	9 4 1 1 3 6 2 5 2 5	8 5 5 9 8 3 2 2 3 2	4 5 3 9 3 8 8 8 9 9
9 8 9 1 6 2 9 7 8 8	4 7 6 5 7 4 8 7 1 3	7 9 7 2 9 1 9 1 5 4	7 4 2 6 9 5 2 1 8 4
4 7 4 6 2 1 8 4 7 2	2 3 2 9 8 1 6 8 7 6	5 3 8 3 6 4 1 8 2 3	6 1 4 2 5 6 6 5 6 8
6 5 7 9 8 8 3 1 3 6	6 2 4 6 1 2 4 6 9 4	9 7 6 1 2 9 3 9 4 8	8 6 5 3 2 1 9 2 7 6
3 9 5 3 3 4 2 6 9 5	8 9 7 8 6 8 1 4 5 8	1 2 3 6 7 6 6 3 7 7	2 8 9 5 7 7 1 4 3 5
7 6 6 2 9 3 6 5 6 4	7 6 9 3 9 7 3 3 4 2	4 6 4 4 4 5 7 7 6 9	1 9 1 7 6 3 4 6 4 3
8 2 2 8 4 9 7 2 2 7	5 1 8 2 5 9 7 1 6 1	3 8 2 5 1 2 5 5 8 6	5 2 8 8 1 9 7 9 1 7
3 3 2 3 6 7 4 6 7 5	8 3 8 5 8 4 1 2 2 5	2 1 7 6 9 6 1 5 6 5	7 1 6 3 7 5 5 2 7 1
2 6 3 2 1 3 3 1 3 2	5 2 2 9 7 7 4 3 6 4	3 3 8 1 1 2 4 9 8 6	2 6 5 1 9 9 7 7 8 7
9 4 8 8 4 8 5 7 8 7	9 8 4 6 5 1 3 1 8 2	7 6 6 5 5 1 9 2 1 8	8 5 1 9 8 6 8 5 2 2
5 2 7 7 2 6 6 3 5 9	4 5 6 1 4 8 5 6 1 9	8 7 9 2 7 5 5 4 7 2	1 8 4 8 5 7 4 4 6 6
4 8 5 1 9 5 1 4 6 8	3 4 7 7 3 9 6 9 7 6	1 4 2 3 2 4 3 7 3 9	6 3 7 4 4 2 9 9 5 8
8 7 4 5 3 9 7 9 9 3	2 7 9 8 6 3 7 5 4 1	9 2 5 9 6 3 2 3 2 1	9 4 2 6 6 4 3 1 4 9
6 1 6 4 5 2 9 5 4 1	7 6 5 4 1 6 8 7 5 8	4 9 1 7 4 9 8 6 9 7	4 7 9 5 2 3 2 3 1 3
7 9 9 9 7 4 8 8 1 4	6 9 3 2 2 5 2 8 3 3	6 5 3 4 8 8 7 8 4 3	3 2 3 7 1 8 1 6 9 5
1 5 1 6 8 1 2 2 2 6	1 1 1 3 9 2 9 4 9 7	5 8 4 8 3 7 6 1 5 4	5 9 8 2 3 1 6 8 3 4
5 9 5 3 4 5 9 5 9 4	7 8 2 2 1 9 2 3 6 2	6 5 8 7 7 4 7 3 3 5	1 3 5 5 4 6 3 4 6 8
7 5 7 7 6 8 2 3 3 2	8 9 5 4 5 3 9 8 1 8	5 3 1 8 2 9 3 4 2 9	5 7 8 7 6 2 9 8 4 3
9 7 3 8 5 3 6 9 1 6	9 4 7 1 6 8 8 4 8 6	7 9 5 6 9 5 8 1 5 4	6 2 2 3 1 9 5 9 7 4
2 4 8 5 9 1 3 1 6 9	6 2 6 3 9 7 4 9 2 1	9 7 2 5 8 1 4 8 4 2	7 5 6 4 2 5 2 3 3 1
4 3 4 6 3 4 4 8 2 1	2 6 3 5 3 1 3 6 7 9	4 6 6 2 6 3 5 6 6 8	4 6 9 8 3 4 8 2 1 5
3 8 6 4 2 6 5 7 7 3	4 3 4 6 8 6 1 7 5 7	8 4 7 9 1 8 6 5 9 3	2 1 7 9 9 8 6 6 9 7
6 6 2 9 1 9 8 2 5 8	1 1 9 2 4 7 2 9 4	2 1 3 4 4 2 2 2 1 6	3 9 3 2 7 1 7 7 5 9
1 2 9 2 8 2 1 6 4 7	3 5 8 7 4 2 5 5 4 3	1 8 9 3 5 7 1 7 8 1	9 4 1 6 8 7 4 1 2 2
8 1 1 1 7 7 7 4 8 5	5 7 9 8 7 5 6 1 3 5	3 2 4 1 3 6 9 9 7 7	8 8 4 1 5 3 1 5 8 6
1 2 7 2 3 2 2 1 3 9	2 4 4 1 3 9 6 5 1 1	2 4 7 4 1 2 2 7 9 4	8 6 8 4 2 6 1 6 9 1
4 6 1 5 4 9 3 6 1 5	1 2 6 4 1 4 1 2 5 4	1 9 6 6 4 6 9 9 6 7	2 7 5 3 8 1 8 3 5 7
3 5 4 1 2 4 8 4 8 4	3 9 5 8 4 5 5 7 9 2	8 2 2 3 2 8 5 1 4 9	6 5 6 2 3 8 6 2 6 3
8 7 8 3 7 6 7 9 7 8	9 5 8 7 6 3 4 9 2 3	7 5 1 7 9 5 1 2 3 1	9 1 1 1 1 4 3 7 8 2
7 3 3 7 9 8 9 3 5 6	5 8 7 6 8 1 7 1 8 6	6 7 9 8 5 4 6 6 5 5	3 3 4 8 7 3 7 5 1 4
2 9 2 9 1 5 1 7 6 1	8 7 1 2 9 2 2 3 7 7	5 8 4 9 3 7 3 5 7 8	5 8 9 6 6 2 2 1 2 8
6 8 9 8 6 7 5 8 2 3	7 3 2 9 2 7 9 8 4 8	3 3 5 1 7 9 8 3 2 3	7 2 3 7 5 9 4 8 4 9
9 1 5 6 8 3 6 5 4 2	6 1 3 5 7 6 3 4 6 9	9 6 3 2 6 1 4 4 8 2	4 9 7 9 4 5 9 4 7 6
5 4 6 4 5 1 4 2 9 7	4 6 9 3 5 8 8 6 3 5	4 1 8 5 8 3 7 8 1 6	1 4 2 5 9 7 5 9 3 5
7 4 1 1 6 7 9 5 4 4	8 2 2 9 9 3 5 4 6 9	5 7 8 8 9 3 7 9 6 1	2 8 2 1 3 3 2 7 5 1
5 8 3 9 3 8 5 3 7 1	3 6 1 5 1 1 4 3 7 1	2 1 9 1 3 1 2 3 4 2	4 2 4 8 1 1 3 2 3 3
2 7 4 2 4 1 3 9 3 2	7 1 7 3 8 7 9 9 3 2	4 3 1 9 4 6 4 4 3 8	8 7 6 5 9 2 8 3 4 6
9 5 9 5 7 5 4 1 9 5	1 5 3 8 3 9 6 8 9 8	8 5 7 2 2 5 1 8 1 4	3 4 8 2 5 4 9 6 8 5
3 9 2 6 2 4 7 6 1 7	6 4 4 6 6 4 7 6 8 4	9 9 5 5 8 7 9 2 8 7	9 1 9 4 6 6 1 9 1 7
1 3 6 4 9 8 3 9 4	5 8 6 1 5 2 8 5 5 7	3 8 4 3 5 4 6 6 2 6	5 9 1 6 4 8 4 4 9 4
4 6 8 7 5 6 6 8 2 6	2 7 9 7 2 6 3 7 2 5	1 4 2 4 1 9 5 7 5 5	7 5 7 9 2 5 5 8 6 2
8 2 7 8 1 3 8 2 6 3	9 9 5 2 4 8 2 1 4 3	6 2 3 7 7 8 8 5 9 9	1 6 5 7 7 9 7 5 2 8
6 1 5 3 8 2 1 7 5 8	4 3 8 4 7 5 1 2 1 6	7 6 6 6 6 2 3 1 7 3	6 3 3 3 8 7 6 1 7 9
8 7 6 3 5 5 9 5 6 7	8 5 1 6 1 9 3 3 2 4	7 6 1 9 8 5 4 6 6 6	3 3 4 9 4 5 3 6 6 6
6 6 2 6 8 8 4 2 8 3	6 3 8 4 4 4 1 4 6 8	8 1 6 1 1 8 8 5 3 5	5 6 7 1 8 3 6 5 2 4
9 3 1 5 9 9 7 8 7 5	3 4 5 8 6 3 8 2 5 6	2 7 8 5 7 3 5 7 9 3	9 5 6 2 5 9 9 8 8 8
4 2 4 7 1 4 8 3 9 4	2 8 7 5 9 8 5 6 7 7	4 5 2 6 5 7 1 3 4 8	4 8 8 6 1 2 4 1 1 7
1 8 7 9 2 6 3 1 4 2	7 7 6 3 2 2 9 7 9 1	5 9 3 2 3 2 9 4 2 7	1 2 1 3 2 4 7 2 9 9
2 4 8 2 4 7 1 4 2 8	9 2 2 7 7 1 4 9 8 2	9 4 5 4 6 4 2 2 1 9	6 1 3 8 3 7 2 3 4 3
3 5 9 1 3 2 6 6 5 9	5 6 9 2 8 7 2 1 4 5	6 2 4 3 4 1 6 9 5 2	7 9 9 5 7 1 5 9 3 5
7 9 5 8 7 3 5 9 1 1	4 1 3 1 5 5 6 5 1 9	1 8 7 7 2 6 7 8 7 1	2 4 5 4 9 6 8 7 7 2
5 1 3 4 6 1 2 7 3 6	1 9 4 9 3 6 7 8 3 3	3 3 9 8 9 9 3 1 8 4	8 7 2 7 6 8 1 4 5 1

EXPERIMENTS: DESIGN AND ANALYSIS

Table A.7   Random orderings of numbers 1–9 (*continued*)

```
2 9 7 6 8 3 4 7 2 1     5 8 6 8 2 9 7 7 2 1     1 4 5 8 6 4 8 2 2 4     9 5 6 3 4 9 8 1 9 3
6 5 3 2 4 4 5 8 5 9     3 6 2 2 4 3 4 6 4 2     8 5 4 6 2 1 7 3 7 5     8 6 8 8 6 3 7 6 7 7
7 6 6 3 6 9 8 9 1 8     1 2 7 7 7 1 1 4 7 7     9 6 9 1 8 3 9 5 8 1     7 1 9 7 3 5 5 5 1 5
8 3 5 4 5 7 9 2 6 5     6 9 5 4 3 6 6 3 9 9     2 7 7 9 7 6 4 1 4 6     2 3 1 5 7 1 2 4 2 8
9 8 1 7 9 8 7 6 4 2     2 5 8 5 5 5 5 5 1 3     7 9 8 2 4 2 2 4 5 8     4 4 2 4 9 7 1 2 3 2
5 4 9 9 2 6 3 4 3 3     4 3 4 9 9 7 9 1 6 4     5 8 2 5 9 8 3 7 9 3     5 2 4 1 1 4 9 3 5 6
4 2 2 1 7 1 6 3 9 7     7 7 3 1 8 8 2 9 3 6     6 3 6 3 3 7 1 9 3 2     3 8 3 9 2 6 4 8 4 9
1 7 4 8 3 5 2 5 8 6     8 4 1 3 1 2 3 8 8 5     4 1 1 4 5 9 6 8 6 9     1 9 7 6 8 8 6 7 8 4
3 1 8 5 1 2 1 1 7 4     9 1 9 6 6 4 8 2 5 8     3 2 3 7 1 5 5 6 1 7     6 7 5 2 5 2 3 9 6 1

8 6 8 8 4 1 7 7 5 8     5 9 7 1 2 8 5 3 1 9     1 8 7 9 2 8 9 7 1 1     5 3 7 1 4 7 4 4 2 1
5 9 7 1 9 7 8 9 4 7     7 1 4 6 8 3 2 7 3 7     3 9 1 5 4 9 5 9 8 5     9 9 2 8 3 9 3 6 9 2
3 5 4 6 1 3 5 3 7 4     1 2 6 3 4 2 6 4 8 5     5 4 4 1 6 3 7 8 9 6     3 7 6 7 1 6 6 9 6 7
7 2 1 5 6 9 1 5 8 2     6 6 8 7 9 7 3 1 5 3     2 5 3 8 9 7 4 4 4 8     7 6 8 5 8 5 8 2 8 8
9 4 5 2 3 2 2 4 9 3     9 8 2 8 3 1 4 2 6 4     8 7 6 3 1 6 8 2 3 4     4 4 5 4 6 1 2 3 4 9
1 3 3 4 7 6 3 6 2 1     4 4 5 5 6 6 7 5 7 1     6 3 9 7 8 5 2 5 2 7     6 2 9 2 2 2 1 7 5 4
6 7 9 3 2 5 6 2 6 9     8 5 1 2 7 4 1 6 2 6     9 6 8 2 3 2 1 3 7 2     8 5 3 6 5 3 9 1 1 3
4 1 2 7 5 4 9 1 3 5     2 7 3 4 1 9 8 9 9 2     4 2 2 6 7 1 3 1 6 9     1 8 1 9 9 4 5 5 7 5
2 8 6 9 8 8 4 8 1 6     3 3 9 9 5 5 9 8 4 8     7 1 5 4 5 4 6 6 5 3     2 1 4 3 7 8 7 8 3 6

5 2 1 1 6 7 7 1 9 8     9 2 2 1 3 8 1 5 3 2     3 5 6 9 8 3 6 4 5 5     4 9 4 9 3 7 4 3 6 1
2 7 6 9 1 6 4 9 6 7     4 4 1 9 8 3 4 2 6 9     4 1 4 2 4 7 3 8 3 2     6 2 6 8 1 4 1 8 8 5
8 1 7 2 2 5 8 7 8 1     6 5 5 5 7 5 2 9 8 6     1 3 9 8 6 1 4 2 7 8     3 6 1 1 4 5 3 5 4 4
1 9 4 7 3 3 1 2 2 4     3 8 7 3 4 7 3 1 7 3     7 6 3 4 1 9 9 3 1 7     7 5 7 6 7 8 2 6 2 3
6 3 8 5 8 1 3 4 4 5     5 6 8 7 6 9 8 3 1 1     9 9 1 6 7 6 2 9 2 4     5 4 8 7 5 2 7 1 3 7
3 8 5 3 5 9 5 5 7 3     1 1 3 8 1 6 7 6 9 8     6 4 7 5 5 4 7 6 6 3     9 8 5 2 9 6 6 9 1 8
9 6 9 4 7 2 9 8 5 6     8 9 4 4 9 2 5 4 4 5     5 7 2 3 3 2 8 1 8 6     8 3 9 4 8 3 8 2 7 9
4 5 2 6 9 8 6 3 3 2     7 7 6 2 2 1 9 7 2 4     2 8 8 1 9 5 1 7 4 9     2 1 3 5 6 9 9 7 9 2
7 4 3 8 4 4 2 6 1 9     2 3 9 6 5 4 6 8 5 7     8 2 5 7 2 8 5 5 9 1     1 7 2 3 2 1 5 4 5 6

3 9 5 4 4 7 2 9 4 6     6 7 3 9 6 7 9 3 8 7     7 8 9 5 1 6 9 6 8 6     2 8 4 7 3 9 4 2 1 2
4 1 3 5 1 9 4 4 5 4     3 8 2 6 1 2 5 7 3 5     3 1 8 3 3 1 6 1 7 3     7 4 1 1 2 1 9 8 9 7
1 3 6 6 8 4 6 7 6 7     4 1 8 2 4 5 1 6 5 4     4 3 1 7 4 2 7 5 4 9     4 1 7 2 8 5 7 5 2 6
6 8 4 7 2 5 1 1 7 5     5 2 4 7 9 9 4 2 2 6     9 4 6 8 6 3 3 9 3 1     6 7 2 3 6 8 5 6 8 5
7 5 7 1 5 1 7 2 2 8     8 3 9 1 8 8 7 9 9 3     5 5 5 4 7 8 4 7 9 4     1 5 9 5 7 6 6 1 4 8
9 2 2 2 6 6 3 5 8 1     2 6 5 3 2 3 2 4 4 9     8 9 4 6 5 7 8 3 5 2     9 2 8 4 1 4 2 9 7 9
8 6 1 3 3 3 9 8 9 3     9 9 1 4 7 4 6 8 7 1     2 7 7 1 8 5 1 4 2 8     5 6 6 6 4 2 1 3 5 4
5 7 8 9 7 2 8 6 1 9     1 4 7 8 3 6 3 1 1 2     1 6 2 2 4 2 8 6 7       3 9 5 8 5 3 8 4 6 3
2 4 9 8 9 8 5 3 3 2     7 5 6 5 5 1 8 5 6 8     6 2 3 9 9 9 5 2 1 5     8 3 3 9 9 7 3 7 3 1

2 9 1 8 8 7 9 1 3 2     8 7 9 5 2 1 6 6 6 9     2 1 7 9 2 5 5 4 6 2     1 8 4 1 8 7 4 8 5 4
6 2 9 4 1 5 5 3 7 3     9 5 5 3 6 4 3 4 4 3     9 2 3 5 9 9 8 6 1 6     6 2 5 8 1 1 6 4 4 3
9 3 3 9 5 1 8 6 1 8     7 1 2 8 9 6 1 8 7 2     6 7 1 8 4 7 1 5 2 1     2 7 6 4 2 4 8 3 9 6
8 4 7 5 4 2 1 9 2 4     3 8 6 7 4 3 2 5 3 4     8 8 2 2 7 4 9 7 5 4     8 5 2 2 5 3 9 6 1 2
4 7 4 7 9 4 2 5 6 6     2 6 1 4 7 8 4 7 2 7     4 9 4 6 6 8 2 2 8 5     7 9 8 9 9 6 5 1 2 5
1 6 5 3 7 3 3 8 9 5     4 3 3 6 3 2 8 2 8 5     5 4 8 1 5 2 7 8 3 3     4 6 7 6 3 2 1 5 8 8
7 5 8 6 6 6 6 2 8 7     6 4 8 9 1 5 9 1 5 1     1 3 6 7 3 3 4 3 7 8     3 3 9 7 7 8 7 2 3 1
3 8 2 1 2 9 7 4 5 9     5 2 7 2 5 9 7 9 1 8     7 5 9 4 8 1 6 1 9 9     5 1 3 3 6 5 3 7 7 9
5 1 6 2 3 8 4 7 4 1     1 9 4 1 8 7 5 3 9 6     3 6 5 3 1 6 3 9 4 7     9 4 1 5 4 9 2 9 6 7

6 4 9 2 9 6 9 6 8 3     6 6 4 2 4 2 9 1 9 8     5 5 5 9 6 3 2 4 9 6     9 7 2 1 4 3 7 1 6 6
2 3 6 6 2 2 8 9 4 8     5 5 6 9 1 7 6 5 2 7     8 8 2 7 1 1 9 6 2 5     5 1 8 5 1 2 5 3 9 3
8 8 4 3 7 5 3 2 5 5     4 9 7 8 3 3 3 4 8 6     7 9 1 5 4 9 3 5 1 3     8 4 9 3 6 7 3 8 2 7
9 1 3 1 1 9 7 4 6 9     9 7 5 7 7 1 2 7 3 5     9 7 3 6 5 7 1 2 7 7     7 2 1 9 5 1 2 6 7 9
7 2 1 4 5 4 1 7 2 2     7 4 3 4 6 8 4 2 5 2     1 4 8 8 2 6 5 7 5 2     3 5 4 2 2 8 4 9 8 1
5 9 2 9 4 3 5 1 3 1     3 1 1 6 8 5 8 6 4 9     4 1 7 1 8 2 7 1 4 9     4 3 3 4 7 6 8 5 5 2
1 6 7 8 3 7 6 3 1 7     1 3 8 5 9 4 5 3 1 3     6 6 4 3 9 5 8 8 8 1     2 9 5 6 3 4 6 2 3 4
4 5 5 7 6 8 2 5 7 6     2 2 2 3 5 9 1 8 7 1     3 3 6 2 3 8 6 9 6 4     1 8 6 8 8 5 9 4 4 5
3 7 8 5 8 1 4 8 9 4     8 8 9 1 2 6 7 9 6 4     2 2 9 4 7 4 4 3 3 8     6 6 7 7 9 9 1 7 1 8
```

Table A.8   Random orderings of numbers 1–16

```
11 16 12  5 13 16 13  2  2    11  8 11  9  7 14 13  9 12  8     7  6  5  7  8  4 10  3  4 15
14  3 10  8  1  9  3  3  6    14 16 12 12 11 11 15 16  5 16     3  9  6  2  2  6  9 14 16  5
 5  4  4  1  4  4  2 15 16     6 11  7  4  5 16 10 13 13 10    12  8  7 12  5 14 12  9  7  8
 9  2 13 15  6  2  7 16  1     1  1  4 15 16  3  7  7  6  4    14  4  8  9 15 13  5  7 10  4
 8  5  3 14  7 10 14  7  3     9  9  1  2 14 13  2  6  7 13     4  5 16 14 11  5  6  8 15 16
10 12  7 10 14  3  9  6  9    15 10 13 11  9  8  4  1 10  5    10 10  2 15 16  7 14 13 13 11
 7  6 15  6 11  8 15 10 13     5  6  2 14  6  4  8 12  1 14    16 11 10  5 12 12  7 15 11  6
16  7 14  2 10 13 12 14  8    13  2  6  6  2  7 14 15  3  2    13  1  3 13  7 10 16  2  2 13
 2  8  2  4  3 15  4  9 15     7 12 16  5  1  1  9 10 14  6     8 13 13 16  4 11 15  4  9  7
 1 14  5 11  5  6  5 12 11     2  5 10  7 13  9  6 14 16  7     6  3 14 10  9  1 13  5  1  1
 4 15  6  9 15 14 16  4  7    10  3 15 10 10 15 11  4 11 12     9  7 12 11 14  9  4  1  6  3
 3 13  9 12  9  7 11 11 14     8  7  5  3  8  6  1  2 15  1     2  2  4  6  1  3  8 12 14  9
 6 10 16 13  8 11  6 13  4    12 13  9  1  3  5 12  8  8  3    11 12 11  3 13  8 11 16  3  2
13 11 11  3 16  1  1  8  5     4  4  3 13  4  2 16 11  2  9     5 14 15  8  6 15  2 10  5 10
15  1  8 16  2 12  8  5 10    16 14 14 16 12 12  3  3  9 15     1 16  9  4 10 16  3 11 12 12
12  9  1  7 12  5 10  1 12     3 15  8  8 15 10  5  5  4 11    15 15  1  1  3  2  1  6  8 14

16  7 13 13  8 15  1  3 12     7 10 16 16  9  5 16 16 15 14    12  4 11  1  9 15 13 14  9 11
 5  2  7  2 11 11  8  2 14    14  2  9  7 12 16  1  1 11  3     5 14 12  5 16 10  8  6 11  7
12  3  5  4 12 12 13  8  9     1  6  7  8  4 12  7  8  5 16     1 13  9 15  6 16  7 10 16 10
 4  5 15 11  2 14 16  5  7    10 16  6  2  3  1  4  3 12  1    16 10  8 16 15 13  3 13 12 13
15 14  6 16 14  4  9  6  2    11 14 10  4  2  2  5 10  7  6     2  8  4 12 10  7 16 15  4 12
14  6 11  6 16 13  6 15 11     4 13  2  3  8 13 11 14 13  2     3  3  2  2  2 12 15  1  5  5
 1  9  3 14  6  1 11 16 13    12  3 14  9  6  8 12  5  9 13    15 11  6  8  3 14  5  2 13  8
 2  8 15  8  5 16  7 14 15    13 15 12  1 13 11 15  6  3  8     4  1  1 11 13  4  6  7  1  9
 5  7  4 12  7  3 15  7  1     9 12  5 13 14 10  8  9  1  4    14  5 15  6  8  9  9  4  2 15
13 10  8 10  4  9  4 12  3     5 11 13 14  5  4  6  7 14 10     7 16  3  4  1  5  2 16  6  1
 9  1  2 15  1  6  2  4  4     8  4  3  6 10 15 14 10  5        13 12 16 14 12  3  1  8  7  4
 3 11  1  1 15 10 14 11  5    16  5  4 12 16  9  9 15  6  7     9  9  7 13  5  6 12 12  8  6
 2 16 10  3 13  2 10  1 16     2  1  8 15 11 14 10 13  4 11     8 15 14  7  4 11 11  3 10 16
10  8  9  9 10  8 12 10  8    15  9 11  5  1  3  3  2 16 12    11  7  5 10  7  8 10  9 15  2
 6 12 12  5  3  5  5 13 10     3  7 15 10  7  6  2  4  8  9     6  6 13  9 11  2  4 11 14 14
11 13 16  7  9  7  3  9  6     6  8  1 11 15  7 13 12  2 15    10  2 10  3 14  1 14  5  3  3

 7 12 15  7  3 16  3 15  8  9   1  5  6  3  1  3 12  2 15 10    6 16  4 12  9  6  5 15  1 16
 6  4  1 15  2 14 16  7  5  7   5  7  7  7 15 16 10  1  9 13    1  1  5  3  2 15 16  6  7  8
 1 16  4 11 11  7  4  4  4  6   9  1  9 13 13  2  9  3  2  9   14  4 16  1  4  4  2  9 11  2
 3  1  5 12  8 15  5  1  3 10  16  9 11  8 14 11  3 10 13 11   10 12  1  9 14  7  6 16 13 10
 8 14 12 16 16 11 15 14 13 14  11 11 12 15 12  7  1 15 10  3    7  8 12  6 16  3 12  8  4 14
 2 13  8 10 12  3 10  9  6 12  13 15  3  4  3  1  2 12 11  1    9  5 14 15 11  2 10 10  5  3
 4  3  7  6 14  6  6 16 14 11  14  8 10  4  4  7  6  3 14      5  6  3  7  1 12  3  1 15  1
10  2  9 13 10  8  7 11  7 13   2 13  5 11  9 12 11  4  8  2    3 15 15 11 15 16  8  3 10 15
 3  7  6  3  4 12  2  8 10  3   3 10 15 16 16 10  5  8  6  7   15  2 13  4 10  9  1 12  2  7
 2  6 11  4  7 13 12  6  9  5   6  6 13  2  6  9  8 14 14 16    4  3  2 14 13 13 13 13  3  6
 4  8 10  1  6  5  8  3  1  4  15  3  4 14  7  8 13  9  5 12   16  9  6  5  7 11 14  7  6 12
 1 10  3  8  9  1 13  5 16  1  10 16 14  1 10  6 15  7 12  5   13 13  7  8  6  5 11 11 16  5
 9  5 16  9  5  9  9  2  2  8   7 14  8  6  5  5 14  5  7  8    2  7  8 10  3 14  4 14 14 13
 6  9  2  5 13  2  1 13 15 16   4  2 16 12  8 13 16 13 16  6   11 14  9 16 12  1 15  5  9  9
 9 15 13  2  1  4 10 11 12  2   8  4  1  9  2 15  6 16  1 16    8 11 10 13  5 10  7  2  8 11
 5 11 14 14 15 10 11 12 12  2  12 12  2 10  8 14  4 11  4  4   12 10 11  2  8 13  9  4 12  4

 6 14  8 16  5 10 15  5  6  1   9 11  1  2  9  7  8  2  7 11    2  7 14 11  3  7  7  9 10  8
 6 13  1 14 12 13  9 11  5  7   6  6  7 12  2  9  7 15 13 15    8 15  2 15 13  8 10  4  6 12
 4 10 10 15  8  9 12  2  7  3   7 10 13  8 15  1  6 14  1  4    5  1  5 10  8 12  2 12 14  5
 5 16 16  9  1 10 16 13 13     13  3  9 13  7 13 14 12  5  3   14  6  1  8  7  4 15 11 13 10
 0  8 11  4  1  6  7 15 16 11  15 13 11  7  3 14 13  6  2  7   13  5 13 12 10 16  4  7 15 16
 4  1 14  5 10 15  2 12  2 16   5  5  8 15 10 16  9 13 14  2   11 16  3  5 15  2 12  2 12  4
 3 11  2  6  3 11  1  9  8 15  10 14 10 14 16  2 12  5  8  1    7 12 15 16  4  5 13 16  2  1
 9  6  9 13  2  5  5  1 15 14   4  4 15 16 12  8 16  7 11 10    4  9  7  4 12  3  1  5  5 15
 1  7  5  1 11 14  3  6 11  5   3 12 16  6 13  4 10 11 16  6    1 13 11 14 10  9  6  9  6  3
 2 15  7  3 16  2 14  3 10  9  14  2  3  9  4 15  3  8  4 13   16 14  8  9 14 11  3 10  4  6
 1  9  3 10 13 12 13  7  3  6  12  1  5  4  6 11  2  1  9 12   10 10 10  7  6  1  6 13 16 14
 2  4  4 11  7  4  8 13 12  8   2  9 14  3  1  3  5  4 12  5   12  8  6 13  5 13 14  3  3 13
 8 12  6 12 14  7  4  4  9  4   1 15 16 11 14 12  4 16 15 14    9  3 12  6  2  9 16 14  7  2
 5  2 13  8  6  8  6  8  1  2  11  8  4  5  1  6 15  9  6 16   15 11 16  1 11 15  5  8 11 11
 3  3 12  2  4  3 16 10  4 10   8  7  6  1  5 10 11  3 10  8    6  2  9  2 16 14 11 15  1  9
 7  5 15  7 15 16 11 14 14 12  16 16  2 10 11  5  1 10  3  9    3  4  4  3  9  6  8  1  8  7
```

Table A.8 Random orderings of numbers 1–16 (continued)

```
 9  1  6  8 10  5 12 16  8  2      5 12  9 14  5  8 16 11  6  5      5  1 16 12 14 11  6 10 12
16 16 14 11  2  1 16  9 16 16      1  6  7 15 12  4  4 14  2 11      8  9  7 11 12  4  1  8  8
 2  8  5 14  5 16  1  3  4  1      8  5 16  1  4 15  6  5 14  6     13  6  1  5  7  9 15 15  5
 5 10  8 13 11  6  2  1 10 11      7  9  5  4 10 14 11  2  1 10      3 14 15 13  3 16 10 11 13
13  9 12  2  6  4 10  8 12  7      3 14 13  5 16  1  5  7 11  3     12 16  2 14 10 15 14  6 16
10 11 13 16  7  2  7 11  9  4      9 16  3  7 11  2 15 12  4  8     11  4 14  7  6 14 16  1 14
 4 12  2 15  9 14 11  2 15  8     16  7  1 11 15 10  1 10 16 14      6  7 10  6  9  8  9 12  3
 6  3  4  7  4  7  6  4  3  6     12 15  8 16  7  6  7  1  9  7     16  5  8  4 15 13  7 13  4
 1 13 16  4  8 11 15  6 11 15     14  1 11  6  1  5 14  3 12 13      2  3 13  8 13 10  8  4 10
15  6 10  5 12 10  5 15 14  9     15  2  2  2  8  7  3  9  7 15     15 15 11 16  5  2  3  7  6
 3  5 15  6 13 13  9 10  5 13     10 11 12  9 14 11 12 13 13  9     14  8  3 10  2  7  2  3  7
11 14 11  3 16  3 14 12  2 14      4 13 10 12 13  3 10 15 15 16      7 12  9  3 16  1 11 16 15
 8  2  3 10 15  9 13 14  1 12     13  8 15 10  3  9  9 16 10  1      1 11  4 15 11  6  4  9  1
14  4  1  9 14 12  8  7  7 10      2 10  6  8  9 12  8  6  8  4     10  2  6  2  1  3 13  2  9
12 15  7  1  1  8  4 13  6  5     11  3 14  3  2 13  2  4  5  2      9 10  5  9  4 12  5  5  2
 7  7  9 12  3 15  3  5 13  3      6  4  4 13  6 16 13  8  3 12      4 13 12  1  8  5 12 14 11

10 14 10 11  5 10  7  5  3  7     11 12  7  8  1 13  2 15  6 13     16 16  4 15  5  9  1 11  5
 8 10  3  7  3  4 13  3 12 11      5 14  3  6  5 16  9  7  8 12      1 10 14 13  1  4 16 12  8
14  4  1 10 13 11  3  8  2  5     12  3 11 16 10  9  1  9 15 10      9  7 15  2 13  6  8  1 14
 1  1  8  5  9 16 11  7  5 14     13 13 16 13 13 10 16  3 10  6      2  6  5 10  8  1 12  5 12
11 11 14 16 16  9  4  9  9 10      8 10 10 11  9  7 12  1 12  7      7 15 11  1  6  2 14 14  7
16  7  6  1 10 12  2  6  8 15      3 15  8 12  8  4  5 13  5  1      3 14  8  6 14  8  9  4 11
 4  5 13  3  1  7 16 15  6  6      6  7 14  1  7 14 10 14  7 15     13  1 10 12 12  3  7  7  6
 3  2  2 13 12  3 15  4  1  2      1  9  2 14 12 11 14 11  1  9      8 12 16  8  7 16  5  2  2
 7 15 12  4  8  8  5  1 10  3     14  6  5 15 14 15  4  4  4 11      6  4  7  3 16 10 15  3  1
 2 16  7  8  2 14 14 14 11 12      9  4  6  5 15  8  8 16 16  3     15  9  1  7 15  7 11  8  9
 5  6  5 14 14  2  8 10 14  8     10  8 12  4  2  3  3  8 14 14      4  8  9 16 10  5  4  9  4
13  8  4 15  4  6  9  2  7 16     16 16 13  3 11  5  6 10  3 16     14 13  3  5  2 11  6 13 13
12  9 16  6  6 15 12 11 13  4      7  1  4 10 16  6  7  2 11  2     11  5 13  9 11 12 13 10  3
15  3  9  2  7  5  1 12 16  1      2 11  1  2  3  2 11  5  9  4     10 11 12 11  4 13 10 15 10
 9 12 15  9 11  1 10 16  4  9      4  5 15  9  6  1 13  6 13  5     12  3  6  4  9 15  2  6 16
 6 13 11 12 15 13  6 13 15 13     15  2  9  7  4 12 15 12  2  8      5  2  2 14  3 14  3 16 15

 9  5  6 16  1  4  4  8 11  5     13 15  8 12  9  4  6  9  5 10      7 15  6  3  9  8 16 11  5
 5  1  3  6  6  6  8  7 12  9      3  3  7  4 13  8 10 15  3  7      6  2 10  8  2  5 10  7 14
16  2  8  1 16  8  7  6  9 11      6 12 15 10  4 16  1 16  1  2     14 11  7  5  5 14  7  3 15
 6  3 12  9 13 10  9 12  2 12     14 16  6  2 12 10 11  4  8  3     13  9 15 16 11  9 15 13  1
11  4 16 13  9  1  1  1 10 14     15  8 11  3  5  3  3 11  7 15      9 12  3 11 12  4  4 14  4
12 12  1 14  5  3 16  4  7 10      7 10 12 13 15 14 13  8  6  9      8  4 12  6 13  2  1  5  6
 7 14  4  2  4 16  3 10  4  4     16 13  4  7  7 12  7  6  2 13      1 16  2  4  8 10 11 12 10
 1 13 11 12 15  9 12 13  6  6      1 11 10 14  1  1  9  5 16  8      5 14  5  9 16 13  2  6 11
14  9  7  5  2  2 10 14  8  3     12  7  9  1 16  5  5 14 15  1      3  5 14 15 15 15  6 15 16
13  8  5  8  7 11  2  1  1  1      9  4  2 16  2 15  4  2 10 16     12  7 13 13  4  1  9 10  9
 3  7  2  7 10 11  5 11 15  2      5 13 15  5  8  2 15  1 13  4     15  3 11  2  7  6  8  4  8
 8 16 13 11  3 14  2  9 16 13      2  6 16  6  3 11  8  7  9 14     11  8 16 10 14  3 12 16  3
 4 11 10  3 12 13 15  5  3  8     11  9  3 15 10 13 14 12 14 11     10  1  9  7  6  7  3  1  7
10  6  9 15  8 15 14 15  5  7     10  1  5  8 14  6 12 10 12  6     16  6  4 12  1 12 14  2  2
 2 10 14 10 14 12  6  3 14 16      4 14 14 11  6  7 16 13  4  5      4 10  1 14 10 16 13  8 13
15 15 15  4 11  5 13 16 13 15      8  2  1  9 11  9  2  3 11 12      2 13  8  1  3 11  5  9 12

14  4  3 13  8  7  9  6 12  5     10 13  6 13 15  3  2 14 12 10      7 12  9  6  5  6 11 12  6
 8  9 11  4  2 14 11 11 14  6      8  9 10  8 14  5  5 15 13 13     16  6 14 11  7 16  9  3  9
 1  5  9  7 14 11 14  3  4 13     12 10  8 11  6  8  4  5  8  4      3  5  4 16 15  5  8 11 15
13  8  6  3  4  5  2 12 11 14      4  8 16  6  8  9 10 16 15 15      5 14 12 10  1  2 16 15  1
 2 16  7 14  3 16 16 14 10 10     16 16 12 15 16 13 13  8  4  5      8  7  1  1  4 15 15  6 14
 6 12  4 10  1 13 15  4  1  8     15 11  7  9 13 12 16  6  7  3     14 10  8 15 10 12 12  8  2
12  2 13 16  5 10 10 16  2 16      3 12  1  4 10  4  1  2  1  1     12  9 15  3 13 11  6 13  3
11  3  1  9  7  9  5  8  9 11     13  2  3  3  3  7  3 10  5 16      2 13 10 13  3  1 10 14 11
15  1  2  1 16 12  6 10  6  7      2  1  4 14  2 11 12  1  3  6      1  3 16  8  9  7 13  2  7
16 14  8  2 11  4 12 13  3  9     11  4 11  2 12 15 11  7  6  9      9 11  5  2 13  3  1 10
 5 13 12 11 13  1  1  1 15  4      9  5 15  7  7  1  8 11  9  7     10 15  7  9 12 14  1 16  4
 3  7 16 15  6  3  8  2  7 12     14 15  2 12  1  2  9 12 16  8     11  1  3 12  8  9  5  7  8
 9 15 15 15  6  3  5 16  3  2      5  7 13  1 11 16 14  9  2 12      6  2 13  7 14  4  4  5 12
 7 11  5  8  9  8  7 15  8  3      6  3  9  9 10 15 13 11  2  2     15 16  6  5 16  8  2  9 13
10  6 10  6 12  2  4  7  5  1      1 14  5 10  5 14  7  3 10 14     13  8 11  4 11  3  7  4 16
 4 10 14 12 10 15 13  9 13 15      7  6 14 16  4  6  6  4 14 11      4  4  2 14  6 10 14 10  5
```

Table A.9 Random orderings of numbers 1–25

Top section — left block:

16	11	7	2	6	18	25	12	12
22	21	16	13	16	4	5	8	4
13	4	17	7	20	11	16	13	23
11	10	11	17	12	15	23	18	5
18	5	1	19	22	19	18	16	25
25	18	12	9	17	3	11	24	9
23	14	5	10	7	12	13	14	6
8	16	22	23	19	21	6	6	16
12	20	6	21	14	13	9	7	2
20	7	3	5	1	14	1	23	10
2	13	8	22	23	25	24	9	20
5	23	2	4	18	1	22	4	17
15	15	19	20	4	8	15	25	21
1	9	20	16	2	2	17	22	1
6	17	10	18	24	24	4	2	19
24	3	24	14	15	9	8	17	7
7	24	14	1	9	16	10	1	13
4	25	13	8	25	10	7	20	15
14	19	18	25	10	5	2	11	22
3	6	4	24	3	6	19	15	8
19	1	25	15	8	7	14	10	24
17	8	23	11	13	22	3	19	14
21	22	21	12	21	20	21	3	11
9	2	9	3	5	23	20	5	18
10	12	15	6	11	17	12	21	3

Top section — middle block:

14	24	15	5	4	15	24	24	20	11
3	16	16	2	25	17	13	2	9	5
13	12	10	25	7	9	20	14	6	10
19	2	14	17	10	10	8	22	13	1
6	9	6	6	14	16	14	21	21	18
11	19	24	16	13	13	23	7	3	20
2	5	4	8	15	25	22	1	17	4
10	25	23	11	24	8	3	11	15	22
21	21	8	21	20	19	2	13	2	21
17	13	11	18	5	18	9	4	22	25
7	14	18	19	2	3	15	10	24	17
15	6	1	13	17	20	10	6	5	6
24	20	12	7	11	6	18	9	4	16
25	10	17	23	1	4	16	18	11	12
23	4	13	24	23	22	6	19	14	7
12	8	19	22	12	23	17	15	1	15
4	11	9	12	18	5	19	16	10	23
9	3	3	10	19	21	11	5	18	19
20	22	22	4	9	12	5	20	7	2
1	18	7	1	22	7	7	12	25	13
22	17	25	3	3	11	1	8	23	14
8	1	2	14	21	1	12	17	16	8
5	7	5	9	16	2	4	23	19	3
18	15	21	15	8	24	25	25	12	24
16	23	20	20	6	14	21	3	8	9

Top section — right block:

5	15	12	25	11	3	10	22	16	14
7	24	11	15	3	9	8	12	12	15
9	3	7	1	4	2	9	4	25	12
4	5	21	12	12	13	24	17	7	9
23	1	1	19	8	18	21	16	18	25
8	17	9	3	7	17	1	24	14	11
13	12	2	17	17	5	19	14	20	21
19	18	14	10	24	10	4	3	1	23
20	6	3	23	19	25	11	5	24	1
24	21	24	14	6	16	13	18	15	6
2	25	18	18	2	11	6	7	4	20
16	8	17	22	21	23	7	23	23	16
3	10	13	9	18	8	25	13	2	4
25	7	8	8	5	20	14	1	9	8
21	2	23	5	16	15	2	2	5	18
15	19	25	24	9	14	16	6	6	24
14	9	20	16	15	22	12	10	19	2
22	22	5	11	14	12	23	20	21	10
12	16	6	13	22	21	20	19	22	19
18	20	16	7	13	24	15	21	3	22
17	13	19	2	10	4	3	11	10	7
10	23	22	21	23	19	18	15	8	13
1	4	10	20	1	7	17	9	11	3
11	14	15	6	25	6	5	8	17	5
6	11	4	4	20	1	22	25	13	17

Bottom section — left block:

1	6	19	5	13	7	2	25	12
4	22	5	24	5	12	19	23	21
5	13	9	25	18	20	5	9	22
20	9	4	20	25	1	16	13	8
6	20	14	15	17	23	1	10	14
24	24	2	7	7	22	25	24	15
23	17	17	4	8	6	8	19	13
17	16	24	12	11	8	7	4	16
15	15	21	1	1	9	9	21	20
9	8	8	2	15	5	20	11	18
19	21	20	21	4	19	10	7	4
11	14	15	9	2	11	15	2	3
21	25	10	14	22	2	13	5	7
16	11	16	19	24	25	22	16	25
13	18	1	3	6	14	12	14	5
22	3	23	6	23	18	24	15	2
2	12	6	18	16	16	6	6	19
12	2	7	23	3	13	3	3	17
18	10	22	22	14	15	14	8	9
14	4	18	13	10	17	17	22	10
25	1	3	16	12	4	18	17	1
7	5	11	17	20	3	11	12	24
3	23	12	8	19	21	4	20	11
10	19	25	10	9	10	21	18	6
8	7	13	11	21	24	23	1	23

Bottom section — middle block:

21	14	4	5	7	6	7	19	20	25
5	4	19	14	13	4	13	4	7	1
14	10	5	9	10	13	17	10	6	6
8	11	21	13	3	16	1	22	8	11
24	1	18	7	8	15	8	14	4	2
12	12	14	19	1	3	20	6	3	5
17	13	9	3	2	21	19	7	24	23
11	9	7	6	22	22	6	9	13	14
20	3	17	11	24	1	16	13	25	20
19	24	16	17	21	18	11	17	23	4
9	21	11	24	23	23	24	8	17	9
25	25	24	12	16	20	15	1	19	12
13	16	25	4	5	25	14	12	21	10
16	6	8	8	25	5	4	21	1	24
7	23	10	16	19	10	23	20	9	17
2	19	12	22	18	8	12	23	10	3
6	15	15	20	17	24	9	3	5	18
4	7	1	15	12	17	21	16	18	15
22	8	23	10	15	14	5	25	15	16
1	17	13	18	9	9	10	2	2	13
3	22	6	21	20	12	22	11	12	21
23	5	2	1	11	7	25	18	16	7
10	20	3	23	6	11	3	24	22	19
15	18	20	2	14	19	18	5	14	22
18	2	22	25	4	2	2	15	11	8

Bottom section — right block:

18	10	8	19	25	15	20	7	13	2
25	12	18	7	11	1	7	23	11	21
22	17	21	14	24	2	23	20	18	22
21	3	5	15	6	6	19	5	8	17
6	15	10	12	15	13	1	11	22	19
3	19	11	21	1	22	10	25	2	24
9	6	17	9	21	20	12	6	19	16
11	11	25	22	23	14	6	9	9	11
7	16	13	16	7	10	14	24	20	14
10	21	23	10	12	18	21	2	12	7
5	8	20	4	10	24	16	19	21	9
1	18	12	5	20	23	13	22	7	1
12	5	14	11	19	3	9	21	15	12
2	4	24	1	13	4	22	12	17	15
24	1	7	6	3	5	8	13	10	3
4	9	9	23	22	16	5	10	23	4
13	23	2	17	16	7	18	17	3	23
15	22	15	13	14	11	11	18	14	5
20	2	16	2	4	21	3	15	4	6
8	14	22	3	8	17	25	8	25	8
17	25	19	8	5	19	4	14	24	25
19	7	4	24	17	25	2	3	1	18
16	20	3	25	18	8	15	16	6	13
23	13	1	18	2	9	24	4	5	10
14	24	6	20	9	12	17	1	16	20

Table A.10   Random orderings of numbers 1–36

3	20	18	36	26	13	1	21	31	34	20	23	3	21	26	12	27	27	24	26	3	36	2	21	31	33	16	35	27	11	26	8	19	36	31	33
16	14	32	19	2	36	9	11	36	7	32	32	30	25	29	32	33	28	2	25	25	4	36	6	13	13	30	3	26	6	29	15	23	19	13	16
12	25	11	5	21	2	21	6	21	4	23	15	32	18	33	6	28	36	14	6	26	23	18	11	17	31	9	19	33	18	11	35	9	23	32	35
5	34	29	6	20	9	27	18	4	30	19	12	36	11	31	18	31	34	7	4	29	7	17	13	8	30	22	13	9	8	28	36	14	34	9	27
34	1	10	27	13	16	24	31	16	21	26	23	10	25	26	15	30	35	4	29	20	30	22	8	4	22	36	8	24	11	30	11	30	16	2	11
13	28	23	14	28	24	32	22	23	36	10	18	25	7	14	30	20	28	29	1	36	22	24	35	7	20	1	4	36	21	20	5	27	6	8	26
33	8	35	3	22	30	12	16	31	1	4	25	22	30	1	3	22	24	11	27	34	24	12	3	36	27	24	30	1	33	26	18	20	25	4	8
7	35	3	26	21	13	16	31	13	13	27	34	19	13	32	18	19	36	35	30	9	13	13	33	2	34	36	16	27	15	34	22	25	7	15	19
18	3	11	22	14	4	30	32	18	10	34	27	17	27	34	31	27	24	16	9	20	32	23	30	36	35	29	6	18	22	16	9	23	20	23	36
26	26	25	20	18	30	34	13	20	33	27	35	28	13	27	13	2	16	29	6	16	34	16	6	33	28	9	25	23	18	20	30	25	19	16	31
23	2	20	14	19	31	32	12	14	22	7	7	21	30	35	3	19	5	14	11	17	31	24	17	13	29	4	29	20	22	22	14	20	23	22	15
2	21	29	18	21	33	4	20	29	34	5	5	36	15	7	26	27	34	23	15	23	10	28	18	24	28	13	17	22	11	19	23	27	21	4	13

Bibliography

Books on experimental design

Chew, V. (ed.) (1958). *Experimental Designs in Industry.* Wiley, New York.
Cochran, W. G. and Cox, G. M. (1957). *Experimental Designs.* Wiley, New York.
Cox, D. R. (1958). *Planning of Experiments.* Wiley, New York.
Davies, O. L. (ed.) (1956). *Design and Analysis of Industrial Experiments.* Oliver & Boyd, London.
Federer, W. T. (1955). *Experimental Design.* Macmillan, New York.
Finney, D. J. (1960). *An Introduction to the Theory of Experimental Design.* Univ. of Chicago Press, Chicago.
Fisher, R. A. (1960). *The Design of Experiments.* Oliver & Boyd, Edinburgh.
John, P. W. M. (1971). *Statistical Design and Analysis of Experiments.* Macmillan, New York.
Kempthorne, O. (1952). *The Design and Analysis of Experiments.* Wiley, New York.
Raghavarao, D. (1971). *Constructions and Combinatorial Problems in Design of Experiments.* Wiley, New York.
Vajda, S. (1967). *The Mathematics of Experimental Design.* Griffin, London.

Bibliographies on experimental design

Herzberg, A. M. and Cox, D. R. (1969). Recent work on the design of experiments: A bibliography and a review. *J. Roy. Statist. Soc., A,* **132**, 29–67.
Federer, W. T. and Balaam, L. N. (1972). *Bibliography on Experiment and Treatment Design pre-1968.* Oliver & Boyd, Edinburgh.

Books on statistical methods

Snedecor, G. W. and Cochran, W. G. (1967). *Statistical Methods.* Iowa State Univ. Press, Ames.
Davies, O. L. and Goldsmith, P. L. (ed.) (1972). *Statistical Methods in Research and Production.* Oliver & Boyd, Edinburgh.
Draper, N. R. and Smith, H. (1966). *Applied Regression Analysis.* Wiley, New York.

Statistical tables

Fisher, R. A. and Yates, F. (1963). *Statistical Tables.* Oliver & Boyd, Edinburgh.
Pearson, E. S. and Hartley, H. O. (ed.) (1966). *Biometrika Tables for Statisticians.* Vol. 1. Cambridge Univ. Press, Cambridge.

Book on matrix algebra

Graybill, F. A. (1969). *Introduction to Matrices with Applications in Statistics.* Wadsworth, Belmont, N. C.

References on experimental design

This bibliography lists those papers and other books referred to in the text, together with a further selection of papers on various aspects of experimental design. As far as possible they have been grouped according to the chapters to which their subject-matter is most relevant. This classification does not mean, however, that the papers are irrelevant to the material in other chapters.

Chapter 1

Anscombe, F. J. (1948). The validity of comparative experiments. *J. Roy. Statist. Soc., A,* **111**, 182–211.

Box, G. E. P. and Guttman, I. (1966). Some aspects of randomisation. *J. Roy. Statist. Soc., B,* **28**, 543–58.

Cox, D. R. (1961). Design of experiments: the control of error. *J. Roy. Statist. Soc., A,* **124**, 44–8.

Eisenhart, C. (1960). Some canons of sound experimentation. *Bull. I.S.I.,* **37**(3), 339–50.

Finney, D. J. (1956). The statistician and the planning of field experiments. *J. Roy. Statist. Soc., A,* **119**, 1–17.

Finney, D. J. (1957). Stratification, balance and covariance. *Biometrics,* **13**, 373–86.

Greenberg, B. G. (1951). Why randomise? *Biometrics,* **7**, 309–22.

Hirschboeck, J. S. (1941). Delayed blood coagulation in methyl methacrylate (boilable "lucite") vessels. *Proc. Soc. Expt. Biol. Med.,* **47**, 311–12.

Kempthorne, O. (1955). The randomisation theory of experimental inference. *J. Amer. Statist. Assoc.,* **50**, 946–67; **51**, 651.

Kendall, M. G. (1975). *Multivariate Analysis.* Griffin, London and High Wycombe.

Michaels, S. E. (1964). The usefulness of experimental designs. *Appl. Statist.,* **13**, 221–35.

Morrison, D. F. (1967). *Multivariate Statistical Methods.* McGraw-Hill, New York.

Yates, F. (1938). The comparative advantages of systematic and randomised arrangements in the design of agricultural and biological experiments. *Biometrika,* **30**, 440–66.

Yates, F. (1967). A fresh look at the basic principles of the design and analysis of experiments. *Proc. 5th Berkeley Symp. Math. Statist. & Prob.,* **4**, 777–90.

Youden, W. J. (1972). Randomisation and experimentation. *Technometrics,* **14**, 13–22.

Chapter 2

Bartlett, M. S. (1937). Some examples of statistical methods of research in agriculture and applied botany. *J. Roy. Statist. Soc., B,* **4**, 137–70.

Biggers, J. D. (1959). The estimation of missing and mixed-up observations in several experimental designs. *Biometrika,* **46**, 91–106.

Bliss, C. I. and Marks, H. P. (1939). The biological assay of insulin. II. The estimation of drug potency from a graded response. *Quart. J. Pharm. Pharmacol.,* **12**, 182–205.

Bose, R. C., Shrikhande, S. S. and Parker, E. T. (1960). Further results on the construction of mutually orthogonal Latin squares and the falsity of Euler's conjecture. *Can. J. Math.,* **12**, 189–203.

Bose, S. S. and Mahalanobis, P. C. (1938). On estimating individual yields in the case of mixed-up yields of two or more plots in field experiments. *Sankhyā,* **4**, 103–20.

Carmer, S. G. and Swanson, M. R. (1973). An evaluation of ten pairwise multiple comparison procedures by Monte Carlo methods. *J. Amer. Statist. Assoc.,* **68**, 66–74.

Finney, D. J. (1946). Standard errors of yields adjusted for regression on an independent measurement. *Biometrics,* **2**, 53–5.

Haseman, J. K. and Gaylor, D. W. (1973). An algorithm for non-iterative estimation of multiple missing values for crossed classifications. *Technometrics,* **15**, 631–6.

Healy, M. J. R. and Westmacott, M. H. (1956). Missing values in experiments analysed on automatic computers. *Appl. Statist.,* **5**, 203–6.

John, J. A. and Prescott, P. (1975). Estimating missing values in experiments. *Appl. Statist.,* **24**, 190–2.

Miller, R. G. (1966). *Simultaneous Statistical Inference.* McGraw-Hill, New York.

Nair, K. R. (1940). The application of the technique of analysis of covariance to field experiments with several missing or mixed-up plots. *Sankhyā,* **4**, 581–8.

Pearce, S. C. (1948). Randomised blocks with interchanged or substituted blocks. *J. Roy. Statist. Soc., B,* **10**, 252–6.

Pearce, S. C. (1965). *Biological Statistics: An Introduction.* McGraw-Hill, New York.

Pearce, S. C. and Jeffers, J. N. R. (1971). Block designs and missing data. *J. Roy. Statist. Soc., B,* **33**, 131–6.

Preece, D. A. (1971). Iterative procedures for missing values in experiments. *Technometrics,* **13**, 743–54.

Preece, D. A. and Gower, J. C. (1974). An iterative computer procedure for mixed-up values in experiments. *Appl. Statist.,* **23**, 73–4.

Rubin, D. B. (1972). A non-iterative algorithm for least squares estimation of missing values in any analysis of variance design. *Appl. Statist.,* **21**, 136–41.

Thomas, D. A. H. (1973). Multiple comparison among means—a review. *The Statistician*, **22**, 16–42.
Yates, F. (1933). The analysis of replicated experiments when the field results are incomplete. *Emp. J. Exp. Agric.*, **1**, 129–42.
Yates, F. (1936). Incomplete Latin squares. *J. Agric. Sci.*, **26**, 301–15.

Chapter 3

Draper, N. R. and Stoneman, D. M. (1964). Estimating missing values in unreplicated two-level factorial and fractional factorial designs. *Biometrics*, **20**, 443–58.
Good, I. J. (1958). The interaction algorithm and practical Fourier analysis. *J. Roy. Statist. Soc.*, B, **20**, 361–72; **22**, 372–5.
Quenouille, M. H. (1955). Checks on the calculation of main effects and interactions in a 2^n factorial experiment. *Ann. Eugen.*, **19**, 151–2.
Rayner, A. A. (1967). The square summing check on the main effects and interactions in a 2^n experiment as calculated by Yates's algorithm. *Biometrics*, **23**, 571–3.
Shearer, P. R. (1973). Missing data in quantitative designs. *Appl. Statist.*, **22**, 135–40.
Wright, G. M. (1958). The estimation of missing values in factorial experiments. *New Zealand J. Sci.*, **1**, 1–8.
Yates, F. (1937). The design and analysis of factorial experiments. *Imp. Bur. Soil. Sci. Tech. Comm. No. 35*, 1–95.

Chapter 4

Biggers, J. D. (1961). Estimation of missing observations in split-plot experiments where whole-plots are missing or mixed-up. *Biometrika*, **48**, 468–72.
Davis, J. F., Cook, R. L. and Baten, W. I. (1942). A method of statistical analysis of a factorial experiment involving influence of fertilizer analyses and placement of fertilizer on stand and yield of cannery peas. *J. Amer. Soc. Agron.*, **34**, 521–32.
Harter, H. L (1961). On the analysis of split-plot experiments. *Biometrics*, **17**, 144–9.
Taylor, J. (1950). The comparison of pairs of treatments in split-plot experiments. *Biometrika*, **37**, 443–4.
Williams, E. J. (1952). The interpretation of interactions in factorial experiments. *Biometrika*, **39**, 65–81.
Woodman, R. M. and Johnson, D. A. (1947). The effect of time of sowing and water supply on the bolting and growth of lettuce. *J. Agric. Sci.*, **37**, 95–112.

Chapter 5

Barnard, M. M. (1936). An enumeration of the confounded arrangements in the 2^n factorial design. *J. Roy. Statist. Soc., Suppl.*, **3**, 195–202.
Finney, D. J. (1947). The construction of confounded arrangements. *Emp. J. Exp. Agric.* **5**, 107–12.
Yates, F. (1935). Complex experiments. *J. Roy. Statist. Soc., Suppl.*, **2**, 181–247.

Chapter 6

Binet, F. E., Leslie, R. T., Weiner, S. and Anderson, R. L. (1955). Analysis of confounded factorial experiments in single replications. *North Carolina Agric. Exp. Station, Tech. Bull. No. 113*.
Bose, R. C. (1947). Mathematical theory of the symmetrical factorial design. *Sankhyā*, **8**, 107–66.
Bose, R. C. and Kishen, K. (1940). On the problem of confounding in the general factorial design. *Sankhyā*, **5**, 21–36.
Cotter, S. C., John, J. A. and Smith, T. M F. (1973). Multi-factor experiments in non-orthogonal designs. *J. Roy. Statist. Soc.*, B, **35**, 361–7.
Dean, A. M. and John, J. A. (1975). Single replicate factorial experiments in generalized cyclic designs. II. Asymmetrical arrangements. *J. Roy. Statist. Soc.*, B, **37**, 72–6.
John, J. A. (1973). Generalized cyclic designs in factorial experiments. *Biometrika*, **60**, 55–63.

John, J. A. and Dean, A. M. (1975). Single replicate factorial experiments in generalized cyclic designs. I. Symmetrical arrangements. *J. Roy. Statist. Soc.*, *B*, **37**, 63–71.

John, J. A. and Smith, T. M. F. (1972). Two factor experiments in non-orthogonal designs. *J. Roy. Statist. Soc.*, *B*, **34**, 401–9.

Kishen, K. and Shrivastava, J. N. (1959). Mathematical theory of confounding in asymmetrical and symmetrical factorial designs. *J. Ind. Soc. Agric. Statist.*, **11**, 73–110.

Wilkie, D. (1961). Confounding in 3^3 factorial experiments in nine blocks. *Appl. Statist.*, **10**, 83–92.

Chapter 7

Addleman, S. (1962). Orthogonal main effect plans for asymmetrical factorial experiments. *Technometrics*, **4**, 21–46.

Addleman, S. (1963). Techniques for constructing fractional replicate plans. *J. Amer. Statist. Assoc.*, **58**, 45–71.

Addleman, S. (1969). Sequences of two-level fractional factorial plans. *Technometrics*, **11**, 477–509.

Box, G. E. P. and Hunter, J. S. (1961). The 2^{k-p} fractional factorial designs. *Technometrics*, **3**, Part 1, 311–52; Part 2, 449–58.

Box, G. E. P. and Wilson, K. B. (1951). On the experimental attainment of optimum conditions. *J. Roy. Statist. Soc.*, *B*, **13**, 1–45.

Brownlee, K. A., Kelly, B. K. and Loraine, P. K. (1948). Fractional replication arrangements for factorial experiments with factors at two levels. *Biometrika*, **35**, 268–76.

Burton, R. C. and Connor, W. S. (1957). On the identity relationship for fractional replicates in the 2^n series. *Ann. Math. Statist.*, **28**, 762–7.

Connor, W. S. and Young, S. (1961). Fractional factorial designs for experiments with factors at two and three levels. *Nat. Bur. Stand. App. Math. Ser. No. 58*.

Connor, W. S. and Zelen, M. (1959). Fractional factorial experiment designs for factors at three levels. *Nat. Bur. Stand. App. Math. Ser. No. 54*.

Connor, W. S., Zelen, M. and Deming, L. (1957). Fractional factorial experiment designs for factors at two levels. *Nat. Bur. Stand. App. Math. Ser. No. 48*.

Daniel, C. (1958). On varying one factor at a time. *Biometrics*, **14**, 430–1.

Daniel, C. (1960). Parallel fractional replicates. *Technometrics*, **2**, 263–8.

Daniel, C. (1962). Sequences of fractional replicates in 2^{p-q} series. *J. Amer. Statist. Assoc.*, **57**. 403–29.

Daniel, C. (1973). One at a time plans. *J. Amer. Statist. Assoc.*, **68**, 353–60.

Finney, D. J. (1945). The fractional replication of factorial arrangements. *Ann. Eugen.*, **12**, 291–301.

Finney, D. J. (1946). Recent developments in the design of field experiments. III. Fractional replication. *J. Agric. Sci.*, **36**, 184–91.

Fry, R. E. (1961). Finding new fractions of factorial experimental designs. *Technometrics*, **3**, 359–70.

John, P. W. M. (1962). Three quarter replicates of 2^n designs. *Biometrics*, **18**, 172–84.

John, P. W. M. (1966). Augmenting 2^{n-1} designs. *Technometrics*, **8**, 469–80.

Margolin, B. H. (1967). Systematic methods for analysing $2^n 3^m$ factorial experiments with applications. *Technometrics*, **9**, 245–59.

Margolin, B. H. (1968). Orthogonal main effects $2^n 3^m$ designs and two factor interaction aliasing. *Technometrics*, **10**, 559–73.

Margolin, B. H. (1969). Resolution IV fractional factorial designs. *J. Roy. Statist. Soc.*, *B*, **31**, 514–23.

Nelder, J. A. (1963). Identification of contrasts in fractional replication of 2^n experiments. *Appl. Statist.*, **12**, 38–43.

Plackett, R. L. and Burman, J. P. (1946). The design of optimum multifactorial experiments. *Biometrika*, **33**, 305–25.

Quenouille, M. H. and John, J. A. (1971). Paired comparison designs for 2^n factorials. *Appl. Statist.*, **20**, 16–24.

Rao, C. R. (1950). The theory of fractional replication in factorial experiments. *Sankhyā*, **10**, 81–6.

Webb, S. R. (1971). Small incomplete factorial designs for two and three level factors. *Technometrics*, **13**, 243–56.

Youden, W. J. (1961). Partial confounding in fractional replication. *Technometrics.* 3, 353–8.

Chapter 8

Grundy, P. M. and Healy, M. J. R. (1950). Restricted randomisation and quasi-Latin squares. *J. Roy. Statist. Soc., B,* 12, 286–91.
Rao, C. R. (1946). Confounded factorial designs in quasi-Latin squares. *Sankhyā,* 7, 295–304.

Chapter 9

Addleman, S., Gaylor, D. W. and Bohrer, R. E. (1966). Sequences of combination chemotherapy experiments. *Biometrics,* 22, 730–46.
Becker, N. G. (1968). Models for the response of a mixture. *J. Roy. Statist. Soc., B,* 30, 349–58.
Becker, N. G. (1969). Regression problems when the predictor variables are proportions. *J. Roy. Statist. Soc., B,* 31, 107–12.
Becker, N. G. (1970). Mixture designs for a model linear in the proportions. *Biometrika,* 57, 329–38.
Bose, R. C. and Draper, N. R. (1959). Second order rotatable designs in three dimensions. *Ann. Math. Statist.,* 30, 1097–112.
Box, G. E. P. and Draper, N. R. (1959). A basis for the selection of a response surface design. *J. Amer. Statist. Assoc.,* 54, 622–54.
Box, G. E. P. and Draper, N. R. (1963). The choice of a second order rotatable design. *Biometrika,* 50, 335–52; 52, 305.
Box, G. E. P. and Hunter, J. S. (1957). Multifactor experimental designs for exploring response surfaces. *Ann. Math. Statist.,* 28, 195–241.
Box, G. E. P. and Hunter, J. S. (1958). Experimental designs for the exploration and exploitation of response surfaces. In *Experimental Designs in Industry* (ed. V. Chew), 138–90.
Box, G. E. P. and Wilson, K. B. (1951). On the experimental attainment of optimum conditions. *J. Roy. Statist. Soc., B,* 13, 1–45.
Box, M. J. and Draper, N. R. (1971). Factorial designs, the $|X'X|$ criterion and some related matters. *Technometrics,* 13, 731–42.
Cornell, J. A. (1973). Experiments with mixtures: a review. *Technometrics,* 15, 437–56.
Cox, D. R. (1971). A note on polynomial response functions for mixtures. *Biometrika,* 58, 155–9.
Draper, N. R. (1960). Second order rotatable designs in four or more dimensions. *Ann. Math. Statist.,* 31, 23–33.
Draper, N. R. (1961). Missing values in response surface designs. *Technometrics,* 3, 389–98.
Draper, N. R. and Herzberg, A. M. (1968). Further second order rotatable designs. *Ann. Math. Statist.,* 39, 1995–2001.
Draper, N. R. and Lawrence, W. E. (1965). Mixture designs for three factors. *J. Roy. Statist. Soc., B,* 27, 450–65.
Draper, N. R. and Lawrence, W. E. (1965). Mixture designs for four factors. *J. Roy. Statist. Soc., B,* 27, 473–8.
Dykstra, O. (1971). The augmentation of experimental data to maximise $|X'X|$. *Technometrics,* 13, 682–8.
Goldsmith, P. L. (1974). A conversational computer program for tailored experimental designs in factorial situations. Presented to Roy. Statist. Soc. Conf. Warwick.
Gorman, J. W. (1970). Fitting equations to mixture data with restraints on compositions. *J. Qual. Tech.,* 2, 186–94.
Gorman, J. W. and Hinman, J. E. (1962). Simplex lattice designs for multi-component systems. *Technometrics,* 4, 463–87.
Hebble, T. L. and Mitchell, T. J. (1972). "Repairing" response surface designs. *Technometrics.* 14, 767–79.
Hermanson, H. P., Gates, C. E., Chapman, J. W. and Farnham, R. S. (1964). An agronomically useful three-factor reponse surface design based on dodecahedron symmetry. *Agronomy J.,* 56, 14–17.

Herzberg, A. M. (1967). A method for the construction of second order rotatable designs in k dimensions. *Ann. Math. Statist.*, **38**, 177–80.

Hill, W. J. and Hunter, W. G. (1966). A review of response surface methodology: A literature survey. *Technometrics*, **8**, 571–90.

Kennard, R. W. and Stone, L. A. (1969). Computer aided design of experiments. *Technometrics*, **11**, 137–48.

Kurotori, I. S. (1966). Experiments with mixtures of components having lower bounds. *Ind. Qual. Control*, **22**, 592–6.

Lambrakis, D. P. (1968a). Experiments with mixtures: a generalisation of the simplex-lattice design. *J. Roy. Statist. Soc.*, *B*, **30**, 123–36.

Lambrakis, D. P. (1968b). Experiments with p-component mixtures. *J. Roy. Statist. Soc.*, *B*, **30**, 137–44.

Lambrakis, D. P. (1969). Experiments with mixtures: an alternative to the simplex-lattice design. *J. Roy. Statist. Soc.*, *B*, **31**, 234–45.

McLean, R. A. and Anderson, V. L. (1966). Extreme vertices design of mixture experiments. *Technometrics*, **8**, 447–54.

Mitchell, T. J. (1974). Computer contruction of "D-optimal" first-order designs. *Technometrics*, **16**, 203–20.

Murty, J. S. and Das, M. N. (1968). Design and analysis of experiments with mixtures. *Ann. Math. Statist.*, **39**, 1517–39.

Quenouille, M. H. (1959). Experiments with mixtures. *J. Roy. Statist. Soc.*, *B*, **21**, 201–2.

Scheffé, H. (1958). Experiments with mixtures. *J. Roy. Statist. Soc.*, *B*, **20**, 344–60; **21**, 238.

Scheffé, H. (1961). Reply to Mr. Quenouille's comments about my paper on mixtures. *J. Roy Statist. Soc.*, *B*, **23**, 171–2.

Scheffé, H. (1963). The simplex-centroid design for experiments with mixtures. *J. Roy. Statist, Soc.*, *B*, **25**, 235–63.

Smith, H. and Rose, A. (1963). Subjective responses in process investigation. *Ind. Eng. Chem.*, **55**, 25–8.

Snee, R. D. (1973). Techniques for the analysis of mixture data. *Technometrics*, **15**, 517–28.

Thompson, W. O. and Myers, R. H. (1968). Response surface designs for experiments with mixtures. *Technometrics*, **10**, 739–56.

Chapter 10

Bose, R. C. (1942). A note on the resolvability of balanced incomplete block designs. *Sankhyā*, **6**, 105–10.

Bose, R. C. and Nair, K. R. (1939). Partially balanced incomplete block designs. *Sankhyā*, **4**, 337–72.

Bose, R. C. and Shimamoto, T. (1952). Classification and analysis of partially balanced designs with two associate classes. *J. Amer. Statist. Assoc.*, **47**, 151–90.

Clatworthy, W. H. (1955). Partially balanced incomplete block designs with two associate classes and two treatments per block. *J. Res. Nat. Bur. Stand.*, **54**, 177–90.

Clatworthy W. H. (1973). Tables of two-associate-class partially balanced designs. *Nat. Bur. Stand. Appl. Math. Ser. No. 63*.

David, H. A. (1963). The structure of cyclic paired comparison designs. *J. Aust. Math. Soc.*, **3**, 117–27.

David, H. A. (1965). Enumeration of cyclic paired comparison designs. *Amer. Math. Monthly*, **72**, 241–8.

David, H. A. (1967). Resolvable cyclic designs, *Sankhyā*, **29**, 191–8.

Freeman, G. H. (1967). The use of cyclic balanced incomplete block designs for directional seed orchards. *Biometrics*, **23**, 761–78.

John, J. A. (1967). Reduced group divisible paired comparison designs. *Ann. Math. Statist.* **38**, 1887–93.

John, J. A., Wolock, F. W. and David, H. A. (1972). Cyclic designs. *Nat. Bur. Stand. Appl. Math. Ser. No. 62.*

Pearce, S. C. (1963). The use and classification of non-orthogonal designs. *J. Roy. Statist. Soc.*, *A*, **126**, 353–77.

Preece, D. A. (1966). Some balanced incomplete block designs for two sets of treatments. *Biometrika*, **53**, 497–506.

Preece, D. A. (1967). Nested balanced incomplete block designs. *Biometrika*, **54**, 479–86.
Rao, C. R. (1947). General methods of analysis of incomplete block designs. *J. Amer. Statist. Assoc.*, **42**, 541–61.
Tocher, K. D. (1952). The design and analysis of block experiments. *J. Roy. Statist. Soc.*, *B*, **14**, 45–100.
Welch, H., Putnam, L. E. and Gamboa, A. M. (1945). Correlation of the purity of penicillin sodium with intra-muscular irritation in man. *J. Amer. Med. Assoc.*, **127**, 74–6.
Yates, F. (1936). Incomplete randomised blocks. *Ann. Eugen.*, **7**, 121–40.
Yates, F. (1940). The recovery of inter-block information in balanced incomplete block designs. *Ann. Eugen.*, **10**, 317–25.

Chapter 11

Agarwal, K. N. (1968). Analysis of experiments on crop rotations. *J. Ind. Soc. Agric. Statist.*, **20**, 26–48.
Berenblut, I. I. (1964). Change-over designs with complete balance for first residual effects. *Biometrics*, **20**, 707–12.
Berenblut, I. I. (1967). A change-over design for testing a treatment factor at four equally spaced levels. *J. Roy. Statist. Soc.*, *B*, **29**, 370–3.
Berenblut, I. I. (1967). The analysis of change-over designs with complete balance for first residual effects. *Biometrics*, **23**, 578–80.
Berenblut, I. I. (1968). Change-over designs balanced for the linear component of first residual effects. *Biometrika*, **55**, 297–303.
Cochran, W. G. (1939). Long term agricultural experiments. *J. Roy. Statist. Soc.*, *Suppl.*, **6**, 104–48.
Cochran, W. G., Autrey, K. M. and Cannon, C. Y. (1941). A double change-over design for dairy cattle feeding experiments. *J. Dairy Sci.*, **24**, 937–51.
Crowther, F. and Cochran, W. G. (1942). Rotation experiments with cotton in the Sudan Gezira. *J. Agric. Sci.*, **32**, 390–405.
Davis, A. W. and Hall, W. B. (1969). Cyclic change-over designs. *Biometrika*, **56**, 283–93.
Federer, W. T. and Atkinson, G. F. (1964). Tied-double-change-over designs. *Biometrics*, **20**, 168–81.
Grizzle, J. E. (1965). The two period change-over design and its use in clinical trials. *Biometrics*, **21**, 467–80.
Lucas, H. L. (1957). Extra-period Latin squares change-over design. *J. Dairy Sci.*, **40**, 225–39.
Patterson, H. D. (1950). The analysis of change-over trials. *J. Agric. Sci.*, **40**, 375–80.
Patterson, H. D. (1951). Change-over trials. *J. Roy. Statist. Soc.*, *B*, **13**, 256–71.
Patterson, H. D. (1953). The analysis of the results of a rotation experiment on the use of straw and fertilizers. *J. Agric. Sci.*, **43**, 77–88.
Patterson, H. D. (1959). The analysis of a non-replicated experiment involving a single four-course rotation of crops. *Biometrics*, **15**, 30–59.
Patterson, H. D. (1964). Theory of cyclic rotation experiments. *J. Roy. Statist. Soc.*, *B*, **26**, 1–45.
Patterson, H. D. (1965). A factorial combination of treatments in rotation experiments. *J. Agric. Sci.*, **65**, 171–82.
Patterson, H. D. (1968). Serial factorial design. *Biometrika*, **55**, 67–81.
Patterson, H. D. (1970). Non-additivity in change-over designs for a quantitative factor at four levels. *Biometrika*, **57**, 537–49.
Patterson, H. D. (1973). Quenouille's changeover designs. *Biometrika*, **60**, 33–46.
Patterson, H. D. and Lowe, B. I. (1970). The errors of long term experiments. *J. Agric. Sci.*, **74**, 53–60.
Patterson, H. D. and Lucas, H. L. (1959). Extra-period change-over designs. *Biometrics*, **15**, 116–32.
Patterson, H. D. and Lucas, H. L. (1962). Change-over designs. *North Carolina Agric. Expt. Station Tech. Bull. No. 147.*
Pearce, S. C. and Taylor, J. (1948). The changing of treatments in a long-term trial. *J. Agric. Sci.*, **38**, 402–10.
Rees, D. H. (1969). Some observations on change-over trials. *Biometrics*, **25**, 413–17.

Williams, E. J. (1949). Experimental designs balanced for the estimation of residual effects of treatments. *Aust. J. Sci. Res.*, *A*, **2**, 149–68.

Williams, E. J. (1950). Experimental designs balanced for pairs of residual effects. *Aust. J. Sci. Res.*, *A*, **3**, 351–63.

Yates, F. (1949). The design of rotation experiments. *Comm. Bur. Soil Sci. Tech. Comm. No. 46.*

Yates, F. (1954). The analysis of experiments containing different crop rotations. *Biometrics*, **10**, 324–46.

Chapter 12

Bliss, C. I. and Dearborn, R. B. (1942). The efficiency of lattice squares in corn selection tests in New England and Pennsylvania. *Amer. Soc. Hort. Sci. Proc.*, **41**, 324–42.

Cochran, W. G. (1941). An examination of the accuracy of lattice and lattice square experiments on corn. *Iowa Agric. Exp. Station Res. Bull.*, **289**, 400–15.

Folks, J. L. and Kempthorne, O. (1960). The efficiency of blocking in incomplete block designs. *Biometrika*, **47**, 273–83.

Grundy, P. M., Healy, M. J. R. and Rees, D. H. (1954). Decision between two alternatives —How many experiments? *Biometrics*, **10**, 317–23.

Hudson, H. G. (1939). Population studies with wheat. *J. Agric. Sci.*, **29**, 76–109.

Pearce, S. C. (1970). The efficiency of block designs in general. *Biometrika*, **57**, 339–46.

Yates, F. (1938). The gain in efficiency resulting from the use of balanced designs. *J. Roy. Statist. Soc.*, **5**, 70–4.

Yates, F. (1940). The recovery of inter-block information in balanced incomplete block designs. *Ann. Eugen.*, **10**, 317–25.

Chapter 13

Cochran, W. G. (1937). Problems arising in the analysis of a series of similar experiments. *J. Roy. Statist. Soc.*, *Suppl.*, **4**, 102–18.

Cochran, W. G. (1951). Testing a linear relation among variances. *Biometrics*, **7**, 17–32.

Cochran, W. G. (1954). The combination of estimates from different experiments. *Biometrics*, **10**, 101–29.

Curnow, R. N. and Sharpe, E. (1962). The analysis of covariance as a means of reducing standard errors in certain experiments involving sequences of treatments. *Biometrics*, **18**, 410–13.

Greenwood, M. L. and Salerno, R. (1949). Palatability of kale in relation to cooking procedure and variety. *Food Res.*, **14**, 314–19.

Hall, I. J. (1972). Some comparison of tests of equality of variances. *J. Statist. Comp. Sim.*, **1**, 183–94.

Lee, H. M., Robbins, E. B. and Chen, K. K. (1942). The potency of stilbestrol in the immature female rat. *Endocrinology*, **30**, 469–73.

Miller, R. G. (1968). Jacknifing variances. *Ann. Math. Statist.*, **39**, 567–82.

Patterson, H. D. and Henderson, R. (1973). Recovery of information in the analysis of serial factorial experiments. *Proc. 39th Session I.S.I.*, **1**, 508–14.

Prescott, P. (1974). Normalizing transformations of Student's *t* distribution. *Biometrika*, **61**, 177–80.

Stoate, J. T. and Lane Poole, H. (1938). Application of statistical methods to some Australian forest problems. *Bull. Comm. For. Timb. Bur. Aust.*, **21**, 1–20.

Wallace, D. L. (1959). Bounds on normal approximation to Student's *t* and the chi-square distributions. *Ann. Math. Statist.*, **30**, 1121–30.

Watson, D. J. (1939). Field experiments on the effect of applying a nitrogenous fertilizer to wheat at different stages of growth. *J. Agric. Sci.*, **29**, 379–98.

Yates, F. and Cochran, W. G. (1938). The analysis of groups of experiments. *J. Agric. Sci.*, **28**, 556–80.

Chapter 14

Andrews, D. F. (1971). Significance tests using residuals. *Biometrika*, **58**, 139–48.

Anscombe, F. J. (1948). The transformation of Poisson, binomial and negative binomial data. *Biometrika*, **35**, 246–54.

Anscombe, F. J. (1960). Rejection of outliers. *Technometrics*, **2**, 123–47.

Anscombe, F. J. (1961). Examination of residuals. *Proc. 4th Berkeley Symp. Math. Statist. & Prob.*, **1**, 1–36.

Anscombe, F. J. (1967). Topics in the investigation of linear relations fitted by the method of least squares. *J. Roy. Statist. Soc.*, *B*, **29**, 1–52.

Anscombe, F. J. and Tukey, J. W. (1963). The examination and analysis of residuals. *Technometrics*, **5**, 141–60.

Bartlett, M. S. (1947). The use of transformations. *Biometrics*, **3**, 39–52.

Beall, G. (1942). The transformation of data from entomological field experiments so that the analysis of variance becomes applicable. *Biometrika*, **32**, 243–62.

Behnken, D. W. and Draper, N. R. (1972). Residuals and their variance patterns. *Technometrics*, **14**, 101–12.

Birnbaum, A. (1959). On the analysis of factorial experiments without replication. *Technometrics*, **1**, 343–57.

Box, G. E. P. and Cox, D. R. (1964). An analysis of transformations. *J. Roy. Statist. Soc.*, *B*, **26**, 211–52.

Cochran, W. G. (1947). Some consequences when assumptions for the analysis of variance are not satisfied. *Biometrics*, **3**, 22–38.

Daniel, C. (1959). Use of half-normal plots in interpreting factorial two-level experiments. *Technometrics*, **1**, 311–41.

Daniel, C. (1960). Locating outliers in factorial experiments. *Technometrics*, **2**, 149–56.

Draper, N. R. and Hunter, W. G. (1969). Transformations: some examples revisited. *Technometrics*, **11**, 23–40.

Draper, N. R. and Stoneman, D. M. (1964). Estimating missing values in unreplicated two-level factorial and fractional factorial designs. *Biometrics*, **20**, 443–58.

Eisenhart, C. (1947). The assumptions underlying the analysis of variance. *Biometrics*, **3**, 1–21.

Finney, D. J. (1971). *Probit Analysis*. Cambridge Univ. Press, Cambridge.

Freeman, M. F. and Tukey, J. W. (1950). Transformations related to the angular and the square root. *Ann. Math. Statist.*, **21**, 607–11.

Hoyle, M. H. (1973). Transformations—An introduction and a bibliography. *Int. Statist. Rev.*, **41**, 203–23.

John, J. A. and Prescott, P. (1975). Critical values of a test to detect outliers in factorial experiments. *Appl. Statist.*, **24**, 56–9.

Neyman, J. and Scott, E. L. (1960). Correction for bias introduced by a transformation of variables. *Ann. Math. Statist.*, **31**, 643–55.

Sparks, D. N. (1970). Half normal plotting, AS30. *Appl. Statist.*, **19**, 192–6.

Stefansky, W. (1972). Rejecting outliers in factorial designs. *Technometrics*, **14**, 469–79.

Tukey, J. W. (1949). One degree of freedom for non-additivity. *Biometrics*, **5**, 232–42.

Tukey, J. W. (1955). Query no. 113. *Biometrics*, **11**, 111–13.

Index